Pearson Education

AP* Test Prep Series

AP*PHYSICS B

For:
Physics, Third Edition
By James S. Walker

Connie J. Wells
Pembroke Hill School

PEARSON

Prentice
Hall

Upper Saddle River, NJ 07458

Project Manager: Christian Botting
Assistant Editor: Jessica Berta
Senior Editor: Erik Fahlgren
Editor-in-Chief, Science: Dan Kaveney
Editorial Assistant: Fran Falk
Executive Managing Editor: Kathleen Schiaparelli
Senior Managing Editor: Nicole M. Jackson
Assistant Managing Editor: Karen Bosch Petrov
Production Editor: Robert Merenoff
Supplement Cover Manager: Paul Gourhan
Supplement Cover Designer: Christopher Kossa
Manufacturing Buyer: Ilene Kahn
Manufacturing Manager: Alexis Heydt-Long

© 2007 Pearson Education, Inc.
Pearson Prentice Hall
Pearson Education, Inc.
Upper Saddle River, NJ 07458

Printed in the United States of America

10 9 8 7 6 5 4 3

ISBN 0-13-173079-7

Pearson Education Ltd., *London*
Pearson Education Australia Pty. Ltd., *Sydney*
Pearson Education Singapore, Pte. Ltd.
Pearson Education North Asia Ltd., *Hong Kong*
Pearson Education Canada, Inc., *Toronto*
Pearson Educación de Mexico, S.A. de C.V.
Pearson Education—Japan, *Tokyo*
Pearson Education Malaysia, Pte. Ltd.

About the Author

Connie Wells has a Master of Science Degree in Physics from the University of Kansas and is a Physics and Advanced Placement Physics teacher, as well as Science Department Chair, at Pembroke Hill School in Kansas City, Missouri. She has coached her Science Olympiad teams to the National Science Olympiad Competition for eighteen of the past twenty years. During the past seventeen years as an A.P. Physics teacher, she has been active in test scoring and development for the College Board, serving on the AP Physics Test Development Committee from 1997-2001. She has been a Reader, Table Leader, and Question Leader for the A.P. Physics Reading and has presented teacher workshops throughout the country and abroad. In November 2003, Connie received the 2003-04 Siemens Award for Advanced Placement Teaching sponsored by the College Board and Siemens Foundation.

Acknowledgments

I would like to express my gratitude to my husband and sons for their inspiration and support, the Pembroke Hill AP* Physics Class of 2006 for their patience and editorial suggestions, and, in particular, Nathan Evert, for his technical expertise in the production of this text. I would also like to acknowledge the physics reviewers—especially George and Patricia Zober, John Garnevicus, and Maria Di Stefano—for their insightful suggestions.

Inspiration for this—and all my work—has come from my parents, who together taught high school students for over eighty-five years, and from many dinner-table discussions of physics problems and applications with my father and brothers.

Preface: To the Student

This book, which should provide essential review for any student preparing for the AP* Physics B Examination, is designed to be used with James S. Walker's <u>Physics, 3rd edition</u>. It is coordinated with the Walker text, with each section from the textbook directly linked to the published AP* Physics B syllabus. This review summarizes major concepts and examples that are representative of the AP* syllabus, and sample problems given within each chapter are written to resemble typical problems that might appear on an AP* exam. Chapter problems from the Walker text that most closely resemble actual AP* problems are targeted for student practice, with the suggestion that the student use these for extra practice in areas in which more work is needed. A full-length exam in the last section is provided as a personal assessment, along with sample scoring suggestions. Additionally, this review volume provides hints for you, as the student, that may help to remove some of the "hurdles" of exam taking and improve your confidence as you face the actual exam. An entire section on Laboratory Work describes techniques that should assist your preparation for that inevitable lab question on each examination.

Your review will be most effective if you read the overview within each chapter, examine the equations and bold-face terms, then test yourself with the sample questions and problems at the end of the chapter. If you encounter a section on which you do not perform well, use the textbook references to read about that topic more in depth and practice further with the recommended textbook problems. After your review, use the sample test provided to further assess your readiness, studying the explained answers to clarify your understanding. In the days just prior to the exam, go back over the equations and "Final Hints" provided in each chapter for those last-minute reminders.

After your comprehensive review, go into the examination prepared and confident that you will perform your best.

Good luck!

CONTENTS

INTRODUCTION: *How to Use This Text to Prepare for the AP* Physics B Examination*

This review manual is designed for use with James S. Walker's <u>Physics</u>, 3rd Edition, to prepare for the Advanced Placement B Physics Examination. It is assumed the student has completed a course in physics using Walker's text. This manual then guides the student through a review prior to the exam, refreshing physics concepts and providing sample questions and a practice exam to familiarize the student with AP question style. Along the way, the review guide author provides insights into how to approach certain types of questions as well as tips and techniques to approach the test itself. The idea here is to remove as many hurdles as possible for the student so he or she can focus on the physics on exam day.

In **Section I**, each section of the AP Exam is described in detail, with descriptions of question styles and suggestions on how to optimize performance on the Multiple Choice and Free Response portions.

Section II is outlined according to the parts and chapters in Walker's text, highlighting those sections that correlate most directly to the AP Examination. Chapters open with the equations that pertain to that topic box-outlined, using the exact notation and style used on the AP* Physics B Equations sheet. The idea in doing it this way is to familiarize students with the notations that will be provided with the AP* Exam.

Within each chapter, major terms, equations, and concepts are reinforced with references to specific examples and diagrams in the text. At the end of each chapter, a set of Sample Questions with answers and explanations serves as a checkpoint for student understanding. The author has chosen to take a "common sense" approach to significant figures—as do the AP* readers—rounding to a useful number of significant figures, based upon data given and the context of the problem.

Section III discusses the laboratory skills a student may need to demonstrate on the examination, including graphical construction and analysis. A prototype laboratory write-up is included to emphasize the essential components of good laboratory design. For the student who has not had significant laboratory experience, careful examination of this section may at least set a framework for the student to approach a laboratory question.

Section IV has a full-length practice examination for student self-assessment and for practice in gauging time constraints on the actual exam. The Multiple Choice section has questions representing the various question styles often used on the exam and contains a distribution of question topics that closely correlates with the percentages on topics in the syllabus. The Free Response section of the practice exam contains six "15 point" questions, similar to the exam, with distribution of topics again closely correlated to topic percentages on the AP syllabus. Answers with brief explanations are given for both sections. Additionally, instructions are given for the student to compute a score for his or her performance.

SECTION I
THE AP* EXAM

The Advanced Placement* Examination is constructed using the following syllabus, with questions on the exam covering concepts according to these percentages.

AP Physics B Topics	Textbook Correlations
Newtonian Mechanics [35%]	**Chapters 2-14**
A. *Kinematics [7%]*	*Chapters 2 and 3*
• Position, Distance, and Displacement	Chapter 2
• Average Speed and Velocity	
• Instantaneous Speed and Velocity	
• Motion with Constant Acceleration	
• Freely Falling Objects	
• Vectors and Vector Components	Chapter 3
• Adding and Subtracting Vectors	
• Displacement, Velocity, and Acceleration Vectors	
• Relative Motion	Chapter 4
• Motion in Two Dimensions	
• Projectile Motion	
B. *Newton's Laws of Motion [9%]*	*Chapters 5 and 6*
• Force and Mass	Chapter 5
• Newton's Laws of Motion	
• Forces in Two Dimensions	
• Types of Forces and Free Body Diagrams	Chapter 6
• Applications of Newton's Laws	
• Static Equilibrium	
C. *Work, Energy, Power [5%]*	*Chapters 7, 8, and 10*
• Work Done by a Constant Force	Chapter 7
• Kinetic Energy and Work-Energy Theorem	
• Work Done by a Variable Force	
• Power	
• Potential Energy	Chapter 8
• Conservative and Nonconservative Forces	
• Conservation of Mechanical Energy	Chapter 10
D. *Systems of Particles, Linear Momentum [4%]*	*Chapter 9*
• Linear Momentum and Newton's Second Law	
• Impulse	
• Conservation of Linear Momentum	
• Elastic and Inelastic Collisions	
• Center of Mass	

E. *Circular Motion and Rotation [4%]*	*Chapters 6, 10, and 11*
• Uniform Circular Motion	Chapter 6
• Torque and Rotational Statics	Chapter 11
• Rotational Kinetic Energy	Chapter 10
F. *Oscillations and Gravitation [6%]*	*Chapters 12 and 13*
• Newton's Universal Law of Gravitation	Chapter 12
• Kepler's Laws of Orbital Motion	
• Gravitational Potential Energy	
• Simple Harmonic Motion	Chapter 13
• Spring and Pendulum	
• Energy Conservation in Harmonic Motion	
Fluids Mechanics and Thermal Physics [15%]	**Chapters 15-18**
A. *Fluids [6%]*	*Chapter 15*
• Density, Pressure, and Static Equilibrium in Fluids	
• Archimedes' Principle	
• Fluid Flow and Continuity	
• Bernoulli's Equation	
B. *Temperature and Heat [2%]*	*Chapter 16*
• Temperature and Temperature Scales	
• Thermal Expansion	
• Mechanical Equivalent of Heat	
• Heat and Mechanical Work	
• Conduction, Convection, and Radiation	
C. *Kinetic Theory and Thermodynamics [7%]*	*Chapters 17-18*
• Ideal Gases and Kinetic Theory	Chapter 17
• Laws of Thermodynamics	Chapter 18
Electricity and Magnetism [25%]	**Chapters 19-23**
A. *Electrostatics [5%]*	*Chapters 19 and 20*
• Electric Charges, Forces, and Fields	Chapter 19
• Coulomb's Law	
• Electric Fields and Flux	
• Charging by Induction	
• Electric Potential and Electric Potential Energy	Chapter 20
• Potentials of Point Charges	
• Equipotential Surfaces	
B. *Conductors and Capacitors [4%]*	*Chapters 20 and 21*
• Insulators and Conductors	Chapter 20
• Capacitors	Chapter 21
• Electrical Energy Storage	

C. *Electric Circuits [7%]*
   • Electric Current and Resistance
   • Ohm's Law
   • Electrical Energy and Power
   • Series and Parallel Circuits
   • Circuits Containing Capacitors
   • Ammeters and Voltmeters
	Chapter 21

D. *Magnetic Fields [4%]*
   • Magnetic Fields and Forces
   • Motion of Charged Particles in Magnetic Fields
   • Forces on Current-Carrying Wires
   • Biot-Savart Law and Ampere's Law
	Chapter 22

E. *Electromagnetism [5%]*
   • Current Loops and Magnetic Torque
   • Induced EMF
   • Magnetic Flux
   • Faraday's Law of Induction
   • Lenz's Law
	Chapters 22 and 23
	Chapter 22
	
	Chapter 23

Waves and Optics [15%]	**Chapters 14, 25, 26, 28**

A. *Waves[5%]*
   • Types of Waves
   • Harmonics and Music
   • Sound Waves and Sound Intensity
   • Superposition, Interference, and Beats
   • Doppler Effect Electromagnetic Waves
	Chapters 14 and 25
	Chapter 14

B. *Physical Optics [5%]*
   • Electromagnetic Spectrum
   • Superposition and Interference
   • Young's Double Slit Experiment
   • Diffraction
	Chapter 28

C. *Geometric Optics [5%]*
   • Reflection and Mirrors
   • Ray Tracing
   • Refraction and Lenses
   • The Thin-Lens Equation
   • Dispersion
   • Critical Angle
	Chapters 26 and 28

Atomic and Nuclear Physics [10%]	**Chapters 30-32**

A. *Atomic and Quantum Physics [7%]*
   • Photon Theory
   • Photoelectric Effect
   • Compton Scattering
   • Atomic Energy Levels
	Chapters 30,31
	Chapter 30
	
	Chapter 31

B. *Nuclear Physics [3%]*
   • Nuclear reactions
   • Conservation of Mass Number and Charge in Reactions
   • Mass-Energy Equivalence
	Chapter 32

The Advanced Placement Physics B examination is divided into two separate parts, each ninety minutes in length and each counting equally toward the calculation of the student's final score.

Exam Section I – Multiple Choice: Part I of the exam consists of <u>seventy Multiple Choice questions</u> to be answered in <u>ninety minutes</u>. The student may not use either a formula sheet or a calculator on this section of the exam, but a Table of Information containing useful data is provided. The student is penalized for guessing on this section. The final score on the Multiple Choice section is determined by counting the total number of correctly answered questions and subtracting 25% of the number answered incorrectly. Thus, the student who does not feel sure of the answer should be able to eliminate enough incorrect choices to narrow the number of choices to two or three before guessing. [Opinion varies on how far the field should be narrowed before guessing; many of my esteemed colleagues recommend narrowing to three before guessing, but I recommend to my students that they narrow to two choices before guessing.]

Multiple Choice questions all have five answer choices—A, B, C, D, or E—and all answers are "bubbled" onto an answer sheet with a pencil. Since an Equation Sheet is not provided and calculator is not allowed, the questions are either conceptual or are problems involving calculations that can be determined using simple mathematical relationships or "quick cancellation". On this section, it is recommended that a g value of 10 m/s^2 be used to make calculations easier. Numerical answers given as choices are spread out enough in value that a quick estimation should provide a clear answer choice.

The questions on the Multiple Choice section are of several common styles. Familiarity with these will make the student's work easier. For sake of reference, we will call these: (1) Calculations, (2) Grouped Sets, (3) Tables, (4) Graphical Interpretation, (5) Conceptual-Factual, (6) Symbolic, and (7) Choice Combinations. A brief description and example of each type follows, with its solution:

(1) <u>Calculation questions</u> provide numerical data, either given or to be interpreted from a diagram or graph. The student should be familiar enough with equations to write an equation or formula, substitute the given values, cancel, and estimate the answer. Units and signs on the answer choices should be examined as clues to the correct solution. *Example:*

> **1.** A 500 kg test car engages a parachute from the rear of the vehicle to slow down. Initially, it is traveling at 70 m/s in the positive direction, and in 4 seconds it has slowed down to 30 m/s in the positive direction. What is the average force exerted on the car by the parachute?
>   A. 150 N
>   B. 300 N
>   C. -500 N
>   D. 1000 N
>   E. -5000 N
>
> Answer: **E** Using $v_f = v_o + at$, the acceleration is -10 m/s^2. Then using $F = ma$, the average force on the car during the time given is (500 kg)(-10 m/s^2), or –5000 newtons. Note that the force is negative, since it must oppose the motion of the car in order to slow it down. We can quickly narrow our answer choices to the two negative answer choices—even if we don't know how to calculate it.

(2) <u>Grouped sets</u> will show up on the exam as an underlined header telling which numbered questions are in the group, generally followed by a diagram and a "stem" (description of the situation). [Note: Don't be tempted to skip the stem, as critical information will be provided here.] A group of two to four questions will then be asked related to the diagram and stem. Generally, these are grouped in one column of the page, but the student should note which questions are included, from the underlined header. *Example:*

The drawing shows the path of a projectile that was launched at an angle from the ground, with point A just after the projectile leaves the ground and point E just before the projectile hits the ground again. Use the labeled points on the diagram to answer the questions that follow. Neglect air friction.

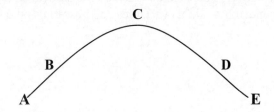

2. When is the velocity zero?
   A. points A and E
   B. point C
   C. points A and B
   D. points A, C, and E
   E. at no point

3. When is the acceleration zero?
   A. points A and E
   B. point C
   C. points A and B
   D. points A, C, and E
   E. at no point

4. When is the speed of the projectile a minimum?
   A. points A and E
   B. point C
   C. points A and B
   D. points A, C, and E
   E. at no point

Answers:
2. **E** By reading the stem given with the diagram, it's clear that the projectile is moving at points A and E. Even though the vertical velocity is zero at point C (the peak of the parabola), the projectile still has horizontal velocity.
3. **E** A gravitational force acts on the projectile during the entire trip, so the acceleration is always *g*.
4. **B** Since the projectile has a constant horizontal velocity component in the absence of air friction, the velocity is minimum at point C, where the vertical velocity is zero.

(3) <u>Questions presented as a table</u> generally have answer choices that have a combination of statements that must all be true in order for that answer choice to be true. *Example:*

5. What must be true for an object to be in equilibrium?

	velocity	**acceleration**
A.	constant, nonzero	constant, nonzero
B.	positive	positive
C.	constant, zero or nonzero	equal to zero
D.	equal to zero	constant
E.	constantly changing	constantly changing

Answer: **C** Since there would be no net force on the object at equilibrium, acceleration must be zero and velocity must be constant (either zero or a constant value).

(4) <u>Graphical interpretation</u> questions may show up in any of the other styles or groups—either as part of the "stem" for the question(s) or as answer choices to questions. The student should be well familiar with independent (*x*-values) and dependent (*y*-values) variables and how to use the slopes and areas to come to conclusions. *Example*:

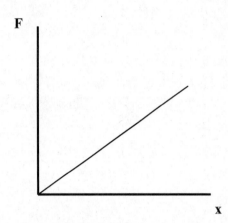

6. The above graph represents the trend for data gathered by adding masses to a spring and plotting the weight of each mass added, **F**, as a function of the distance the spring stretched, **x**. The slope of this plot would represent:
   A. work done on the spring in stretching
   B. work done by the spring as it was stretched
   C. potential energy of the spring
   D. kinetic energy of the spring
   E. elastic spring constant

   Answer: **E** From Hooke's Law, $\mathbf{F} = k\mathbf{x}$, the applied force is directly proportional to the extension distance of the spring. The elastic spring constant, k, is the constant of proportionality and thus the slope of the graph.

(5) <u>Conceptual questions</u> are common on the exam, as most questions are written to determine students' understanding of concepts rather than ability to memorize facts. *Example:*

7. Collisions between two objects that involve no net force during the collision:
   A. conserve only kinetic energy
   B. are always elastic
   C. conserve both momentum and kinetic energy
   D. conserve momentum
   E. are always inelastic

   Answer: **D** Since such a collision will conserve momentum but not necessarily kinetic energy, we don't have enough information to determine whether or not the collision is elastic. Thus we can conclude only that the collision conserves momentum.

(6) <u>Symbolic questions</u> use only the symbols for variables. Answers to these can occasionally be determined by examining the units on variables and comparing the result to units on the desired answer. *Example:*

8. A rock of mass m is thrown horizontally at a speed v from a cliff of height h. The rock's final kinetic energy as it hits the ground below is:

A. mgh
B. mv^2/h
C. $\frac{1}{2}mv^2 + mgh$
D. $\frac{1}{2}mv^2$
E. mv

Answer: **C** The total kinetic energy at the base of the cliff is the original kinetic energy of the rock as it leaves the thrower's hand plus the kinetic energy gained as the rock falls the distance h, which is equal to the loss in gravitational potential energy.

(7) <u>Choice Combination</u> questions provide three answer choices that may be used in combination for the final answer. The key to these questions is determining which of the choices is(are) correct—or narrowing the answer selection. Sometimes, by eliminating just one of the answer choices, the final answer will become apparent by the combination remaining after you eliminate that answer from the selections. *Example:*

9. Which of the following statements are true for totally inelastic collisions?

    I. Total mechanical energy is conserved.
   II. Momentum is conserved.
  III. The objects stick together.

  A. **I**
  B. **II**
  C. **I** and **II**
  D. **II** and **III**
  E. **I, II,** and **III**

Answer: **D** Since the collision is totally inelastic, the colliding objects stick together and become one mass after the collision. Thus, choice I is not true and we can immediately eliminate answer choices A, C, and E. Even if we are not sure about statements II and III, we have narrowed the answer selection to choices B or D.

Exam Section II – Free Response: This section consists of <u>six or seven Free Response questions</u> to be completed in a <u>ninety-minute</u> time period. The student may use a calculator on this section of the exam, and both a sheet of Equations and Table of Information are provided. The point value of each question may vary from ten to fifteen points, clearly stated on the question. In recent years, directions at the beginning of each question also carry a recommendation for the amount of time to be spent on that question. Topics for these questions are generally distributed according to the topic percentages in the AP syllabus, with some questions blending several different topics. However, to avoid unreasonably "contrived" situations that try to exactly match those percentages, the topics on this section are only loosely matched to the syllabus, with the difference made up by questions on the Multiple Choice section. The student may notice, for example, an abundance of questions on the topic of fluids on the Multiple Choice part if there are no fluids questions on the Free Response.

Since there are no penalties for guessing on the Free Response section, the student is advised to try every question, making the best effort possible to provide an answer in each space. As you take the Free Response test, remember that scoring is based upon work shown in the space provided. On each problem, clearly show the formulas used with substitution of values and units. There is no penalty for substitution of an incorrect value obtained from a previous section. Thus, if a value is needed from a previous section that you were not able to work, you might define a value to substitute by simply stating, for example, "assume that the answer to part (a) is 2 m/s". Then use that value in your substitution and go ahead with the solution of the problem. [Note: It's not advisable to select the number one as a substitute answer, since there is the temptation for that "1" to become an assumed value in later calculations—and not count for substitute credit.] <u>Keep in mind that the readers who score the Free Response section of the A.P. Physics Exam are looking for indications that you understand the physics of the problem</u>. Communicate what you know to the readers by showing your work clearly and explaining your reasoning in brief but clear statements. No extra credit is given to lengthy answers, and a student will sometimes lose credit by saying too much and contradicting a previous correct statement.

Even though duplicate Free Response questions are provided in a pink booklet and a green one, the pink copy is the only one that is sent in for scoring. Since time is limited, do all your work on the pink copy and use the green copy only for reference as you work. Generally speaking, you want to spend the same number of minutes on each problem as the point value of the problem. However, recent tests are providing the student with a recommended time frame for each problem that may or may not correspond to the point value.

Students are often asked to provide conceptual justifications or explanations for problem situations, and it is helpful to understand some key phrases that test writers often use:
> (1) "Calculate" means show all the work leading to your final answer, whether it is numerical or symbolic.
> (2) "What is" and "determine" simply mean give the answer. Work leading to the answer does not have to be explicitly shown, since it may be easily obvious—but it's always a good idea to show your thinking if time allows.
> (3) "Derive" means the student should start with a fundamental equation (perhaps one from the equation sheet), then clearly show all substitutions of symbols or numerical values and all steps to the solution.
> (4) The words "justify" and "explain" mean the student should back up the answer with explanations, calculations, diagram, sketches, graphs, equations—anything that helps to clarify and point out why the answer works or how it was obtained.

Scoring: For <u>multiple-choice</u> questions, there is a penalty for answering incorrectly, as opposed to leaving the question blank. The base score on this section is:

> *(Number of questions answered correctly) - ¼ (Number of questions answered incorrectly)*

For example, suppose a student answered 40 of the 70 multiple-choice questions correctly, left 10 questions blank, and answered 20 questions incorrectly. That student's score would be calculated thus: $40 - ¼ (20) = 35$.

Since the multiple-choice section counts as half the overall score on the exam, the score on the multiple choice section is multiplied by a factor 1.286 (or by 90/70) to make the value of that section equivalent to the 90 points assigned to the free-response section. In the example above, the student has then made a multiple-choice score of 35 x 1.286, or 45 points, which will be added to the free-response score to obtain the test total.

Each <u>free-response</u> question is assigned a point value, usually 10 or 15 points, for scoring. The faculty consultants scoring a particular question set up scoring guidelines that define carefully what answers will be accepted for each section of that question and how many points will be assigned to each section. Each paper is then assigned a score from 0 to 10 or 0 to 15, based up the quality and accuracy of answers. The total score on the free-response section is simply the sum of the scores on each of the questions, for a maximum possible score of 90 points. The free-response total is added to the multiple-choice score to determine the final test score.

SECTION II
REVIEWING THE PHYSICS
The AP Syllabus and Walker's Text, <u>Physics</u>, 3rd Edition*

Each of Chapters 1 through 32 in this section correlates to a chapter in Walker's <u>Physics</u>. Within each review chapter, references to specific sections, page numbers, diagrams, and sample problems within Walker's <u>Physics</u> help to focus on material that will be covered on the exam as you review. The following features are designed to focus the review on AP topics:

- **<u>Chapter Titles:</u>** Each chapter is numbered and titled identically to Walker's text.

- **<u>Equations:</u>** Equations developed in each chapter are highlighted for reference, using the same symbols for variables that are used on the AP* Examination Formula Sheet.

- **<u>Overview:</u>** In each chapter, main topics and related equations are highlighted, along with clarifications of the scope of each topic that might be expected on the examination.

- **<u>Sample Questions:</u>** At the end of each chapter, sample multiple-choice questions similar to actual AP* questions allow the student to self-test on those topics before moving on to the next chapter. For best practice, these should be answered without the aid of formula sheets or calculator. However, reference to the Table of Information would be appropriate when necessary.

- **<u>Sample Problems:</u>** Free-response questions allow the student to apply concepts to the solutions of related problems. Reference to the Equations Sheet and Table of Information would be appropriate here, as well as use of a calculator.

- **<u>Solutions to Sample Questions and Problems:</u>** The correct answer and explanation is given for each sample multiple-choice question, and a complete solution is provided for each free-response problem, along with important techniques and hints for quick solution.

- ▶**<u>Recommended Problems for Further Practice:</u>** If the student needs more work on that topic, recommended problems from the textbook are provided. Though any work from the problems provided in the text would be helpful, the problems selected are those that most closely resemble both topic and style that might be experienced on the AP Examination. The problems selected either have solutions provided within the text or have answers provided at the back of the book.

- √ **<u>Reminders:</u>** Special hints or references are provided to help the student with solution insights or to help the student avoid common errors on the exam. It would be helpful to go over all of these just prior to exam day.

Chapter 1

Introduction and Mathematical Review

Although the Advanced Placement Physics B Examination does not require the use of calculus for any solutions, advanced algebra skills and knowledge of trigonometric relationships are essential. Additionally, it is helpful to have a working knowledge of vectors.

Geometry and Trigonometry
The following equation list is provided only on the free-response section of the exam. Familiarity with these relationships should also be helpful on the multiple-choice section.

Equations

Area of rectangle: $A = bh$
Area of triangle: $A = \frac{1}{2} bh$
Volume of parallelepiped: $V = lwh$
Circumference of circle: $C = 2\pi r$
Area of circle: $A = \pi r^2$
Volume of cylinder: $V = \pi r^2 h$
Surface area of cylinder: $A = 2\pi r l + 2\pi r^2$
Volume of sphere: $V = \frac{4}{3} \pi r^3$
Surface area of sphere: $A = 4\pi r^2$

Right triangle trigonometry:

$$a^2 + b^2 = c^2$$
$$\sin \theta = \frac{a}{c}$$
$$\cos \theta = \frac{b}{c}$$
$$\tan \theta = \frac{a}{b}$$

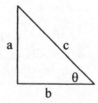

Even though the information sheet provided on both sections of the exam contains sine, cosine, and tangent functions for 30°, 45°, and 60°, it is often helpful to be able to recognize quickly the relationships between side lengths in several special triangles. These "special" triangles are often used in question development, and knowing the ratios of lengths of two sides can help you quickly determine the length of a third side.

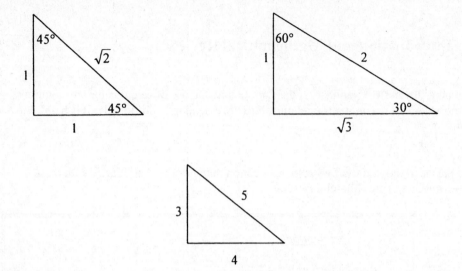

Vectors

Remembering that a vector has both magnitude and direction, the student should be aware in reading questions that questions often ask only for the magnitude in the answer to a question involving vector quantities. Thus, a numerical answer with units will suffice, and a direction is then not required. It is important, when asked to draw vectors (e.g., forces on free body diagrams) to put the arrows on them indicating the direction. <u>In this text, and on the AP* Equations Sheet, **vector** quantities will be shown in **bold** font.</u>

When adding vectors diagrammatically to find the vector resultant, remember to add them "tip to tail," with the resultant from the beginning of the first vector to the end of last. As an example:

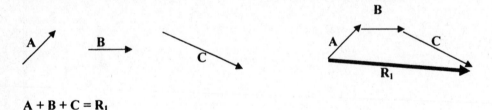

A + B + C = R₁

As in simple mathematics with numbers, subtraction is simply the addition of a negative. The same applies to vectors, so subtracting a vector is the same as adding its negative. The negative of a vector has the same magnitude as the vector but the opposite direction:

Here's another example, using the same three vectors defined in the first example:

A + B − C = A + B + (-C) = R₂

Unit Vectors and Multiplying Vectors

The AP* Physics B Syllabus does not strictly include or require solutions using the methods of vector calculus. However, the concepts underlying vector products are essential to the understanding of physics, and using straightforward methods of finding these products can simplify many solutions. Thus, the discussion that follows regarding unit vectors and vector and scalar products is not essential for your preparation for the B Examination but is provided as a tool if you feel ready to use it.

The **scalar product**, or "dot" product, of two vectors is written as **A·B** and is defined as $|AB|\cos\theta$. This product of two vectors results in a scalar value. Essentially, the dot product finds the product of the components of those vectors that lie in the same direction. An example of scalar product is in determining work, where the force and displacement are both vectors, and the work is found by finding the components of force and displacement that are in the same direction.

Example: In the diagram, a 10 Newton force acting at an angle 30° above horizontal pushes an object 5.0 meters across a smooth, level surface.

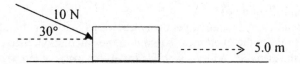

Work done, ignoring friction, in moving the object can be found by using the formula:

$$W = Fs\,\cos\theta$$
$$W = (10\ N)(5.0\ m)(\cos 30°) = 43\ joules$$

Using the scalar product method, work done is the dot product of the force and displacement. To find the dot product, we find the component of force that lies in the same direction as the displacement. That component is F cos 30°, so we get the same answer as before:

$$W = \boldsymbol{F\cdot s} = (F\cos 30°)(s) = (10\cos 30°\ N)(5.0\ m) = 43\ joules$$

The **vector product**, or "cross" product, of two vectors is written as **AxB** and is defined as $|AB|\sin\theta$. This product of two vectors results in a quantity that is also a vector. Essentially, the cross product finds the product of the components of those vectors that lie perpendicular to each other. This new vector then has a direction that is determined using the **right-hand rule**—or lies in a third dimension to the component vectors. For example, if we have a vector that lies along the *x*-axis crossed with a vector that lies along the *y*-axis, the cross product of those vectors will be in the direction of the *z*-axis. To determine the direction of a vector cross product, use the fingers of your right hand in the following way:

1. Orient your fingers so your index finger points ahead of you, your other fingers point to your left, and your thumb points to the ceiling.
2. Your right hand should be creating a three-dimensional set of directions so that your index finger, other fingers, and thumb are all perpendicular to each other.
3. To use the right-hand rule, use your index finger as the first vector and your fingers as the second vector. (The order in which this is performed <u>does</u> matter.) Your thumb is the direction of the vector product.

Though vector cross products may seem a little strange, remember that this notation has simply been devised to describe what happens in nature. We will see in later chapters that there are many applications for the right-hand rule.

Unit vector notation is used to specify direction for a vector or in formulas involving vectors. A unit vector has a magnitude of one, so it does not change the magnitude of an answer when used in multiplication—only supplies a direction. The notation $\hat{x}$, for example, denotes a direction along the positive x-axis. The vector $5\hat{x}$ has a magnitude of 5 and a direction along the positive x-axis. Usually, to avoid confusion with the symbols x, y, and z, which are often used as variable unknowns, the symbols $\hat{i}$, $\hat{j}$, and $\hat{k}$ are used instead. Now, the vector $5\hat{i}$ has a magnitude of 5 and a direction along the x-axis. Likewise, the vector $4\hat{j}$ has a magnitude of 4 and a direction along the y-axis.

Now we can multiply vectors using the unit vector notation. Here are several examples:

$(3\hat{i}) \times (4\hat{j}) = 12\hat{k}$, a vector of magnitude 12 in the positive z direction

$(3\hat{j}) \times (-4\hat{k}) = -12\hat{i}$, a vector of magnitude 12 in the negative x direction.

Note that since the vectors we are multiplying here are perpendicular to each other, the magnitude of the product is $(3)(4)(\sin 90°)$, which is 12.

Estimations and Order of Magnitude [Chapter 1, Section 6]
The multiple-choice section of the exam does not allow calculators, yet many questions involve computations. The student should use space on the exam page to write the quantities required in the calculation, then cancel as much as possible, making a quick estimation of the answer. When quantities involve powers of ten, it often is necessary only to use orders of magnitude to select the correct answer from choices given. Since the exam is designed to be taken without a calculator, the answer choices should be spread out enough in value for a quick estimation to determine the correct answer. On this section, you are advised to use $g = 10$ m/s^2.

Dimensional Analysis and Units [Chapter 1, Sections 3 and 4]
Using units as you substitute values for variables to make your calculations can not only assure that you have made the necessary conversions but can help in determining relationships in formulas in those situations on the Multiple Choice section when you are not provided formulas. Occasionally, the units on multiple-choice answers can be a giveaway to the correct answer. On Free Response, points are often assigned for the correct units on answers.

Graphing and Graphical Analysis
Analysis of information from graphs will show up on both the multiple-choice and the free-response sections of the AP* Examination. Often, questions will involve simply reading values from the graph and using those values to answer questions. However, it is also very important to understand the meanings of slope and area in relationship to each graphical representation of data. Examples of these will be given within each chapter review.

When presented with data to graph, remember that the **independent variables** are generally plotted on the x-axis and the **dependent variables** are plotted on the y-axis. The graph title is then "*y vs. x*", meaning "*y is a function of x*" or the "*dependent variable is a function of the independent variable*". For example, if you are given time and velocity data for an experiment and instructed to plot "*Velocity versus Time,*" the velocity values will be plotted on the y-axis and time values on the x-axis. If the data points appear to form a linear pattern, draw a **best-fit line** through the points, leaving about the same number of points on each side of the line. If the pattern of points is not linear, look for one of the following common curves, with which you should be familiar:

Power Curve

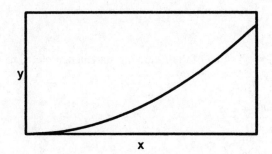

Equation: $y = kx^2$

Root Curve

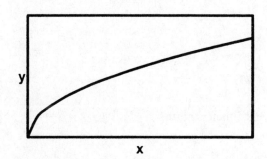

Equation: $y = k\sqrt{x}$

Inverse Curve

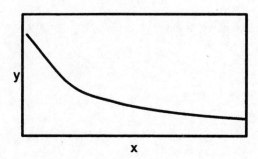

Equation: $y = \dfrac{k}{x}$

Sample Questions

1. If Rick walks the dog 6 blocks north and then 8 blocks east, what is the magnitude of his displacement for the walk?
    A. 2 blocks
    B. 4 blocks
    C. 8 blocks
    D. 10 blocks
    E. 14 blocks

2. The above plot represents displacement as a function of time. Which of the following statements related to the graph is correct?
A. If time is doubled, the displacement will also double.
B. If time is doubled, the displacement will remain unchanged.
C. If time is doubled, the displacement will quadruple.
D. If time is doubled, the displacement will increase by a factor $\sqrt{2}$.
E. If time is doubled, the displacement will decrease by a factor ½ .

3. Given the equation $s = v_o t + \frac{1}{2} a t^2$ and values $s = 640$ m, $t = 4$ s, and $a = 16$ m/s^2, determine the value of v_0. (Remember: No calculator.)
A. 0 m/s
B. 32 m/s
C. 64 m/s
D. 128 m/s
E. 192 m/s

4. What would be the vector cross product of 6 newtons east and 5 meters north?
A. 30 m north
B. 30 N north
C. 30 N·m up
D. 30 N·m down
E. 30 N·m south

5. What would be the vector cross product of 5 meters north and 6 newtons east?
A. 30 m north
B. 30 N north
C. 30 N·m up
D. 30 N·m down
E. 30 N·m south

Sample Problem

Graph the following data, draw a best-fit line, and determine the slope.

mass (kg)	force (N)
0.5	1.3
1	2.67
1.5	3.72
2	4.65
2.5	6.34
3	6.67
3.5	8.4

SOLUTIONS TO SAMPLE QUESTIONS AND SAMPLE PROBLEMS

Multiple Choice Questions:

1. D The 6-block and 8-block segments are legs of a right triangle, with the displacement (difference between final position and original position) as the hypotenuse of that triangle. This special triangle should be recognized as a 3-4-5 right triangle, with the same ratios 6-8-10. Thus, the displacement is 10 blocks.

2. C Since the graph appears to be a power curve of form $y = kx^2$, regardless of the value of k, doubling the value on the x-axis (time) would result in that term being squared to produce a quadrupled value of the y-axis value, which is displacement.

3. D Substituting the values given: $640\ m = v_o(4\ s) + \frac{1}{2}\ (16\ m/s^2)(4\ s)^2$

Now solve and cancel terms where possible : $v_o = \dfrac{640 - (8)(16)}{4} = 160 - 32 = 128\ m/s$

4. C First, the magnitude of the product would be the product of the numerical values (since they are perpendicular and sin 90° equals 1). However, we also need to use the product of the units, which eliminates answers A and B. Now, using the right-hand rule: (1) index finger points east, (2) other fingers point north, (3) thumb points up. The vector product is upward.

5. D We find the solution in a manner similar to question 4, but in this case the order of the product is different, so the direction of the vector product is different. The magnitude is still 30 N-m. To use the right-hand rule: (a) index finger points north, (2) other fingers point east, (3) thumb now points down. The vector product is downward.

Free Response Problem:

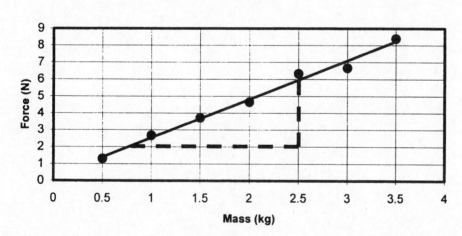

Force vs. Mass

By convention, the first column on the data table is the independent variable, so mass is placed on the x-axis and force is placed on the y-axis. Once an appropriate scale is selected for each axis so the graph fills the given space, the data points are plotted and a best-fit line is constructed. The best-fit line is not extended to the point 0,0 unless that data point is given or unless there is evidence that the force is, indeed, zero when mass is zero. Two points on the line that are easily readable are selected to determine "rise over run" for the slope. Here, we have selected the points (2.5, 6.0) and (0.75, 2.0). Note that the slope carries the units given from the data.

$$slope = \frac{6.0\ N - 2.0\ N}{2.5\ kg - 0.75\ kg} = \textbf{2.29}\ \frac{N}{kg}$$

► **Recommended for further practice (Walker, 3rd ed.):**
- Review Example 1–2 on page 9 and Example 1–3 on page 10, along with the solution methods.
- Chapter Summary on pages 13–14
- Problems on pages 14–16: 9, 29, and 45

√**Reminders**:
- Use the points on a best-fit line—not data points from the data table—to determine slope.
- Slopes have units associated with them—the y-axis units divided by the x-axis units.
- When making any calculations, use the units on substituted values to check for appropriate units on answers and to verify that all units are correctly converted.

PART 1

MECHANICS

Chapter 2

One-Dimensional Kinematics

Equations

Final speed: $v = v_o + at$

Change in position: $x = x_o + v_o t + \frac{1}{2} at^2$

Final speed: $v^2 = v_o^2 + 2a(x - x_o)$

The **kinematics** of an object describes its motion. In this chapter, we will restrict that motion to **translational** motion, where the center of mass of an object changes position, but the object itself does not spin or rotate around its center of mass. That motion will be discussed in a later chapter.

Though the introduction to vectors occurs in the next chapter, it is important to understand the differences between **vector** quantities that have both magnitude and direction and **scalar** quantities that have only magnitude. The following table may help to clarify these distinctions.

Quantity	Symbol	Formula	Definition	Scalar/Vector
distance	d	$d = v_{ave}\, t$	total distance traveled, using average speed	scalar
displacement	Δx	$\Delta x = x - x_o$	change in position	vector
average speed	v	$v = \dfrac{d}{t}$	magnitude of velocity	scalar
average velocity	v	$v = \dfrac{x - x_0}{\Delta t}$	rate of change in position	vector
acceleration	a	$a = \dfrac{v - v_0}{\Delta t}$	rate of change in velocity	vector
time	t			scalar

In each case where the quantity is a vector, it has not only a magnitude (with appropriate units) but also a direction. In one-dimensional motion, considered here, the direction can be designated with either a positive or negative sign. Thus, vector quantities can be positive, negative, or zero. Scalar quantities can only be positive For example, if an object moving toward the west is assigned a positive velocity, then movement to the east is negative. For the same object, a positive acceleration would mean an increase in velocity to the west and a negative acceleration could mean either a decrease in velocity to the west or an increase in velocity to the east.

In addition to the kinematic equations listed in the table above, this equation will be useful:

$$v^2 = v_o^2 + 2a(x - x_o)$$

On the AP*, v^2 is "final velocity squared," and $(x - x_o)$ or Δx is "change in position."

On the following plot of **position as a function of time**, x is the object's position, which could be either horizontal or vertical.

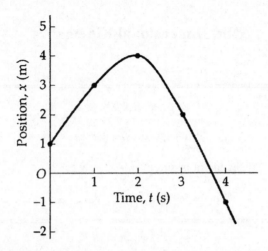

As positive values for position increase (during the first two seconds), the object is moving farther in the positive x-direction, and as values decrease, the object is returning to original position. In this case, the object returns to its starting position at $x = 1$ m at about 3.25 seconds and then continues moving back until it reaches a position two meters behind its starting position at $t = 4$ seconds. The **slope** of the tangent to any point on this graph would be change in position divided by change in time, which is **instantaneous velocity**. Note that from $t = 0$ to $t = 2$ seconds the slope is positive, so the object's instantaneous velocity is positive during that interval. During the interval from $t = 2$ to the end of the plot, the slope is negative. Thus, the object's instantaneous velocity is negative during this entire time, as the object moves backward. At $t = 2$ seconds, the tangent to the curve is horizontal, with zero slope, so the instantaneous velocity at that moment is zero.

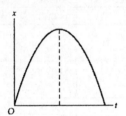

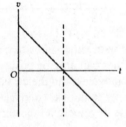

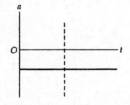

> ### Graphical Analysis Summary:
> 1. The slope of tangent to x vs. t is the instantaneous velocity at that point.
> 2. The slope of tangent to v vs. t is the instantaneous acceleration.
> 3. The area between graph line of v vs. t and the time axis is the change of position during that time interval.
> 4. The area between graph line of a vs. t and the time axis is the change in velocity during that time interval.

In the situation at left, the x vs. t graph is a curve that indicates that the object returns to its starting position. The v vs. t plot for that curve shows that the object starts with a positive velocity and halfway through the given time the object has a velocity of zero—then turns and has a negative velocity. The positive area and negative area under this graph line are equal, so the net change in position is zero, meaning no net displacement at the end of the trip. The a vs. t plot shows constant negative acceleration throughout the trip. The area under that graph line is the total change in velocity for the trip.

An object in free fall under the influence of gravity experiences a constant downward acceleration, known as g, which has a value of 9.81 m/s^2 near Earth's surface. An object dropped at $t = 0$ will have an initial velocity of zero. After falling one second (assume no air friction), the acceleration g means the object has gained 9.81 m/s of speed during that one second. The average velocity during that first second is the average of 0 and 9.81 m/s, which is 4.91 m/s. Thus, the object falls 4.91 meters during that first second.

During the interval from $t = 1$ s to $t = 2$ s, the object gains another 9.8 m/s of speed, so the object's instantaneous velocity after two seconds is 19.6 m/s. The object's average velocity during the 2nd second of fall is the average of 9.8 m/s and 19.6 m/s, or 14.7 m/s. Thus, the object falls another 14.7 meters in the 2nd second, for a total displacement downward of 19.6 meters.

This pattern continues for the duration of the object's fall. **Galileo's Law of Odd Numbers** states that, for an object that falls from rest, the distance the object falls during each time interval follows odd number multiples—falling 4.9 meters in the 1st second, 14.7 meters (3 x 4.9) during the 2nd second, 24.5 (5 x 4.9) meters in the 3rd second, 34.3 meters (7 x 4.9) in the 4th second, and so on. Two more observations are key: (1) The instantaneous velocity after a given time interval is directly proportional to the time; and (2) The total downward displacement after a given time interval is proportional to the square of the time.

$$v = v_o + gt$$

$t_0 = 0$	$v_0 = 0$	$x_0 = 0$
$t_1 = 1$ s	$v_1 = 9.8$ m/s	$x_1 = 4.9$ m
$t_2 = 2$ s	$v_2 = 19.6$ m/s	$x_2 = 19.6$ m
$t_3 = 3$ s	$v_3 = 29.4$ m/s	$x_3 = 44.1$ m
$t_4 = 4$ s	$v_4 = 39.2$ m/s	$x_4 = 78.4$ m

$$x = x_o + v_0t + \tfrac{1}{2} gt^2$$

[Note: Throughout this text and on the AP* Exam, a value of 9.8 m/s^2 will be used for g, except on Multiple Choice questions where 10 m/s^2 will be used for estimations without the use of a calculator. Either value is accepted during scoring of AP* Exams.]

Sample Questions
[Note: Use 10 m/s² for g.]

1. A hockey puck sliding across ice at 8 m/s comes to a stop in 2 seconds. What is the average acceleration of the puck?
   A. -4 m/s^2
   B. -2 m/s^2
   C. -1 m/s^2
   D. 2 m/s^2
   E. 4 m/s^2

2. What is the instantaneous speed of a rock that has fallen for 2 seconds, starting from rest?
   A. 2 m/s
   B. 5 m/s
   C. 10 m/s
   D. 20 m/s
   E. 30 m/s

Questions 3-5. A ball is thrown upward with an initial velocity of 20 m/s.

3. What is its position above the thrower's hand and instantaneous velocity after 2 seconds?

	Velocity	Position
A.	+10 m/s	5 m
B.	+10 m/s	20 m
C.	0	20 m
D.	−10 m/s	10 m
E.	−10 m/s	15 m

4. What is the ball's average velocity between $t = 1$ and $t = 4$ seconds?
   A. 10 m/s
   B. 5 m/s
   C. 0
   D. −5 m/s
   E. −10 m/s

5. How long is the ball in the air?
   A. 2 s
   B. 3 s
   C. 4 s
   D. 5 s
   E. 6 s

Sample Problem

1. The graph below describes the motion of an object along a straight horizontal track, with the object initially moving forward on the track.

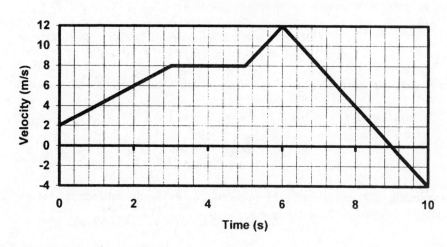

Velocity vs. Time

(a) Find the instantaneous acceleration of the object at $t = 2$ seconds.

(b) Find the change in position of the object from $t = 6$ seconds to $t = 9$ seconds.

(c) During what time period is the object moving backward?

(d) At what time(s) is the object not moving at all?

(e) At what time(s) is the object's speed equal to 2 m/s?

SOLUTIONS TO SAMPLE QUESTIONS AND SAMPLE PROBLEM

Multiple Choice Questions:

1. **A** Use the equation $v = v_o + at$, with initial velocity 8 m/s, final velocity zero, and time 2 seconds:

$$a = \frac{v - v_o}{\Delta t} = \frac{0 - 8\,m/s}{2\,s} = -4\,m/s^2$$

Note that setting the problem up correctly yields the necessary negative acceleration, confirming that the object's velocity is decreasing.

2. **D** Use the equation $v = v_o + at$, with initial velocity zero, time 2 seconds, and acceleration 9.8 m/s²:

$$v = 0 + (10\,m/s^2)(2\,s) = 20\,m/s$$

Chapter 2 – One-Dimensional Kinematics

Note: Here we worked the problem by making the direction of motion, down, a positive value. This is evident by the fact that the value of g is positive. If we had made the direction down negative, a negative value for g would have been used, and the final velocity would also have been negative—simply meaning down. However, this problem only asks for speed, so the answer is positive either way.

3. C Two quick calculations are necessary for this solution, with the observation that the positive value on the initial velocity upward sets the up direction positive and thus down negative in this problem:

$$(1)\ v = v_o + at = 20\ m/s + (-10\ m/s^2)(2\ s) = 0$$
$$(2)\ \Delta x = v_o t + \tfrac{1}{2}\,at^2 = (20\ m/s)(2\ s) + \tfrac{1}{2}\,(-10\ m/s^2)(2\ s)^2 = 20\ m$$

Note: The object is, then, located at the peak of its motion, which is 20 meters above the ground.

4. D First, find the instantaneous velocities at t = 1 s and t = 4 s:

$$v_1 = v_o + at = 20\ m/s + (-10\ m/s^2)(1\ s) = 10\ m/s$$
$$v_4 = v_o + at = 20\ m/s + (-10\ m/s^2)(4\ s) = -20\ m/s$$

Then, since the acceleration is constant during this interval (-10 m/s² for the entire trip), average the two velocities

$$v_{ave} = \frac{v_o + v_f}{2} = \frac{10\ m/s + ^- 20\ m/s}{2} = -5\ m/s$$

5. C Let's consider a couple of ways to do this one:
   (1) Using the knowledge that the initial and final positions of the ball will be the same, so the change in position for the entire trip is zero:
$$\Delta x = v_o t + \tfrac{1}{2}\,at^2$$
$$0 = (20\ m/s)t + \tfrac{1}{2}\,(-10\ m/s^2)t^2$$
$$0 = 20 - 5t$$
$$t = 4\ s$$

   (2) Using the knowledge that without air resistance the ball's final velocity will be the same magnitude but opposite sign of its initial velocity:
$$v_f = v_o + at$$
$$-20\ m/s = +20\ m/s + (-10\ m/s^2)t$$
$$t = 4\ s$$

Free Response Problem:

1. (a) We recognize that the slope of the graph at any given point is the instantaneous acceleration. Since the slope is constant from $t = 0$ to $t = 3$, we can calculate the slope for that entire segment:

$$Acceleration = slope = \frac{rise}{run} = \frac{8\ m/s - 2\ m/s}{3\ s - 0} = 2\ m/s^2$$

(b) The graph lies entirely above the x-axis during the time from 6 seconds to 9 seconds, so the object is traveling forward (since the initial velocity was forward in the problem). The velocity is linear, so the acceleration is constant during this time. Thus, the area between the graph line and the x-axis is the change in position. (See next page.)

$$Distance = area = \tfrac{1}{2}\,Bh = \tfrac{1}{2}\,(3\ s)(12\ s) = 18\ m.$$

Velocity vs. Time

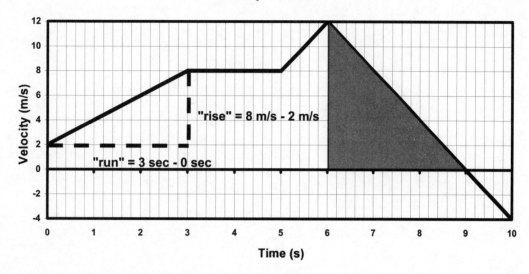

(c) The problem tells us that the object is initially moving forward, which sets forward velocity as positive. Thus, the object is only moving backward when the velocity is negative—**from 9 to 10 seconds**.

(d) The object is not moving when its velocity is zero—instantaneously **at 9 seconds**.

(e) Since speed is the magnitude of the velocity, the object has a speed of 2 m/s at times **0** seconds, **8.5** seconds, and **9.5** seconds.

▶ **Recommended for further practice (Walker, 3rd ed.):**
- Graphical Interpretation on pages 22–23
- Problem Solving Summary, page 45
- Chapter Summary on pages 43–35
- Problems on pages 47–54: 21, 29, 33, 37, 51, 61, 75, 79, 81, 99

√ **Reminders:**
- Assign positive and negative signs consistently to vector quantities such as displacement, velocity, and acceleration.
- It is usually simpler to make motion upward positive and motion downward negative for an object's vertical motion, and, in the horizontal, make the direction of motion positive and any quantity opposite the direction of motion negative.
- For the AP* Exam, use 10 m/s^2 on the Multiple Choice section and either 9.8 or 10 m/s^2 on the Free Response section (though it's important to show clearly in calculations on the Free Response which value was used).
- Do not get into the habit of automatically assigning a negative sign to the gravitational constant, g. Make the sign of g consistent with other vector quantities in the problem, and watch for redundant negative signs that have gravity pushing your object upward!
- Neglecting the effects of air friction, the mass of an object does not affect its motion under the influence of gravity.
- Acceleration is defined as any change in speed or direction.

Chapter 3

Vectors

Vector quantities, such as displacement, velocity, acceleration, and force, require both magnitude and direction to be completely defined. **Scalar** quantities, such as time and energy, have only magnitude. Chapter 1 contains further review of vectors, including vector cross products and dot products. In this text, as well as on the AP* Physics Equations Sheet, <u>the symbols for vector quantities are shown in **bold** font.</u> For example, in the equation for Newton's Second Law, $\mathbf{F} = \mathbf{ma}$, both force and acceleration are vector quantities, and mass is a scalar quantity.

When dealing with vector quantities in one dimension (or along a linear path), it's easy to indicate a vector's direction by assigning a positive or negative value to the magnitude of the vector. If one direction is positive, then the opposite direction is negative. For example, an object moving to the right assigned a positive velocity would have a negative velocity when moving to the left. In another situation, if we decide to assign an object moving upward a positive velocity, then the constant acceleration due to gravity on that object would be negative, since it is constantly downward throughout the trip. Adding two vectors in one dimension is simply a matter of adding their positive or negative values.

<u>Example</u>: Find the vector sum of the displacements 3 meters east, 4 meters west, and 5 meters east.
<u>Solution</u>: If the vectors directed toward the east are assigned positive values, then the vector directed west is given a negative value, so the answer is the sum of +3m, -4m, and +5 m. The **resultant** displacement is 4 meters east.

When combining vector quantities in two dimensions, it's necessary to find vector **components** and add those components in each direction. Before finding components, however, a **frame of reference** must be set up, defining the *x*-direction and *y*-direction.

<u>Example</u>: Find the vector sum of the displacements 3 meters east, 4 meters at 30° north of east, and 5 meters west.

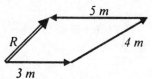

<u>Solution</u>: Adding them "tip to tail," as shown above, we can see the resultant graphically, but finding the magnitude and direction of the resultant requires direct measurements which can be slow and inaccurate. An accurate, quick way to find the resultant is shown below.

(1) Define the coordinates, choosing east in the x-direction, north in the y-direction, etc., and sketch the vectors.

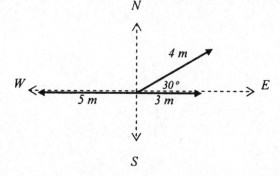

(2) For any vector not aligned in the defined coordinate directions (in this case the 4-meter displacement), split the vector into its components.

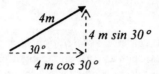

(3) Add vectors and components in the same coordinate direction separately:

   x: $3\,m + 4\,m\,cos30° + (-5\,m) = 1.5\,m$
   y: $0 + 4\,m\,sin30° + 0 = 2.0\,m$

(4) Combine the x and y components, using the Pythagorean Theorem to obtain the magnitude of R:

   $R = [(1.5\,m)^2 + (2.0\,m)^2]^{1/2} = 2.5\,m$

(5) Find the direction of R, using the tangent:

   $tan\,\theta = \dfrac{R_y}{R_x} = \dfrac{m}{1.5\,m} = \dfrac{2.0\,m}{1.5\,m}$ $\theta = 53°$

(6) Identify the resultant vector:

   $R = 2.5\,m\ at\ 53°\ north\ of\ east$

[Note: We know where to place the angle by identifying the quadrant in which the vector lies. Since both the x and y components are positive, the resultant vector lies in Quadrant I, so it is "north of east" by our previous definitions of direction.]

In subsequent chapters, there will be many situations where it will be necessary to find vector components.

Sample Questions

1. **Vector A** and **vector B** are shown here. Which choice below correctly shows the resultant of **A + B**?

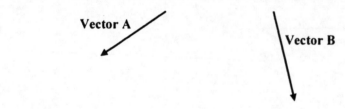

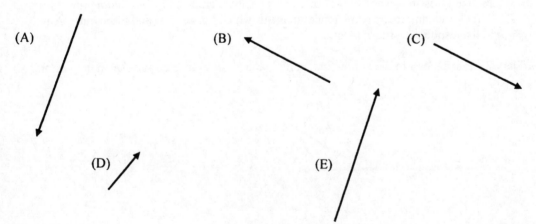

2. Using the same vectors and answer choices as in Question 1, which choice among those on the previous page correctly shows the resultant of **A** − **B**?

3. A velocity vector of 10 m/s is directed at 30 degrees above the positive *x*-axis.
   What is the magnitude of its *y*-component?
   A. 5.0
   B. 10 m/s
   C. 9.1 m/s
   D. 4.2 m/s
   E. 5.0 m/s

4. A vector has components 3.0 m east and 4.0 m north. What is the vector's magnitude and direction?
   A. 7.0 m northeast
   B. 7.0 m north of east
   C. 5.0 m at 37° north of east
   D. 5.0 m at 53° north of east
   E. 1.0 m at 30° north of east

5. A soccer ball is kicked with a velocity of 10 m/s at a 60-degree angle above the ground. What is the vertical component of the ball's velocity when it leaves the ground?
   A. 0
   B. 5 m/s
   C. 8.7 m/s
   D. 10 m/s
   E. 20 m/s

Sample Problems

1. Three horizontal forces are applied to a metal ring, as shown below. One of the forces is 10 newtons, and a second force is 12 newtons at an angle of 100° from the first. Find the third force, such that the ring is in equilibrium; i.e., the sum of the three forces is zero.

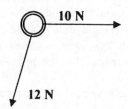

2. A boat with an engine speed of 12 m/s directs its motion straight east across a river that is flowing south at 3 m/s. What is the resultant speed and direction of the boat's path?

SOLUTIONS TO SAMPLE QUESTIONS AND SAMPLE PROBLEMS

Multiple Choice Questions:

1. A

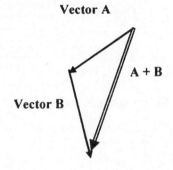

2. B

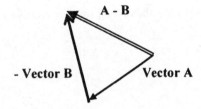

3. E

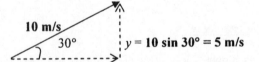 $y = 10 \sin 30° = 5$ m/s

[Note: The question asks for magnitude only, so no direction is required, but the answer must have units.]

4. D

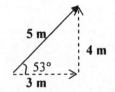

We recognize that the components 3 and 4 are the legs of one of the "special" triangles, a 3-4-5. Either you remember that the angles in this triangle are 37° and 53°, or you select the answer that is most logical. The angle must be larger than 45°, because the y-component is longer than the x-component.

5. C The vertical component of the ball's velocity is positive because we choose upward as positive, and the magnitude of the component is v sin 60°, or 8.7 m/s.

Free Response Problems:

1. For the ring to remain stationary, the force vectors in each dimension must add to zero. (We'll learn more about balancing forces in Chapters 5 and 6.) First, set up a diagram with defined x and y axes. It will make the task easier to set one of the known vectors along one of the axes.

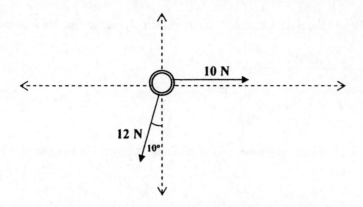

Then find components of each vector in the x and y directions and set up equations so the vector components add to zero in each direction. We'll call the unknown vector R and its components R_x and R_y.

$$x\text{-direction:} \quad 10\,N \; + \; (-12\,N\sin 10°) + R_x \; = \; 0$$
$$y\text{-direction:} \quad R_y + \; (-12\,N\cos 10°) = 0$$

[Note: We assign positive R_x and R_y in the equations without worrying about actual direction. If one of these turns out negative in the solution, we know it's in the negative direction.]

Now solve for the components of the unknown vector and use those components in the Pythagorean Theorem to find the magnitude of the vector:

$$R_x = -10\,N \; + \; 12\,N\sin 10° = -7.92\ N$$
$$R_y = 12\,N\cos 10° = 11.8\,N$$
$$R = \sqrt{7.92^2 + 11.8^2} \; = 14\,N$$

From the signs on these components, the resultant vector lies in Quadrant II. Now use the components to find the angle above the x-axis in Quadrant II.

$$\tan\theta = \frac{11.8\,N}{-7.92\,N} \quad \text{and} \quad \theta = -56°$$

The negative sine on this angle means it is measured counter-clockwise from the negative x-axis, as shown below.

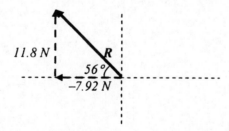

The resultant, which is the balancing force, is **14 N at an angle 136° from the 12 N force**.

2. The boat's velocity vector and the river's velocity vector will simply add to find the resultant velocity vector of the boat:

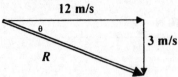

Use the Pythagorean Theorem to find the magnitude of the resultant, then use the tangent of the angle to find the angle.

$$R = \sqrt{12^2 + 3^2} = 12.4 \; m/s$$

$$tan \; \theta = \frac{3}{12} \; and \; \theta = 14°$$

The resultant vector *R* is **12 m/s at 14° south of east**.

▶ **Recommended for further practice (Walker, 3rd ed.):**
- Chapter Summary on pages 132–133
- Problems on pages 74–78: 13, 17, 33, 41, 55, 61

√ **Reminders:**
- Vectors are added graphically "tip to tail," with the resultant from beginning of first vector to end of last vector.
- Vectors are added mathematically by adding components in the *x* and *y* directions and then finding the resultant with these components using the Pythagorean Theorem.
- Subtracting one vector from another is done by adding the second vector's negative, i.e., adding a vector with the same magnitude but direction "flipped" by 180°.
- All vector quantities have both magnitude (with units) and direction. However, when a question asks only for magnitude, don't bother determining angle or direction.

Chapter 4
Two-Dimensional Kinematics

An object in **two-dimensional motion** has components of its motion in two different directions. A ball, for example, thrown at an angle into the air has one component of its velocity in the horizontal direction and another, completely independent, component of its motion in the vertical direction. If we disregard the effect of air friction on both components of motion, the ball experiences constant acceleration in the vertical direction due to the force of gravity. However, in the horizontal direction, without the effect of air friction, the ball moves at constant velocity throughout. This type of motion, sometimes called **projectile motion**, with constant velocity in one dimension and constant acceleration in the second dimension, describes a **parabolic** path for the object. Thus, in any situation where an object experiences a net force in one dimension and no force in the second dimension, the object's path will be a parabola.

Given the initial velocity, or launch velocity, of an object at some angle in two dimensions, the components of that velocity in each dimension must be used in independent equations describing the motion in each dimension. Only the time of travel, which is the same for both dimensions, links the separate and independent equations.

The equations for two-dimensional motion are not new ones, but it is helpful to develop two equations for projectile motion that can be used in any situation where air friction is considered negligible. These equations are not shown in this form on the AP* Equations List.

Projectile Motion Equations

Motion in vertical or y-direction: $y = y_0 + v_{0y}t + \frac{1}{2}gt^2$

Motion in horizontal or x-direction: $x = x_0 + v_{ox}t$

The plot on the next page describes the vertical motion of an object in free motion through the air near Earth's surface. Reading from the graph, the initial vertical velocity of the object is 29.4 m/s. If the object was launched vertically, then 29.4 m/s is also the launch velocity. Since positive values are given for the displacements, the direction "up" is defined as positive for this trip. In this diagram, a value of -9.8 m/s^2 is used for g. After one second, the object's instantaneous vertical velocity has been reduced to 19.6 m/s. After three seconds, the object's instantaneous vertical velocity is zero. However, it's very important to realize that at this moment the acceleration is still -9.8 m/s^2, and the object may still have a horizontal component of its velocity, so it is not necessarily motionless at that instant. The object's velocity is negative from three seconds to six seconds, since the slope of a tangent to the curve ($\frac{\Delta x}{\Delta t}$) is negative. After six seconds, the position of the object relative to the ground is zero, so six seconds is the time in the air. Given the horizontal velocity for this object, the horizontal distance traveled during the six seconds could be calculated.

To reinforce the concept that horizontal and vertical motions are independent of each other, consider a ball launched horizontally and a ball dropped vertically at the same instant. The vertical motion equations for both balls will be identical, since both have initial vertical velocities of zero and both experience the same gravitational acceleration. Thus, both balls will strike the ground at the same time. The ball launched horizontally will also have a horizontal motion equation, so it will travel a distance horizontally—but the horizontal trip is over at the same moment the "dropped" ball hits the ground.

Position vs Time

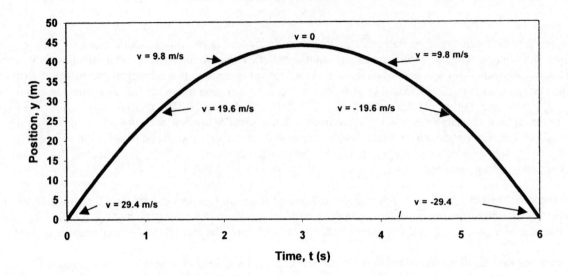

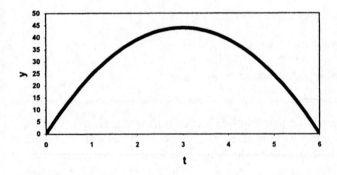

The object's vertical position as a function of time is a parabola. Since the object is launched upward from the ground, where position is defined as zero, all positions are positive. The displacement of the object for the entire trip is zero, since it ends its trip back on the ground.

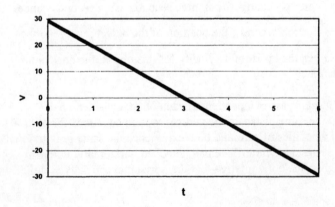

The vertical velocity as a function of time for the above motion is the set of points that are slopes of the tangents to the *Position vs. Time* curve. The object's initial vertical velocity is positive, with velocity decreasing due to the acceleration of gravity. Halfway through the vertical trip, the object's vertical velocity is zero. After that point, the vertical velocity is negative as the object now moves in the opposite direction—back toward the ground.

Acceleration vs. Time

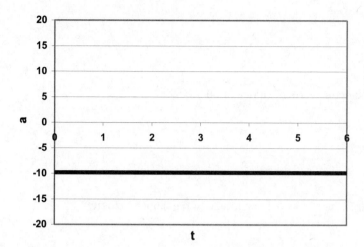

The acceleration as a function of time is a constant value, -9.8 m/s^2 near Earth's surface. At each time, the acceleration is given by the slope of the tangent to the plot of *Velocity vs Time* curve at that particular time.

Sample Questions

1. A soccer ball is kicked at a velocity of 10 m/s at a 60-degree angle above the ground. What is the ball's velocity when it is at the peak of its parabolic path?
    A. 0
    B. 5 m/s
    C. 10 m/s
    D. 8.6 m/s
    E. 2 m/s

Questions 2-5. The plot below describes the vertical motion of a ball thrown upward from the ground.

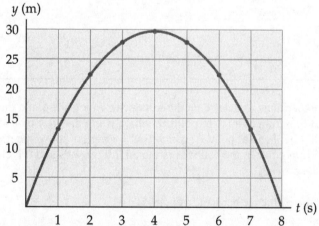

2. What is the total vertical distance traveled by the ball after 8 seconds?
    A. 0
    B. 28 m
    C. 30 m
    D. 32 m
    E. 60 m

3. What is the magnitude of the vertical displacement of the ball after 8 seconds?
   A. 0
   B. 28 m
   C. 30 m
   D. 32 m
   E. 60 m

4. What is the magnitude of the ball's instantaneous vertical velocity at 6 seconds?
   A. –15 m/s
   B. –7.5 m/s
   C. 0
   D. 7.5 m/s
   E. 15 m/s

5. If the ball was initially thrown at a 30° angle, what was the magnitude of the launch velocity?
   A. 5 m/s
   B. 10 m/s
   C. 15 m/s
   D. 20 m/s
   E. 30 m/s

Sample Problems

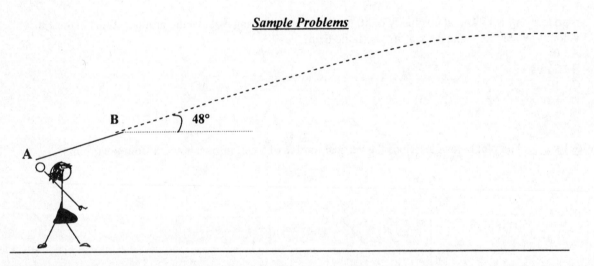

1. Mrs. Wells once did an experiment to determine the force with which she could throw a softball. The softball was accelerated in a straight line from point A to point B, which was a distance of 1.45 m. The mass of the ball was 0.142 kg, and the ball left her hand at point B, which was 1.8 meters above the ground, at an angle of 48 degrees above horizontal. From point B, the ball was in the air 2.0 seconds and traveled a horizontal distance of 16.2 meters before hitting the ground.

(a) With what velocity did the ball leave her hand at point B?

(b) What was the acceleration of the ball while it was in her hand?

(c) What was the average force she exerted on the ball while accelerating it?

(d) Mr. Phillips, another physics teacher, also performed the experiment. When he threw the ball, it was in the air exactly the same amount of time (2.0 seconds) after it left his hand, but Jim threw the ball a horizontal distance of 26 meters. How is this possible? Justify your answer with equations, but without actual calculations, in terms of the comparative force Jim exerted on the ball.

2. A kicker wishes to kick a field goal, so he sets the ball on the ground at a distance of 30 meters from the goal. Assuming he kicks the ball at an angle of 45 degrees at a speed of 27 m/s, what is the ball's height above the ground when it goes over the crossbar?

3. A pumpkin is pushed horizontally at a speed of 2.2 m/s off of a desktop that is 0.8 meters above the floor. How far from the base of the desk will the pumpkin land on the floor?

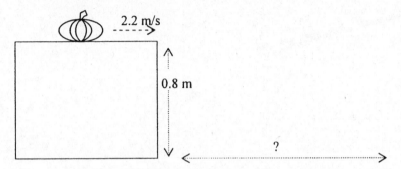

4. A pressurized air rocket fired vertically from the ground stays in the air 6.0 seconds before returning to the ground. (Neglect air resistance throughout these calculations.)

(a) Calculate the launch velocity of the rocket.

(b) How long will the rocket be in the air if it is fired at an angle of 50° with the ground?

(c) What will be the range of the rocket when it's fired at an angle of 50° with the ground?

SOLUTIONS TO SAMPLE QUESTIONS AND SAMPLE PROBLEMS

Sample Questions

1. **B** The ball's vertical velocity is zero at the peak of its motion, but it still has horizontal velocity, which is constant. The horizontal velocity is the horizontal component of the launch velocity, which is:

$$v_{ox} = v \cos 60° = (10 \ m/s)(0.5) = 5 \ m/s$$

2. E The ball is displaced 30 meters upward and then travels the same distance back to the ground, for a total distance traveled of 60 meters.

3. A The ball is displaced 30 meters upward (positive) and then is displaced 30 meters downward (negative). Thus, the sum of the two displacements is zero. Alternately, consider that for the entire trip the ball ends in the same position as it begins; thus the displacement for the entire trip is zero.

4. B

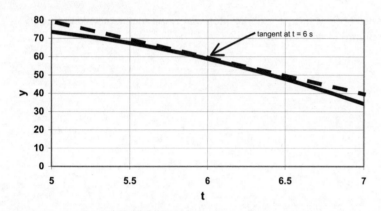

The instantaneous velocity at 6 seconds is the slope of the tangent to the curve. The section of the graph shown here isolates that part of the curve, with a tangent line drawn in (dashed line). First, we can see that the slope is negative, so the answer choices are reduced to the two negative values. Calculating a quick "rise over run," the value is less than ten, so we select the –7.5 m/s answer.

5. E In the same manner as in question 4, take a slope of the tangent to the curve at t = 0, which is about 15 m/s. That is only the vertical component of the launch velocity. If the ball was launched at a 30° angle:

$$v_{launch} \sin 30° = 15 \ m/s$$
$$v_{launch} \ (0.5) = 15$$
$$v_{launch} = 30 \ m/s$$

Sample Problems

1. (a) Use the horizontal displacement and time to find the horizontal component of the velocity:

$$x = (v_{launch} \cos 48°)(t)$$
$$16.2 \ m = v_{launch} \ (\cos 48°)(2 \ s)$$
$$v_{launch} = 12 \ m/s$$

[Note: Since the angle is measured to two significant figures, all answers on this problem are rounded to two significant figures.]

(b) Using the information give for the time the ball was in her hand:

$$v^2 = v_o^2 + 2ax$$
$$(12.1 \ m/s)^2 = 0^2 + (2)(a)(1.45 \ m)$$
$$a = 50 \ m/s^2 \ forward$$

(c) Newton's Second Law (see next chapter):

$$F = ma$$
$$F = (0.142 \, kg)(50 \, m/s^2)$$
$$F = 7.1 \, N \, forward$$

(d) By examining the two projectile motion equations, if the range, x, is larger but time is the same, then the x-component of the velocity must be larger, while the y-component is the same. Mr. Phillips' overall launch velocity is larger than Mrs. Wells'—the result of a larger force exerted on the ball during acceleration ($F = ma$).

$$y = v_{0y}t + \tfrac{1}{2} \, gt^2$$
$$x = v_{ox}t$$

2. Substitute the given values into the two equations for projectile motion, with $v_{ox} = 27 \cos 45° \, m/s$ and $v_{oy} = 27 \sin 45° \, m/s$:

$$x = v_{ox}t$$
$$30 \, m = (27 \cos 45° \, m/s) \, (t)$$
$$t = 1.57 \, s$$
$$y = v_{0y}t + \tfrac{1}{2} \, gt^2$$
$$y = (27 \sin 45° \, m/s)(1.57 \, s) + \tfrac{1}{2} \, (-9.8 \, m/s^2)(0.64 \, s)^2$$
$$y = 18 \, m$$

3. Again, substitute the given values into the two-dimensional motion equations, remembering that the pumpkin's initial velocity as it leaves the table is horizontal, so the initial y-component of velocity is zero. Note also that in the vertical motion equation both the y-displacement downward and the gravitational acceleration are made negative.

$$y = v_{0y}t + \tfrac{1}{2} \, gt^2$$
$$-0.8 \, m = (0)t + \tfrac{1}{2} \, (-9.8 \, m/s^2)t^2$$
$$t = 0.40 \, s$$
$$x = v_{ox}t$$
$$x = (2.2 \, m/s)(0.40 \, s) = 0.88 \, m$$

4. (a) Using only the y equation, with the displacement in the y-direction equal to zero for the entire trip:

$$y = v_{0y}t + \tfrac{1}{2} \, gt^2$$
$$0 = v_{oy}(6 \, s) + \tfrac{1}{2} \, (-9.8 \, m/s^2)(6 \, s)^2$$
$$v_{launch} = v_{oy} = 29 \, m/s$$

(b) Assume the launch velocity of the rocket is the same, regardless of launch angle. Use the vertical motion equation with the y-component of the launch velocity and use y displacement equal to zero for the entire trip.

$$y = v_{0y}t + \tfrac{1}{2} \, gt^2$$
$$0 = (29 \sin 50° \, m/s)(t) + \tfrac{1}{2} \, (-9.8 \, m/s^2)t^2$$
$$0 = 29 \sin 50° \, m/s - 4.9t$$
$$t = 4.6 \, s$$

(c) Apply previous results to the horizontal motion equation:

$$x = v_{ox}t$$
$$x = (29 \cos 50° \, m/s)(4.6 \, s) = 86 \, m$$

▶ **Recommended for further practice (Walker, 3rd ed.):**
- Review Section 4–5 on projectile motion.
- Chapter Summary on pages 97–99
- Problems on pages 101–104: 5, 19, 33, 41, 43, 45, 57, 69

√ **Reminders:**
- Assign a negative value to g only if other vector quantities downward are also assigned negative values.
- The horizontal and vertical motions of an object in projectile motion are independent—linked only by time, which is the same for both.
- Projectile motion is parabolic—defined by constant velocity in the x-direction and constant acceleration in the y-direction.
- The acceleration is g at every point during projectile motion.
- At the vertical peak of an object's trip in projectile motion, the vertical velocity is zero, but the horizontal velocity is constant throughout.
- The values for sine and cosine of 30°, 45°, and 60° angles are given on the Fundamental Constants sheet, which is provided on the Multiple Choice section.

Chapter 5

Newton's Laws of Motion

Equations

Newton's Second Law: $\Sigma F_x = ma_x$

Weight of an object near planet's surface: $W = mg$

Newton's three laws of motion provide the foundation for **dynamics**, the study of the causes of the motions of all objects. All three of these laws discuss **force**, which is a push or pull on an object and is a **vector** quantity— having both **magnitude** and **direction**. Another key element in any discussion of Newton's laws is **mass**, which is the amount of matter in any object, or a measure of the force that is needed to change the object's state of motion. Mass is a scalar quantity, having only magnitude—not direction.

Newton's First Law of Motion states that an object at rest remains at rest or an object in motion remains in motion with a constant velocity unless acted upon by an outside unbalanced force. This law, first proposed by Galileo, is often referred to as the **law of inertia**. In an **inertial frame of reference**, all objects and observers that are moving at the same velocity relative to each other will appear to obey Newton's Law of Inertia. (The A.P. Exam clearly states that all situations on the examination are assumed to be in an inertial frame of reference.) [Refer to example discussed on pages 111–112 in text.] As you sit in your classroom, you are in an inertial frame of reference. You, your desk, your chair, and the objects and people around you seem motionless to you, yet you and all the other bodies are actually moving toward the east on the spinning Earth at a speed inversely proportional to your latitude (about 1000 mi/hr if you are near the Equator). Since everything around you is moving at the same speed, it appears motionless in this inertial frame.

Newton's Second Law of Motion states that the acceleration of an object is directly proportional to the net force acting upon it and inversely proportional to the object's mass, with the net force and acceleration in the same direction. [See Figures 5-3 and 5-4 on pages 112–113.] Symbolically, the formula is written:

$$\Sigma \mathbf{F} = m\mathbf{a}.$$

The bold vector notation on both force and acceleration means mathematically that they must be in the same direction; however, the second law is often written separately in each dimension for clarity:

$$\Sigma F_x = ma_x \qquad\qquad \Sigma F_y = ma_y \qquad\qquad \Sigma F_z = ma_z$$

An important tool in analyzing forces on an isolated object in order to determine its acceleration is the **free-body diagram**. The free-body diagram is so important to the analysis of forces that A.P. Exam questions often ask first for a free-body diagram, as a means of guiding the student to a correct solution method. To construct such a diagram, first isolate the object in question and replace it with a point particle with the same mass. Then draw all the forces acting <u>on</u> the object at that point, using either a given frame of reference or selecting a convenient frame of reference. (Often, it is helpful to use the direction of motion of the object as the positive x or positive y direction.) When solving the problem, use the selected frame of reference to resolve all forces into components that lie along the selected axes; then apply Newton's Second Law to the forces in each coordinate direction. [See Figure 5-5 on page 115 and outlined steps on page 116 in Walker.]

Here is a sample free-body diagram that would be correct for a box sitting on a ramp or a box sliding down a ramp.

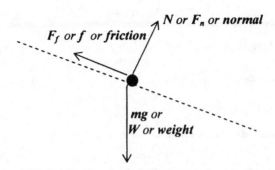

Newton's Third Law of Motion states that for every **action force** that acts on an object there is an equal and opposite **reaction force** exerted by the object, with the action and reaction forces acting on different objects. For example, when you sit in a chair, your weight (the gravitational force on you) causes your body to press upon the chair—an action force called a **normal force**. In return, the chair exerts a reaction force on you—a force that we also call normal force, but this time the normal force is on you and not on the chair. You can feel this reaction force from the chair, as even with your eyes closed, you can feel the chair's force on you when you make contact with it. [See Figure 5-8, page 120.]

Weight is a measure of the gravitational force on an object and is directly proportional to the object's mass, by the equation:

$$W = mg \quad \text{[Figure 5-6, page 126 in Walker.]}$$

Apparent weight arises from a sensation of increased or decreased gravitational pull in an accelerating system, such as when accelerating upward or downward in an elevator. If you were standing on a bathroom scale as you rode an elevator, you would notice a higher reading for your apparent weight when the elevator is accelerating upward. Likewise, you would notice that you seem to weigh less as the elevator decelerates to a stop at the top. The explanation for this apparent change in weight comes from an application of Newton's laws, discussed more in detail in Chapter 7. Another example is the apparent increase in weight astronauts feel as they are propelled upward from the Earth during launch into orbit and the apparent weightlessness the astronauts feel when in orbit. [Figure 5-11, page 128.]

The **normal force** is a force that arises in solids when surfaces come into contact. [Section 5-7, page 130.] The normal force itself is an electromagnetic force between atoms that prevents an object placed on a solid surface from penetrating into the space the atoms of the surface already occupy. The normal force is a **contact force** exerted by a surface that is always perpendicular outward from the surface. [See page 122 for a discussion of contact forces.] For example, a book placed on a desk experiences a normal force from the desk that is perpendicular to the surface of the desk, outward on the book. The desk, in turn, experiences a normal force from the book that is perpendicular to the surface of the book, outward toward the desk.

Tension is a force exerted only as a pull on an object by a string, rope, chain, etc. You will often hear the phrases "massless cord" or "light string" with reference to a tension forces, which means that the tension in each direction can be considered equal. On the AP* Exam, the student is not expected to consider cases where the string or cord itself has mass.

Sample Questions

1. The mass of an object with a weight of 20 newtons on Earth's surface is closest to:
   A. 1 kg
   B. 2 kg
   C. 3 kg
   D. 5 kg
   E. 10 kg

2. Which of the following is a correct free body diagram (without labels) for the situation in which a skier is moving down an icy hill, without any measurable friction?

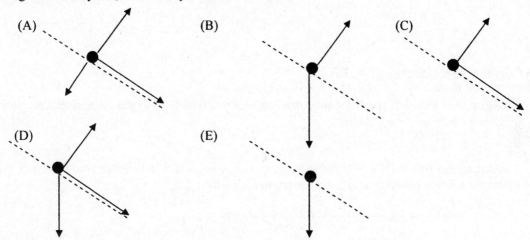

3. A 3 kilogram box sits on a level surface. What is the normal force from the surface on the box?
   A. 3 kg
   B. 6 kg
   C. 3 N
   D. 6 N
   E. 30 N

4. The acceleration due to gravity on the Moon is approximately 1/6 of the value on Earth. A chunk of cheese has a mass of 2.4 kg on Earth. What is its mass on the Moon?
   A. 0.4 kg
   B. 1.6 kg
   C. 2.4 kg
   D. 3.2 kg
   E. 9.8 kg

5. In which of the following situations would the net force on an object be equal to zero?
   I. The object is accelerated.
   II. The object is stationary.
   III. The object is moving at constant speed in a circle.

   A. I only
   B. II only
   C. I and II only
   D. II and III only
   E. I, II and III

1. A box of mass 10 kilograms is being pulled to the right along a level, frictionless surface by a rope that exerts a force of 50 newtons at an angle of 35 degrees above the horizontal.

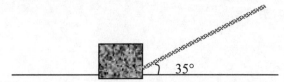

(a) On the dot below, draw a labeled free-body diagram for the box.

(b) Calculate the acceleration of the box.

(c) If the exact same force is applied to the same box on a rough surface, would the acceleration increase, decrease, or stay the same? Explain.

2. A hanging banner that weighs 50 N is supported by two wires as shown in the figure. Draw a free-body diagram for the banner and calculate the tension in each wire.

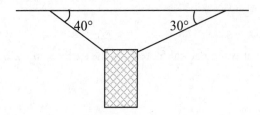

3. A 500 N force acts on a 25 kg object in a direction 45° north of east, and a second force acts on the object with 700 N at 35° south of east. Find the resultant force on the object and the acceleration of the object.

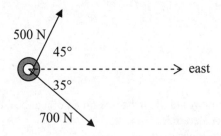

4. A person whose normal weight is 50 newtons has an apparent weight of 45 newtons on an elevator. Find the acceleration of the elevator and explain whether it is moving up or down.

SOLUTIONS TO SAMPLE QUESTIONS AND SAMPLE PROBLEMS

Multiple Choice Questions:

1. B Since $W = mg$ and the value of 20 N given is the weight, then $m = W/g$. Using a value of 10 m/s² for g:

$$m = \frac{20\ N}{10\ m/s^2} = 2\ kg$$

2. B The only forces on the skier are the gravitational force, which should be straight down on the page, and the normal force, which is perpendicular to the surface. A common error here is to include some sort of force "pulling the skier down the slope," but there is no such separate force; the component of the gravitational force parallel to the slope is the force that accelerates the skier down the slope.

3. E The box is on a level surface, so the only two forces acting on it are the weight downward and the normal force upward from the surface. Since the box is stationary, or in equilibrium, these two forces are equal to each other. The normal force equals the box's weight.

$$W = mg = (3\ kg)(10\ m/s^2) = 30\ N$$

4. C Even though the gravitational pull on the cheese would be significantly less when it's on the Moon's surface, the mass of the cheese does not change.

5. B Only in case II is the net force equal to zero. According to Newton's Second Law, when an object is accelerated in a given direction, there is a net force in that direction. The object moving in a circle must have a net centripetal force. [The concepts of centripetal acceleration and centripetal force are not explained until later in this review guide. However, the student should be well aware that acceleration is a change in magnitude or direction of the velocity—and acceleration requires a force, by Newton's Second Law of Motion.]

Free Response Problems:

1. (a) The free-body diagram should be drawn directly on the provided symbol, making sure the arrow tips are provided (since the forces are vectors) and each vector is labeled. Numerical values are not required at this point, and <u>components should not be included unless they are drawn in dashed lines</u>. It would be incorrect to show both the vector and its components. Unless the question specifically asks for the vectors "drawn to scale," the length of each vector does not matter at this point.

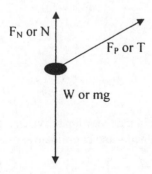

(b) The next step in solving the problem is setting up a frame of reference. In this case, vertical is the **y** direction and horizontal is the *x* direction. Since the tension force does not lie along either of those axes, split the tension into components along the *x* and *y*, using the given angle.

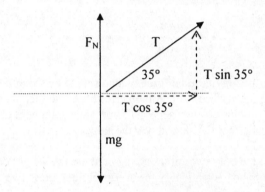

Write Newton's Second Law for the *x* direction: [Section 5-5, starting on page 123, has a good discussion of force vectors and vector components if you need a review of this.]

$$\Sigma F_x = ma_x$$
$$T \cos 35° = ma$$
$$(50 \ N) \cos 35° = (10 \ kg) \ a$$
$$a = 4.1 \ m/s^2$$

(c) If friction is introduced, which the rough surface implies, the friction force would be to the left, in the -*x* direction. Thus, the net force to the right would be less and the acceleration would be decreased. [We will discuss more about friction forces in the next chapter.]

2.   Step 1: Draw a free body diagram for the banner, reducing the banner to a point particle.

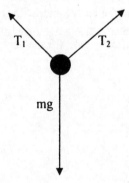

Step 2: Determine coordinate system and resolve vectors into components in that coordinate system. [On the exam, this can be done directly on the free body diagram, as long as components and coordinate axes are shown with dashed lines so they are not confused with the actual forces.]

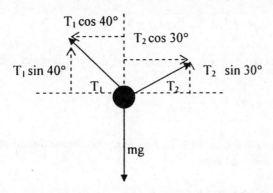

Step 3: Write Newton's Second Law for the forces in each coordinate direction, substitute, and solve.

$$\Sigma F_x = ma_x$$
$$T_2 \cos 30° - T_1 \cos 40° = 0$$
$$T_2 = \frac{T_1 \cos 40°}{\cos 30°} = 0.885 \; T_1$$

$$\Sigma F_y = ma_y$$
$$T_1 \sin 40° + T_2 \sin 30° - mg = 0$$
$$T_1 \sin 40° + T_2 \sin 30° - 50 \; N. = 0$$
$$0.643 \; T_1 + (0.885 \; T_1)(0.5) - 50 = 0$$
$$T_1 = 46 \; N$$
$$T_2 = (0.885)(46) = 41 \; N$$

3.

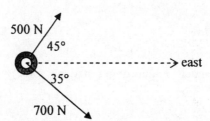

Since "east" provides a coordinate system, first resolve the two forces into their components.
Add the x-components to find the x-component of the resultant:

$$R_x = 500 \cos 45° + 700 \cos 35° = 927 \; N$$

Add the y-components to find the y-component of the resultant:

$$R_y = 500 \sin 45° - 700 \sin 35° = -48.0 \; N \quad \text{[Notice that the } y\text{-component of 700 N is down, or negative.]}$$

Now that we know the components of the resultant force, the magnitude of the resultant can be determined by the Pythagorean Theorem:

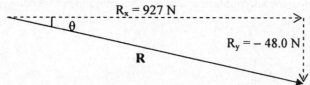

$$|R| = \sqrt{(927\ N)^2 + (-48.0\ N)^2} = 928\ N$$

The direction of the resultant force can best be determined by using the tangent function and the components:

$$\tan \theta = \frac{48.0}{927} \quad and \quad \theta = 3.0°$$

[Note: The negative sign for R_x simply means the angle is in the fourth coordinate quadrant, or south of east.] Thus, the resultant force is **928 N at 3.0° south of east**.

The acceleration is calculated from Newton's Second Law:

$$\Sigma F = ma.$$
$$928\ N. = (25\ kg)\ (a)$$
$$a = 37.1\ m/s^2$$

Since the acceleration is in the same direction as the net force:

$$a = 37.1\ m/s^2\ at\ 3.0°\ south\ of\ east.$$

4.   The apparent weight comes from the normal force the person feels upward from the floor of the elevator (or from a set of scales on which the person is standing—which is also the reading on the scales). Start with a free-body diagram:

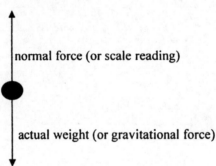

normal force (or scale reading)

actual weight (or gravitational force)

Write Newton's Second Law and solve:

$$\Sigma F_y = ma_y$$
$$N - mg = ma$$
$$45\ N - 50\ N = \left(\frac{50\ N}{9.8\ m/s^2}\right)(a)$$
$$a = 0.98\ m/s^2\ downward$$

Notes:
- Mass is weight divided by g.
- Since the net force is down, the acceleration is down. This could mean speeding up on the way down or slowing down on the way up.

▶ **Recommended for further practice (Walker, 3rd ed.):**

- Work through Example 5-1 on page 115 first, then the Active Example 5-2 on page 125.
- Chapter Summary on pages 132–133
- Problems on pages 136–140: 9, 17, 23, 25, 29, 31, 35, 39, 43

√ **Reminders:**

- Draw a free-body diagram prior to working each problem, with solid arrows for vectors.
- On problem 25, the word *smooth* implies "no friction." Likewise in the next chapter, the word *rough* will mean "with friction."
- Remember that in situations where the object is moving at constant velocity, the problem is solved in the same manner as if the object were stationary, i.e., by setting the net force equal to zero when writing Newton's Second Law.
- Don't show both a vector and its components on a free-body diagram—unless the components are clearly labeled as components (usually with dotted or dashed lines).

Chapter 6

Applications of Newton's Laws

Equations

Newton's Second Law: $\Sigma F_x = ma_x$

Weight near planet's surface: $W = mg$

Friction force: $F_f = \mu N$

In this chapter, we will develop methods for solution of problems using Newton's laws. In addition to the forces previously discussed in Chapter 5 (weight, normal force, tension), some additional forces will be considered.

Friction is a contact force between two surfaces that is essentially an electromagnetic force due to interactions between molecules of the two surfaces. The friction force is along the surface of contact, parallel to the surfaces, and is in a direction that opposes the motion or attempted motion of the object under consideration. Friction depends upon two factors—how hard the surfaces are "pressing" upon each other (the normal force) and the roughness (or smoothness) of the surfaces of contact. The term used to describe this roughness of surfaces is **coefficient of friction**, given the symbol μ. The value of coefficient of friction depends upon both surfaces (thus a single object does not have a μ value) and upon whether or not the surfaces in contact are in movement. Generally, the coefficient of **static** friction, μ_s, is greater than the coefficient of **kinetic** friction, μ_k. The maximum value for friction between two surfaces is:

$$F_f = \mu N$$

Typical Coefficients of Friction		
Materials	Kinetic, μ_k	Static, μ_s
Rubber on concrete (dry)	0.80	1–4
Steel on steel	0.57	0.74
Glass on glass	0.40	0.94
Wood on leather	0.40	0.50
Copper on steel	0.36	0.53
Rubber on concrete (wet)	0.25	0.30
Steel on ice	0.06	0.10
Waxed ski on snow	0.05	0.10
Teflon on Teflon	0.04	0.04
Synovial joints in humans	0.003	0.01

A **spring** force is exerted by a spring that is extended or compressed beyond its relaxed, or **equilibrium**, position. The force exerted by the spring is in the opposite direction of the spring extension, x, so that force is negative. The amount of spring force also depends upon the stiffness of the spring, identified by the value of the **spring constant** or **elastic constant**, k, which is measured in Newtons per meter:

$$F = -kx$$

This is a statement of **Hooke's Law**.

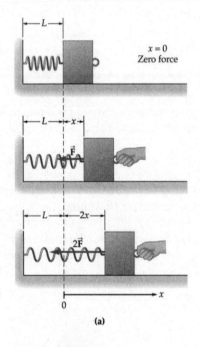

(a)

Spring of relaxed length, L, with no force applied. Spring extension, x, is zero.

Force of magnitude F is applied to the spring, and the spring is extended a distance x. The spring develops a force that opposes the direction of the extension:
$$F = -kx$$

Double the extension of the spring, and a force $2F$ develops in the spring, attempting to restore the spring to its original position.

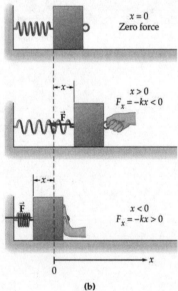

(b)

The constant of proportionality for F and x is the spring constant, k, which is the same for a given spring, regardless of whether the spring is being extended or compressed.

In this **free-body diagram** for an object being pulled by a cord up a ramp, the normal force, friction force (kinetic in this case), weight, and tension are labeled.

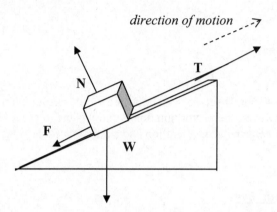

An object in constant **circular motion** must have a force applied to cause the object to continually change direction. The speed of the object does not change, but the direction of motion changes—constantly turning toward the center of the arc or circle. Any force that provides this accelerating force toward the center is termed **centripetal** force. It's important to remember that the word *centripetal*, meaning "center-seeking," describes the nature or purpose of the force—but is not a force in itself. Another force must be identified to provide this centripetal force. The centripetal force is an application of Newton's Second Law, with the force and acceleration in the same direction (toward the center).

$$F_c = ma_c$$

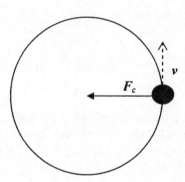

The magnitude of the centripetal acceleration is directly proportional to the square of the object's speed as it moves in the circle and is inversely proportional to the radius of the path:

$$a_c = \frac{v^2}{r}$$

As is evident from the force equation above, the centripetal acceleration is a vector—one that always is directed toward the center of the circular path. One method of designating this in an equation is to use the unit vector $\hat{r}$, meaning radially outward. Since the acceleration vector is not outward but inward, we'll add $-\hat{r}$ to the above equation to mean radially inward. Thus, the centripetal equation in vector form becomes:

$$a = -\frac{v^2}{r}\,\hat{r}$$

The centripetal force equation can also be written:

$$F = \frac{-mv^2}{r}\,\hat{r}$$

Note: The $\hat{r}$ notation is not used on the AP* Physics B Equation sheet, nor is it expected on the examination. Often, only the magnitude is expected in calculations. However, the vector notation is shown here to provide some clarification of the negative sign on the formulas for centripetal acceleration and centripetal force—and to show clear vector notation on both sides of the equation.

Sample Questions

1. A hockey puck (mass 0.2 kg) is attached to a string and swung at a constant 10 m/s velocity in a horizontal circle with a radius of 0.2 meter. What is the tension in the string?
   A. 0.1 N
   B. 1.0 N
   C. 10 N
   D. 20 N
   E. 100 N

2. A hockey puck of weight W attached to a string with tension T is swung in a vertical circle. The centripetal force at the top and bottom is provided in each situation by:

	Top	Bottom
A.	T	T
B.	$T + W$	$T + W$
C.	$T - W$	$T - W$
D.	$T + W$	$T - W$
E.	$T - W$	$T + W$

3. A car that weighs 2×10^4 N rounds a level curve of radius 20 meters at a speed of 10 m/s. What is the coefficient of kinetic friction between the car's wheels and the road?
   A. 0.1
   B. 0.2
   C. 0.3
   D. 0.4
   E. 0.5

4. A vertical spring is at equilibrium with a 100-gram mass attached to it. A second 100-gram mass is then attached to the spring, causing it to stretch a distance of 20 cm. What is the spring constant of the spring?
   A. 20 g-cm
   B. 20 N/m
   C. 10 N/m
   D. 5 g/cm
   E. 5 N/m

5.   A 50-kilogram athlete is climbing a rope. What is the tension in the rope in each situation?

	Accelerating up the rope at 2 m/s²	Accelerating down the rope at 2 m/s²
A.	50 N	50 N
B.	500 N	500 N
C.	600 N	500 N
D.	600 N	400 N
E.	400 N	600 N

Sample Problems

1. In a laboratory experiment, a 3.0-kg box is pulled along a horizontal wooden plank by a 20 N force which acts at a 25° angle to the horizontal. The rate of acceleration of the box is experimentally measured to be 3.60 m/s². Determine the coefficient of kinetic friction between the box and the surface.

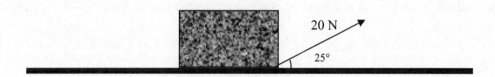

2.

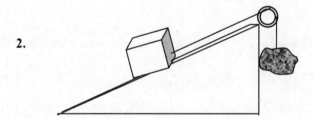

A block of mass 3.2 kg lying on an inclined plane is connected to a rock of mass 3.2 kg by a very light cord passing over a pulley, as shown in the diagram. Determine the acceleration of the block, given a coefficient of friction of 0.15 and an angle of elevation for the ramp of 25°. (Consider the mass and friction of the puller to be negligible.)

SOLUTIONS TO SAMPLE QUESTIONS AND SAMPLE PROBLEMS

Sample Questions

1. **E**   The string tension provides the centripetal force:

$$T = F_c = \frac{mv^2}{r} = \frac{(0.2\, kg)(10\, m/s^2)}{0.2\, m} = 100\, N$$

2. D

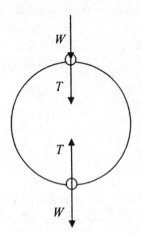

When the ball is at the top of the circle:
The net force providing centripetal force at the top is the sum of the two forces: $T + W$

When the ball is at the bottom of the circle:
The net force providing centripetal force at the bottom is T (toward the center) $- W$ (away from center).

3. E In this case, the centripetal force is provided by friction between wheels and road. On a level surface, the normal force from the road on the car is equal to the weight of the car. Thus, the friction force, which is μN, is equal to μmg:

$$F_c = F_f = \mu N = \mu mg$$

$$\mu mg = \frac{mv^2}{r}$$

$$\mu = \frac{v^2}{gr} = \frac{(10\ m/s)^2}{(10\ m/s^2)(20\ m)} = 0.5$$

4. E The force, F, stretching the spring from the equilibrium position is the weight of the additional mass, and x is the amount stretched when that mass was added:

$$F = -kx$$
$$mg = kx$$
$$(0.1\ kg)(10\ m/s^2) = k(0.2\ m)$$
$$k = 5\ N/m$$

Note: Since the spring constant will have units of force per unit length, the answer choices A and D could immediately be eliminated as having the wrong units.

6.   D Tension has to pull upward on the climber, while weight pulls down. The net force, then, is $T - W$ (up is considered positive), which is equal to ma, by Newton's Second Law:

$$\Sigma F = ma$$
$$T - mg = ma$$

accelerating up: $T = mg + ma = (50\ kg)(10\ m/s^2) + (50\ kg)(2\ m/s^2) = 600\ N$

accelerating down: $T = mg + ma = (50\ kg)(10\ m/s^2) + (50\ kg)(-2\ m/s^2) = 400\ N$

Note: Do <u>not</u> fall into the trap of putting a negative sign on g in these solutions. The gravitational force downward has already been made negative by assigning a negative sign to mg in the original equation. Putting a negative sign on g in the final equation would make gravity push our climber upward!

Sample Problems

1. Step 1: Set up a free body diagram for the object.

Step 2: Determine a frame of reference. Since the object is on a level surface, we will designate to the right the $+x$ direction and up on the page the $+y$ direction.

Step 3: Label forces and determine components for any forces not aligned with the coordinate directions.

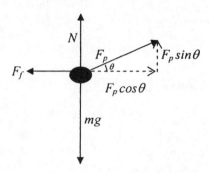

Step 4: Write Newton's Second Law for each coordinate direction.

$$\Sigma F_x = ma_x \qquad\qquad\qquad \Sigma F_y = ma_y = 0$$
$$F_p cos\,\theta - F_f = ma \qquad\qquad N + F_p sin\,\theta - mg = 0$$
$$F_p cos\,\theta - \mu N = ma \qquad\qquad N = mg - F_p sin\,\theta$$

Substitute for N from the second equation:

$$F_p cos\,\theta - \mu(mg - F_p sin\,\theta) = ma$$
$$(20\ N)(cos\ 25°) - \mu[(3.0\ kg)(9.8\ m/s^2) - (20\ N)(sin\ 25°)] = (3.0\ kg)(3.6\ m/s^2)$$
$$\mu = 0.35$$

2.

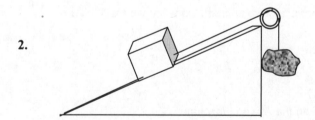

Step 1: Designate the forces on each of the objects—either as a free body diagram or by showing the forces directly on the diagram, as shown here.

Step 2: Determine a frame of reference for each object, with the direction of motion or direction of attempted motion positive for both objects (since they will have the same acceleration and same velocity). However, the frame of reference does not have to be the same for both:. Step 3: Label all forces and determine components for forces that are not aligned with the chosen frame of reference, as shown on the next page.

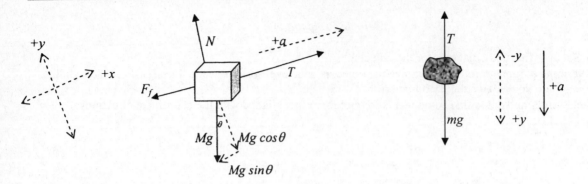

Step 4: Write Newton's Second Law for each coordinate direction:

$$\Sigma F_{x\ (block)} = Ma \qquad\qquad \Sigma F_{y\ (block)} = 0 \qquad\qquad \Sigma F_{y\ (rock)} = ma$$
$$T - F_f - Mg\sin\theta = Ma \qquad N - Mg\cos\theta = 0 \qquad mg - T = ma$$
$$T = \mu N + Mg\sin\theta + Ma \qquad N = Mg\cos\theta \qquad T = mg - ma$$

[Note: In the first and third columns, the <u>direction of motion</u> has been selected as the positive direction. Since the block moves up the ramp, its acceleration is up the ramp, so the tension force on the block is in the positive direction. However, the rock is accelerating downward, so the direction of the acceleration of the rock has to be made positive, since it is the same as the acceleration of the block. We use a different set of reference axes for the rock than for the block. The weight of the rock is made positive, and the tension force on the rock is in the negative direction.]

The accelerations of the box and the rock are equal. Since the string has no mass, the two tensions are equal, and we can substitute:

$$\mu N + Mg\sin\theta + Ma = mg - ma$$
$$\mu Mg\cos\theta + Mg\sin\theta + Ma = mg - ma$$
(All masses are equal, so they will cancel.)
$$(0.15)(9.8\ m/s^2)(\cos 25°) + (9.8\ m/s^2)(\sin 25°) + a = 9.8\ m/s^2 - a$$
$$a = 2.2\ m/s^2$$

The positive acceleration has the box accelerating up the ramp, as we had predicted when we assigned the direction of the friction force.

▶ <u>**Recommended for further practice (Walker, 3rd ed.):**</u>
  - Rules of Thumb for μ_k and μ_s on pages 143 and 147
  - Example 6-3 for a box on a ramp and Example 6-7 on the Atwood machine
  - Chapter Summary on pages 167–168
  - Problems on pages 170–178: 9, 15, 19, 23, 27, 37, 39, 43, 61, 71, 75

√ <u>**Reminders:**</u>
  - A labeled free body diagram is essential for problem solutions.
  - When asked for a free body diagram on the exam, show forces with arrows and proper labels, but do not also show components (unless forces are drawn with solid arrows and components clearly shown with dashed lines, typical of component notation).
  - Watch the negative signs on g, assigning a negative sign to the gravitational force only once during the solution. (See Multiple Choice solution 5.)

Chapter 7

Work and Kinetic Energy

Equations

Kinetic energy: $K = \frac{1}{2} mv^2$

Gravitational potential energy: $U_{grav} = mgh$

Work: $W = F\Delta r \cos \theta$

Power: $P = \dfrac{W}{t} = \dfrac{\Delta E}{t}$

Power: $P = Fv \cos\theta$

Spring force: $F_s = -k\Delta x$

Potential energy of a spring: $U_s = \frac{1}{2} kx^2$

Work is the product of applied force and displacement, with the force and displacement in the same direction. In situations where the force and displacement are not the same direction, you must use the components of force and displacement that are in the same direction. In the equation $W = F\Delta r \cos \theta$ (the form used on the AP* Equation Sheet), $\cos \theta$ selects the component of force in the same direction as the change in position, Δr. In any situation where the force and displacement are perpendicular to each other, there are no components in the same direction and thus no work is done.

Another way to determine work is to write the equation in the form $W = \boldsymbol{F \cdot s}$, where the dot product of the force and displacement vectors literally means "use the components that are in the same direction." This form also emphasizes that even though both force and displacement are vectors, the dot product (work) is a scalar—and has no direction.

As we know, friction forces always oppose the object's motion, so work done by friction is the dot product of friction force and the displacement of the object. There are a couple of ways to think of this. Using the equation $W = F\Delta r \cos \theta$, the friction force is in the opposite direction of the change in position, so the angle between them is 180°. Since cos 180° is −1, the work would be negative if the displacement is considered positive. Another approach is that if the displacement is positive, the friction force is negative, and the product of the two will simply be negative. A very direct way to think of work is that positive work adds energy to the object and negative work removes energy.

Power is the rate at which work is done or the rate of change in energy:

$$\textit{Power: } P = \dfrac{W}{t} = \dfrac{\Delta E}{t}$$

Power is measured in joules per second, which are called **watts**. Another useful way to look at this is to write work as $F \cdot s$, so $P = \dfrac{F \cdot s}{t}$. We recognize $\dfrac{s}{t}$ as velocity, v, so :

$$P = Fv \cos\theta = F \cdot v$$

Kinetic energy is the energy an object possesses due to its motion—a scalar quantity that is a factor of the object's mass and velocity:

$$K = \tfrac{1}{2} mv^2$$

The pendulum below, for example, starts oscillating because work has been done on the pendulum bob to move it to position **A**. When the bob is released, the gravitational potential energy it has at position **A** is converted to kinetic energy at position **B**. The ball's inertia keeps it moving past point **B**, and it loses kinetic energy as it gains potential energy moving to point **C**. Thus, the bob has maximum potential energy at points **A** and **C** and maximum kinetic energy at point **B**. Throughout the motion, disregarding friction, the total mechanical energy (potential plus kinetic) of the pendulum remains constant. **Conservation of energy** is an important concept—and the key to the solution of many physics problems.

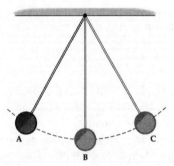

In the previous chapter, Hooke's Law for spring restoring forces was discussed. In this chapter, we will consider the force applied in stretching a spring—and in doing the work of stretching the spring. Remember that the spring force is in the opposite direction of the spring extension: $F_s = -kx$

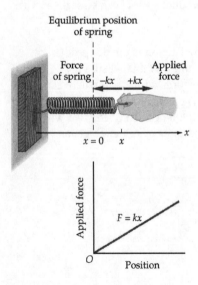

The applied force is in the same direction as the spring extension, so the negative sign doesn't apply:

$$F_{app} = kx$$

Here, the applied force is plotted as a function of spring extension, $F = kx$. The slope of this plot is the spring constant, k. The work done by the applied force in stretching the spring is the area "under the curve," or between the plot line and x-axis. The area is a triangle, $\tfrac{1}{2} Bh$, where the base is the position, x, and the height is the force, kx:

$$W = F \cdot x = \tfrac{1}{2} (kx)(x) = \tfrac{1}{2} kx^2$$

As we will discuss further in the next chapter, the work done by the applied force on the spring is equal to the potential stored in the stretched (or compressed) spring:

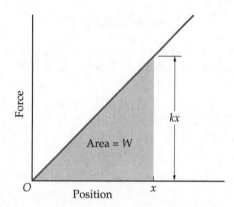

By calculating the area under the plot of *Force vs. Position*, the work done in stretching a spring can be determined. *Force vs. Position* is linear, since it is Hooke's Law, $F_{app} = kx$, with the slope of the line equal to the spring constant, k. The area of this triangle is "one-half times force times the change in position," which is the work done on the spring and the potential energy of the spring in the stretched position. Substituting kx for F helps us to derive the potential energy formula:

$$W = area = \tfrac{1}{2}\,F(x) = \tfrac{1}{2}\,(kx)(x) = \tfrac{1}{2}\,kx^2 = U$$

Essentially, what we are doing by taking the area of the triangle is multiplying the average force along the line ($\tfrac{1}{2}\,F$) by the change in position (from a position of 0 to a position x) to get $\tfrac{1}{2}\,kx^2$ for work and potential energy.

When two springs are connected to each other, they behave as a single spring with a new effective spring constant. The two springs below, with spring constants k_1 and k_2, are connected in series. When a force F is applied, the spring extension is distributed through both springs—but not necessarily with half the extension in each spring (since k values are not the same). The force on each spring is F, since applying a force to spring 2 causes it to try to restore with the same force, pulling with that same force on spring 1. The effective spring constant for two springs connected in series in this way is: $k = \dfrac{k_1 k_2}{k_1 + k_2}$

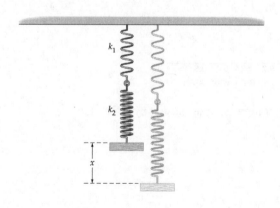

If the same two springs were connected in parallel, i.e., both attached top and bottom to the same weight, the effective k value of the two springs would be: $k = k_1 + k_2$. Each spring would support part of the weight attached, but the extensions would be the same. [See Problem 69 at the end of Chapter 7 in Walker's text.]

Sample Questions

1. A ball of mass 0.2 kg is used to compress a spring a distance of 0.02 meters. When the spring is released, the ball leaves the spring with an initial velocity of 2 cm/s. What is the spring constant?
   A. 0.1 N/m
   B. 0.2 N/m
   C. 1.0 N/m
   D. 2.0 N/m
   E. 4.0 N/m

2. A force of 100 N is used to stop a cart of mass 2.0 kg moving at 1 m/s. What is the work done on the cart by the applied force?
   A. 0.5 J
   B. 1.0 J
   C. 2.0 J
   D. –1.0 J
   E. –0.5 J

3. What is the average power generated by a 1200-kg car as it accelerates from rest to 20 m/s in 10 seconds?
   A. 1200 W
   B. 2400 W
   C. 12,000 W
   D. 24,000 W
   E. 120,000 W

Questions 4-5. Use the plot below of *Force vs. Displacement of a Spring* to answer the following questions.

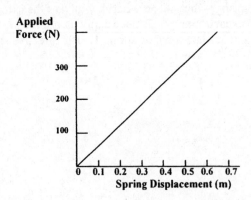

4. What is the work done in compressing the spring by 0.5 meters?
   A. 50 J
   B. 75 J
   C. 100 J
   D. 150 J
   E. 300 J

5. What is the elastic constant of the spring?
   A. 75 N/m
   B. 100 N/m
   C. 200 N/m
   D. 400 N/m
   E. 600 N/m

Sample Problems

1. The plot below describes a variable force acting on an object on a smooth horizontal surface.

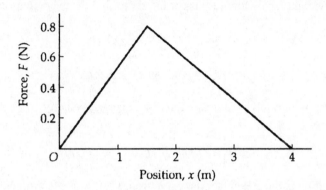

(a) Calculate the work done on the object in moving it from $x = 0$ to $x = 1$ meter.

(b) If the mass of the object is 2 kg, what is the magnitude of its instantaneous acceleration after it has moved 1.5 meters?

(c) What is the instantaneous speed of the object after it has moved 1.5 meters?

(d) What is the instantaneous speed of the object at $x = 3$ meters?

2. A 3.0-kg box is given a quick push across the floor so that it starts moving at 1.0 m/s and comes to a stop in a distance of 4.0 meters.

(a) What is the kinetic energy of the box as it is released after the push?

(b) From where did this energy arise?

(c) Where is the energy once the box comes to a stop?

(d) What was the average friction force on the object?

SOLUTIONS TO SAMPLE QUESTIONS AND SAMPLE PROBLEMS

Multiple Choice Questions:

1. B The kinetic energy gained by the ball is equal to the potential energy given up by the spring (at equilibrium point) when the ball is released. (Watch the units.)

$$\tfrac{1}{2}\,mv^2 = \tfrac{1}{2}\,kx^2$$
$$(0.2\ kg)(0.02\ m/s)^2 = k\,(0.02\ m)^2$$
$$k = 0.2\ N/m$$

2. D Here, with the information given, it's easiest to equate the work done on the cart to the change in kinetic energy of the cart:

$$W = K_f - K_o = 0 - \tfrac{1}{2}\,(2\ kg)(1\ m/s)^2$$
$$W = -1\ J$$

3. D In this case, the easiest method of solution is to multiply average force times average velocity.
(1) Use Newton's Second Law with the mass of the car to find the average force:

$$F = ma = \frac{m(v_f - v_o)}{t}$$
$$F = (1200\ kg)(2\ m/s^2) = 2400\ N$$

(2) Then find power by multiplying average force and <u>average</u> velocity:

$$P = Fv$$
$$P = (2400\ N)(10\ m/s) = 24{,}000\ W$$

4. B Work done on the spring is the area under the curve from $x = 0$ to $x = 0.5$ m. At 0.5 m, the applied force is 300 N.

$$W = \tfrac{1}{2}\,Bh = \tfrac{1}{2}\,(0.5\ m)(300\ N) = 75\ J$$

Note: Another way to think of this is that you are multiplying the spring displacement, 0.5 meter, by the <u>average</u> force applied, which is half of 300 newtons, or 150 newtons.

5. E The elastic constant, or spring constant, is the slope of the graph, since $F = kx$ for applied force. The line has constant slope, so we can use the point (0.5, 300) from the previous problem and (0,0) at the origin.

$$k = \frac{\Delta F}{\Delta x} = 600\ N/m$$

Free Response Problems:

1. (a) The work done is the area under the graph from x = 0 to x = 1 m.

$$W = \tfrac{1}{2}\,(1m)(0.5\ N) = \textbf{0.25 J}$$

(b) Use Newton's Second Law: $F = ma$. The force on the object at that instant is 0.8 newtons.

$$a = \frac{F}{m} = \frac{0.8\ N}{2\ kg} = \textbf{0.4 m/s}^2$$

(c) Since the movement is on a horizontal surface and there is no friction, we can assume all the work goes into an increase in kinetic energy.

$$W = \Delta K = K - K_0 = \text{area under graph line} = \tfrac{1}{2}\,(1.5\ m)(0.8\ N) = 0.6\ J$$

$$K = \tfrac{1}{2}\, mv^2 = 0.6\, J$$
$$v = \boldsymbol{0.77\ m/s}$$

(d) The total kinetic energy at 3 meters is the kinetic energy at 1.5 meters plus the kinetic energy added due to work done from x = 1.5 m to x = 3 m. The additional work is the area of the trapezoid.

$$K = 0.6\, J\ +\ \tfrac{1}{2}\,(0.8 + 0.3)(1.5) = 1.425\, J$$
$$\tfrac{1}{2}\, mv^2 = 1.425\, J$$
$$v = \boldsymbol{1.2\ m/s}$$

2. (a) The kinetic energy is $\tfrac{1}{2}\, mv^2$ or $\tfrac{1}{2}\,(3.0\ kg)(1.0\ m/s)^2$, which is **1.5 joules**.

(b) This gain in kinetic energy is equal to the work done on the box to get it started moving.

(c) Energy is conserved, so the kinetic energy of the box is lost as available mechanical energy, but now exists as thermal energy. Thus, the molecules of the box, the floor, and even the air around them now have more thermal energy and a slightly higher temperature as a result.

(d) The work done in stopping the ball is equal to the loss in kinetic energy, or –1.5 joules. Since friction did the work of stopping the box:

$$W = F_f \cdot s = -1.5\, J$$
$$F_f = \frac{-1.5\, J}{4.0\, m} = \boldsymbol{-0.38\ N}$$

▶ **Recommended for further practice (Walker, 3rd ed.):**
- Conceptual Checkpoint 7-1, page 184
- Chapter Summary on pages 197–198
- Chapter Problems on pages 200–203: 9, 11, 17, 25, 27, 37, 49, 53, 65, 69

√ **Reminders:**
- Work and energy are interchangeable and have the same units (joules).
- Work and energy are scalar quantities, so they do not have directions or components.
- Work done on an object is positive if it increases the object's kinetic energy and negative if it decreases the object's kinetic energy.

Chapter 8

Potential Energy and Conservation of Energy

Equations

Gravitational Potential Energy: $U_G = mgh$

Elastic Potential Energy: $U_S = \frac{1}{2}\,kx^2$

Gravitational Potential Energy: $U_G = -\dfrac{GMm}{r}$

Potential energy is a form of mechanical energy that is stored in a form that can be converted to the kinetic energy of a moving object. An object has **gravitational potential energy** due to its position relative to the Earth's center and gravitational pull on the object. At the center of Earth, the planet would no longer exert a net gravitational pull on the object. However, we use reference positions for the sake of calculating changes in gravitational potential energy, such as the surface of the planet or the floor in a room. For an object near Earth's surface, where the gravitational acceleration is g, its gravitational potential energy is:

$$U_G = mgh$$

where h is the object's height above the surface. In other situations, such as in a laboratory where we are doing an experiment, we may define the gravitational potential energy as mgh, where h is the height above the laboratory floor, since it's not practical to consider the ball falling below that level.

For an object positioned much farther above Earth's surface—several thousand kilometers to make any real difference—the value of g changes. In those cases, the equation to calculate gravitational potential energy becomes:

$$U_G = -\frac{GMm}{r}$$

G is the Universal Gravitational Constant, M is the mass of the planet, m is the mass of the object, and r is the distance from center of the planet to center of the object. We will discuss more about this in Chapter 12 when gravity is discussed in more detail.

An object such as a bowling ball held above one's head possesses gravitational potential energy relative to the floor (and your toes!). If you were foolish enough to drop the ball, its gravitational potential energy would convert to kinetic energy as the ball falls and builds speed. Just before the ball hits the floor, it has no potential energy and maximum kinetic energy. The amount of kinetic energy the ball has at that point is equal to the amount of potential energy it had originally. Under the influence of the gravitational force, a conservative force, the total mechanical energy (potential + kinetic at any point) remains constant.

Conservative forces are those forces, such as the gravitational force and the spring force, that produce movement without loss in **total mechanical energy**, i.e., kinetic plus potential energy.

When an object in equilibrium on the end of a spring is pushed or pulled to cause the spring to be compressed or stretched, the work done in compressing or expanding the spring is now stored as **elastic potential energy.**

$$U_s = \frac{1}{2}kx^2$$

Just as in the case of the bowling ball, when the object on the spring is released, it will move back toward the equilibrium point, building speed as it moves. When the object reaches the equilibrium point, it is no longer distorting the spring, so the elastic potential energy is zero and the kinetic energy is maximum. Again, total mechanical energy is conserved. In the absence of friction or other damping forces, the object on the spring will continue in **oscillation**—constantly converting kinetic energy to elastic potential energy. The kinetic energy is maximum as the mass on the spring passes through equilibrium, where there is no displacement and potential energy is zero. Then, as the spring moves to a point of maximum displacement (sometimes called its **amplitude**) in either direction from equilibrium, the mass is at a **turning point**, where it changes direction and where kinetic energy is zero.

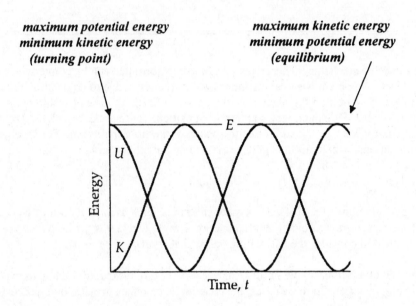

Now let's go back and discuss what happens when a dropped bowling ball hits the floor. It comes to a stop, but the energy has not been lost—it never is. The kinetic energy of the ball when it hits the floor does work on the floor, with the amount of work done on the floor equal to the amount of energy possessed by the ball when it hit the floor. (We will review later the concepts of change in momentum, impulse, and force used to calculate work.) Now what happens to the work? That energy ends up as **thermal energy** in the molecules of both the ball and the floor. If we could take the average temperature of the molecules, we would find that with each drop of the ball onto the floor, the average temperature goes up—an indication that the molecules themselves now are moving with greater average speed. This is the idea of **conservation of energy**—that energy is never lost or gained but is transferred in different forms throughout the Universe.

When a **friction force** acts on an object, we may observe that mechanical energy is not conserved, i.e., stored potential energy may convert to a lesser amount of kinetic energy. The object's mechanical energy may be "lost," but the energy is not lost. The deficit mechanical energy has been used to do work against friction. Again, that work ends up as thermal energy—unavailable to us for mechanical energy. The friction force is an example of a **non-conservative force**, i.e., one that causes a loss in total mechanical energy. When making energy calculations in the presence of non-conservative forces, such as friction, the entire path length the object travels is important in determining how much of the mechanical energy is given up as work against friction. When making energy calculations with only conservative forces, however, one needs only to consider the displacement of the object in determining mechanical energy changes.

Sample Questions

1. Calculate the height to which a 30-gram object must be lifted so that it has 2 joules of gravitational potential energy.
   A. 15 cm
   B. 60 cm
   C. 6.7 cm
   D. 6.7 m
   E. 67 m

2. What is the potential energy stored in a spring that has elastic constant 100 N/m and has been stretched a 2-cm distance?
   A. 0.02 J
   B. 2.0 J
   C. 25 J
   D. 50 J
   E. 200 J

Questions 3-4. A child sits at the top of a playground slide 2 meters above the ground. The child's mass is about 20 kg.

3. If the child falls to the ground from the top, what is his speed when he lands on the playground surface?
   A. 2.2 m/s
   B. 4.0 m/s
   C. 6.3 m/s
   D. 10 m/s
   E. 12 m/s

4. Assuming very little friction on the slide, what is the child's speed when he lands on the ground after sliding down the slide?
   A. 2.2 m/s
   B. 4.0 m/s
   C. 6.3 m/s
   D. 10 m/s
   E. 20 m/s

5. A 20-newton force is used to accelerate a 100-newton box across the floor. The box develops a speed of 2 m/s after being pulled a distance of 1.5 meters. What is the work done against friction?
   A. 5 J
   B. 10 J
   C. 20 J
   D. 50 J
   E. 100 J
   F. 200 J

1. A 20-g "superball" is dropped onto a wooden box from a height of 1.5 meters.

   (a) What is the ball's kinetic energy just before it hits the box?

   (b) If 90% of the ball's kinetic energy is restored to the ball after impact with the box, to what height will it return?

In a second trial, the ball is dropped from the same height onto a small drum, which acts like a spring, depressing to bring the ball to a momentary stop and then sending it back upward.

   (c) If the drum head is depressed a distance of 0.5 cm by the ball's impact, find the effective spring constant of the drum head.

   (d) To what height will the ball return after hitting the drum?

2. The pendulum shown, of length 1.2 meters, is released from point A at a 35° angle. What will be the speed of the pendulum bob when it reaches point B?

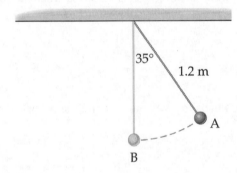

3. A small steel ball of mass m is released from rest at point A at height h on a smooth track. The ball is at height h_A at A and at height h_C at C. Answer the following questions, using only fundamental constants and the given variables.

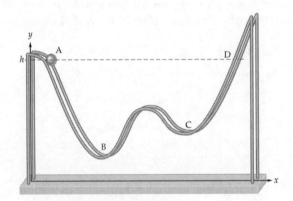

   (a) What is the gravitational potential energy of the ball at point A?

(b) What is the kinetic energy of the ball at point D?

(c) What is the speed of the ball at point C?

(d) Is the speed at point B greater or less than the speed at point C? Explain.

Now, in a second set of trials, the ball is given an initial velocity of v_o at point A as it is released.

(e) What is the new speed of the ball at point C?

SOLUTIONS TO SAMPLE QUESTIONS AND SAMPLE PROBLEMS

Multiple Choice Questions:

1. **C** Remember to convert grams to kilograms to obtain energy in joules.

$$U_G = mgh$$
$$2 J = (0.03 \ kg)(10 \ m/s^2)(h)$$
$$h = \frac{2}{0.3} = 6.7 \ m$$

2. **A** The answers are given in joules, so spring extension needs to be in meters.

$$U_S = \tfrac{1}{2} \ kx^2 = \tfrac{1}{2} \ (100 \ N/m)(0.02 \ m)^2 = 0.02 \ J$$

3. **C** Potential energy is converted to kinetic energy. The child's mass cancels in the problem, so the final speed is the same, regardless of mass.

$$mgh = \tfrac{1}{2} \ mv^2$$
$$v = \sqrt{2gh} = \sqrt{(2)(10 \ m/s^2)(2 \ m)} = 2\sqrt{10} \ m/s = 6.3 \ m/s$$

4. **C** Without friction, the solution here is the same as in question 3, since none of the mechanical energy is given up to work against friction.

5. **B** The input work (average force times distance) goes to increase the box's kinetic energy and to do work against friction.
   (1) Calculate the input work: $W = Fd = (20 \ N)(1.5 \ m) = 30 \ J$
   (2) Use the work-energy theorem, and don't forget to use the <u>mass</u> of the box:

$$W_{input} = K + W_f$$
$$30 \ J = \tfrac{1}{2} \ mv^2 + W_f$$
$$30 = (\tfrac{1}{2})\left(\frac{100 \ N}{10 \ m/s^2}\right)(2 \ m/s)^2 + W_f$$
$$W_f = 30 \ J - 20 \ J = 10 \ J$$

Free Response Problems:

1. (a) The ball's kinetic energy upon impact will be equal to the potential energy lost after its fall.

$$\tfrac{1}{2}\,mv^2 = mgh$$
$$K = (0.020\ kg)(9.8\ m/s^2)(1.5\ m) = \textbf{0.29 J}$$

(b) If 90% of the kinetic energy is returned, then the ball leaves the box with 0.90 times 0.29 joules, or 0.26 joules of kinetic to be converted to potential energy:

$$U = 0.26\ J = mgh$$
$$h = \frac{0.26\ J}{(0.02\ kg)(9.8\ m/s^2)} = \textbf{1.3 m}$$

(c) To be exact, the total change in height for the potential energy calculation is the height above the drum head plus the distance the drum head depresses. That potential energy is then transformed to spring potential energy when the drum head is depressed:

$$mgh = \tfrac{1}{2}\,kx^2$$
$$(0.020\ kg)(9.8\ m/s^2)(1.5\ m + 0.05\ m) = \tfrac{1}{2}\,k\,(0.005m)^2$$
$$k = \frac{(2)(0.020\ kg)(9.8\ m/s^2)(1.55\ m)}{(0.005\ m)^2} = \textbf{24,000 N/m}$$

(d) Since energy was conserved during the collision, the ball will move upward until all its energy is restored to potential energy. Thus it will return to the **1.5 meter** height from which it dropped.

2. Using conservation of mechanical energy, the gravitational potential energy of the pendulum bob at A is equal to the kinetic energy of the pendulum bob at B:

$$mgh_A = \tfrac{1}{2}\,mv_B^2$$

Use a little geometry to determine the height of the pendulum at A, relative to point B:

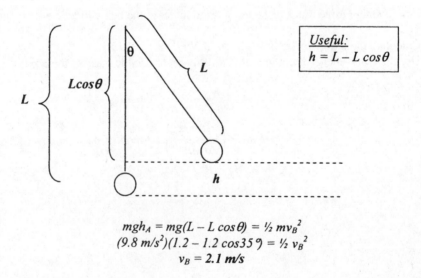

$$mgh_A = mg(L - L\cos\theta) = \tfrac{1}{2}\,mv_B^2$$
$$(9.8\ m/s^2)(1.2 - 1.2\cos35°) = \tfrac{1}{2}\,v_B^2$$
$$v_B = \textbf{2.1 m/s}$$

3. (a) $U_G = mgh_A$ [Note: When giving answers for a symbolic problem such as this on the AP* Exam, make sure the final answer given uses the exact symbols given in the question.]

(b) In the absence of friction, the ball should return to a height that restores potential energy. Since all the energy is potential energy when it returns to the same height ($h_D = h_A$), the kinetic energy at D is **zero**.

$$U_D = mgh_A$$

(c) At point C, the ball has both kinetic and potential energies. The kinetic energy at point C is the difference in the potential energy at A and potential energy at C:

$$U_A = U_C + K_C$$
$$mgh_A = mgh_C + \tfrac{1}{2} mv_c^2$$
$$v_c = \sqrt{2g(h_A - h_C)}$$

(d) Since total mechanical energy is conserved, the ball has less potential energy at B, so it will have more kinetic energy and thus more speed.

(e) Adjusting the equation we used in part (c) to add kinetic energy at point A:

$$U_A + K_A = U_C + K_C$$
$$mgh_A + \tfrac{1}{2} mv_o^2 = mgh_C + \tfrac{1}{2} mv_c^2$$
$$v_c = \sqrt{2g(h_A - h_C) + v_o^2}$$

▶ **Recommended problems for further practice (Walker, 3rd ed.):**
- Active Examples from the Chapter 8
- Applications only of potential energy curves and equipotentials
- Chapter 8 problems from text (pages 233–239): 5, 21, 23, 29, 41, 57, 71, 75

√ **Reminders:**
- No net work is done if an object is moved in a closed loop without a non-conservative force (i.e., without friction).
- Mechanical energy is the sum of all kinetic and potential energies.
- Friction forces cause dissipation of mechanical energy to thermal energy and are called non-conservative forces.
- Positive work done on a system increases the system's mechanical energy, and negative work decreases the mechanical energy.
- Mass has no effect on the period or frequency of a pendulum.
- The value of g does not affect the period or frequency of a spring.

Chapter 9

Linear Momentum and Collisions

Equations

Linear momentum: $p = mv$

Impulse: $J = m\Delta v = F\Delta t$

Newton's Second Law: $F = \dfrac{m\Delta v}{\Delta t}$

The **linear momentum** of an object is, simply, the product of mass and velocity:

$$p = mv$$

Momentum is a vector quantity, so it has magnitude, measured in SI units in kg·m/s, and direction. Changes in momentum may be of more interest to us than momentum alone. The change in momentum is called **impulse** and has the same units as momentum:

$$J = \Delta p = p_f - p_o = m\Delta v$$

[Note: Some authors use **J** for impulse, and some use **I**…and some avoid the symbol for impulse entirely, simply referring to it as Δ**p**.]

Newton's Second Law of Motion, often given as $F = ma$, is more concisely: "Force is rate of change in momentum."

$$\mathbf{F} = \frac{\Delta \mathbf{p}}{\Delta t}$$

It's not difficult to see that by substituting $m\Delta v$ for impulse and $a = \dfrac{\Delta \mathbf{v}}{\Delta t}$, the two forms of the Second Law are equivalent.

Since force is a vector, as are change in momentum and impulse, it's important to keep the directions of the three the same; i.e., the direction of the applied force is the same as the direction of the impulse. To keep these directions the same, one must always keep signs in order:

Important Note
$$\Delta p = p_f - p_o = m(v_f - v_0)$$

In the absence of an external force, total linear momentum is the same before and after any particular occurrence, such as a collision among objects. This is the **Law of Conservation of Linear Momentum.** Momentum is a vector, so direction as well as magnitude will be important.

$$\Sigma \mathbf{p_0} = \Sigma \mathbf{p_f}$$

For interactions among objects in one dimension, direction is determined quite simply by assigning positive and negative signs to objects moving in different directions. For momentum in two dimensions, however, the momentum equations must be written separately for the two dimensions, i.e.:

$$\Sigma p_{0x} = \Sigma p_{fx}$$
$$\Sigma p_{0y} = \Sigma p_{fy}$$

This will involve defining reference axes for the problem situation and finding vector components to use in each equation.

Elastic collisions are those in which both momentum and kinetic energy are conserved. In **totally inelastic collisions**, the separate objects collide and stick to each other, producing one mass with momentum after the collision. It's unlikely that any real collision is perfectly elastic, but just as we often assume negligible friction to make calculations, we also can assume elastic collisions in certain cases for the sake of calculation.

Some special cases for <u>elastic</u> collisions of two objects with identical mass:
1. If a moving object hits a stationary object head-on, they will exchange velocity, i.e., the moving object will stop in the stationary object's position, and the stationary object will move on with the velocity and direction of the moving object.
2. If a moving object hits a stationary object, <u>but not head-on</u>, the two objects will move off at a right angle to each other.
3. If both objects are moving and hit head-on, they will exchange velocities.

Sample Questions

1. A ball of mass 1 kg moving westward at 8 m/s collides with a ball of mass 3 kg moving westward at 4 m/s. The collision is elastic. Which of the following statements is true?
    I. Momentum is conserved in the collision.
    II. Kinetic energy is conserved in the collision.
    III. Both balls will move to the west after the collision if the collision is head-on.

    A. **I** only
    B. **II** only
    C. **I** and **II**
    D. **I** and **III**
    E. **I, II**, and **III**

2. A 3,000-kg car is traveling at 30 mi/hr east and a 2000-kg car is traveling 60 mi/hr west when they collide totally inelastically. What is the magnitude and direction of their motion after the collision?
    A. 30 mi/hr east
    B. 30 mi/hr west
    C. 6 mi/hr east
    D. 6 mi/hr west
    E. They will stop upon impact.

3. Calculate the recoil speed and kinetic energy that a 3-kg rifle would have after firing a 0.22-caliber bullet (mass = 3.0 grams) at a speed of 400 m/s.
    A. 4 m/s and 2.4×10^9 J
    B. 4 m/s and 24 J
    C. 0.4 m/s and 24 J
    D. 0.4 m/s and 0.24 J
    E. 0.1 m/s and 0.24 J

4. A 0.1-kg rubber-tipped dart is thrown at 10 m/s at a brick and rebounds at 8 m/s. The dart knocks the brick over, and the force is determined to be 90 newtons. Calculate the contact time with the brick.
   A. 0.01 s
   B. 0.02 s
   C. 0.1 s
   D. 0.2 s
   E. 0.9 s

5. Air track cart 1 of mass 1.5 kg moving to the right at 1.25 m/s collides elastically with cart 2 of mass 1.5 kg moving to the left at 1.8 m/s. What is the velocity of cart 2 after the collision?
   A. 1.25 m/s to the right
   B. 1.25 m/s to the left
   C. 1.8 m/s to the right
   D. 1.8 m/s to the left
   E. The carts will stop upon impact.

Sample Problems

1. I was taking apart a ballpoint pen, and the spring caused pieces to go flying. The base of the pen, which had a mass of 15 grams, stayed where it was. The ink cartridge, which had a mass of 4 grams, flew to the east at 2 m/s. The pen cap, which had a mass of 3.5 grams, flew off to the south (at a right angle to the cartridge) at a speed of 5 m/s. I would like to find the spring, which has a mass of 2 grams. To do so, I'll need to know the **direction** and **speed** the spring traveled when everything came apart. (Then I can calculate the distance.)

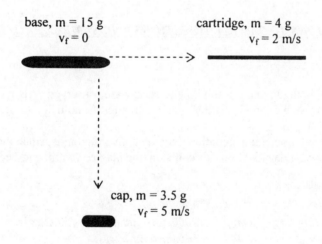

base, m = 15 g
$v_f = 0$

cartridge, m = 4 g
$v_f = 2$ m/s

cap, m = 3.5 g
$v_f = 5$ m/s

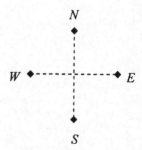

2. A 0.25-kg ball moving toward the east on a frictionless table at 3.0 m/s collides elastically with a 0.40-kg ball that is at rest. All we know about the balls after the collision is that the 0.40-kg ball moves at 30 degrees south of east. Set up but do not solve the equations that can be used to find the speeds of both balls and direction of the first ball after the collision.

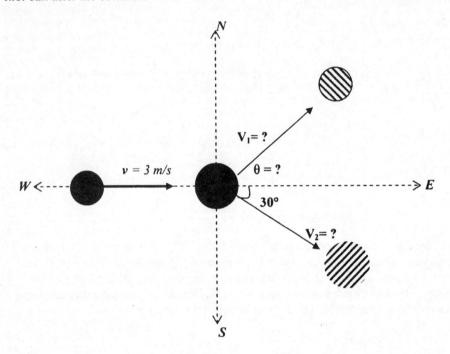

<u>**SOLUTIONS TO SAMPLE QUESTIONS AND SAMPLE PROBLEMS**</u>

Multiple Choice Questions:

1. E In an elastic collision, both momentum and kinetic energy are conserved. Also, since all the momentum before the collision is to the west, we can expect the momentum after the collision to be to the west.

2. D Write a one-dimensional momentum equation, without converting units, since the answer is given in mi/h. We'll make east positive and west negative. In this collision, the masses combine to become one mass after the collision.

$$p_o = p_f$$
$$m_1v_1 + m_2v_2 = (m_1 + m_2)v_f$$
$$(3000\ kg)(30\ mi/h) + (2000\ kg)(-60\ mi/h) = (5000\ kg)v_f$$
$$v_f = -6\ mi/h\ or\ \textbf{6 mi/h west}$$

3. D Write a one-dimensional momentum equation, with no momentum before the gun is fired.

$$p_o = p_f$$
$$0 = m_gv_g + m_bv_b$$
$$0 = (3\ kg)v_g + (0.003\ kg)(400\ m/s)$$
$$v_g = \textbf{-0.4 m/s}$$

$$K = \tfrac{1}{2}\ mv^2 = \tfrac{1}{2}\ (3\ kg)\ (0.4)^2 = \textbf{0.24 J}$$

4. B Use Newton's Second Law, and choose the initial velocity as positive. The final velocity is in the opposite direction, so it is negative. If the dart exerts 90 N of force on the brick, then the brick's force on the dart is equal and opposite, or –90 N. Using care with signs, we come up with the correct velocity change and a positive sign on time.

$$F = \frac{\Delta p}{\Delta t}$$

$$t = \frac{m(v_f - v_0)}{F} = \frac{(0.1\,kg)(-8\,m/s - 10\,m/s)}{-90\,N} = \frac{1.8}{90} = \mathbf{0.02\,s}$$

5. A We quickly recognize this as one of the special cases for equal masses colliding elastically—they exchange velocities. This is easy enough to check:

$$m_1v_1 + m_2v_2 = m_1v_{1f} + m_2v_{2f}$$
$$(1.5\,kg)(1.25\,m/s) + (1.5\,kg)(-1.8\,m/s) = (1.5)(-1.8\,m/s) + (1.5\,kg)(1.25\,m/s)$$

Of course, this equation works. Now let's try the kinetic energy equation:

$$\tfrac{1}{2}\,m_1v_1^2 + \tfrac{1}{2}\,m_2v_2^2 = \tfrac{1}{2}\,m_1v_{1f}^2 + \tfrac{1}{2}\,m_2v_{2f}^2$$
$$(1.5)(1.25)^2 + (1.5)(-1.8)^2 = \tfrac{1}{2}(1.5)(-1.8)^2 + \tfrac{1}{2}(1.5)(1.25)^2$$

So we realize that the only possibility is an exchange in velocities—otherwise they don't change at all, and it's impossible for them to pass each other to retain the same velocity.

Free Response Problems:

1. Since there is no momentum before the pen flies apart, the components of momentum in the x and y directions must add to zero after the pen flies apart. Two of the known pieces fly off at right angles, so we'll set the coordinate axes so that the cartridge flies off in the $+x$ direction and the cap flies off in the $-y$ direction. Then it should be obvious that the x-component of the spring's momentum must be equal to the momentum of the cartridge, and the y-component of the spring's momentum must be equal to the momentum of the cap:

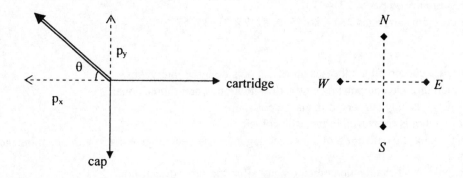

$$p_x = (4\,g)(2\,m/s)$$
$$p_y = (3.5\,g)(5\,m/s)$$
$$p_{spring}^2 = (8\,g\text{-}m/s)^2 + (17.5\,g\cdot m/s)^2$$
$$p_{spring} = 19\,g\cdot m/s$$

Now use the mass of the spring to find its velocity:

$$p_{spring} = 19 \; g \cdot m/s = mv = (15 \; g) \; v$$

$$v = 1.3 \; m/s$$

To find the direction, use the x and y components to find the angle:

$$tan \; \theta = \frac{p_y}{p_x} = \frac{17.5}{8}$$

$$\theta = 65.4° \; \textit{north of west}$$

2. Since the collision is in two dimensions, we write the momentum equations in both dimensions, using the components of velocity in those directions:

$$\Sigma p_{0x} = \Sigma p_{fx}$$
$$(0.25 \; kg)(3.0 \; m/s) = (0.25 \; kg)(v_1 \cos \theta) + (0.4 \; kg)(v_2 \cos 30°)$$

$$\Sigma p_{0y} = \Sigma p_{fy}$$
$$0 = (0.25 \; kg)(v_1 \sin \theta) + (0.4 \; kg)(v_2 \sin 30°)$$

In addition, a kinetic energy equation can be written, since the collision is elastic:

$$\tfrac{1}{2} \; (0.25 \; kg)(3.0 \; m/s)^2 = \tfrac{1}{2} \; (0.25 \; kg)v_1^2 + \tfrac{1}{2} \; (0.4 \; kg)v_2^2$$

The simplified equations are:

$(1) \quad 0.75 = 0.25 \; v_1 \cos \theta + 0.35 \; v_2$
$(2) \quad 0 = 0.25 \; v_1 \sin \theta + 0.2 \; v_2$
$(3) \quad 2.25 = 0.25 \; v_1^2 + 0.4 \; v_2^2$

▶ **Recommended for further practice (Walker, 3rd ed.):**
- Conceptual Checkpoint 9-2
- Example 9-5 on ballistic pendulum
- Chapter Summary on pages 271–273
- Chapter Problems on pages 275–280: 5, 9, 17, 27, 31, 35, 57

√ **Reminders:**
- Momentum is conserved in all cases unless an outside force intervenes.
- Split momentum into components unless the situation is one-dimensional.
- Kinetic energy is only conserved in elastic collisions.
- Only momentum is conserved in inelastic collisions.
- In perfectly inelastic collisions, objects stick together and become one mass with one momentum after the collision.
- Force, impulse, and change in momentum are all in the same direction.

Chapter 10

Rotational Kinematics

The AP* Physics B Syllabus does not usually include topics on rotational kinematics and rotational kinetic energy. However, questions on the AP* regarding conservation of angular momentum and total kinetic energy (i.e., translational kinetic energy plus rotational kinetic energy) do occasionally arise. A basic understanding of moment of inertia, angular velocity, angular acceleration, and angular momentum helps in the explanation of the concept of torque—which is an important topic in the AP* Syllabus. Thus, some basic discussion and a few sample problems are included here as optional review. The equations presented here are not included on the AP* Physics B Formulas Sheet.

Previously, you have studied objects in **translational** motion, where the **center of mass** of the object in motion changes position, or undergoes a displacement. In **rotational** motion, the object spins as a body around a defined axis of rotation, fulcrum, or pivot point—which, incidentally, is not necessarily the center of mass. The Earth, for example, is in rotational motion as it spins on an imaginary axis extending through the planet from the geographic north pole to the geographic south pole.

The amount an object rotates—its **angular displacement** (θ)—is measured in units such as degrees, radians, cyles, turns, or revolutions. The rate at which the object rotates is its **angular velocity** (ω), measured in units such as radians per second, revolutions per minute (rpm), or cycles per second. The rate at which the object changes its rate of rotation is **angular acceleration** (α). The magnitudes of translational (or linear) quantities of motion are related to angular quantities through the radius of rotation. Though angular displacement, velocity, and acceleration are vector quantities, their directions will be discussed later.

$$s = r\theta$$
$$v = r\omega$$
$$a_{tan} = r\alpha$$

For the wheel below, the linear velocity (v) for the wheel is equal to the wheel radius times the angular velocity (ω), which must be in radians per second to obtain velocity in meters per second. The linear displacement (s) for the wheel is equal to the radius of the wheel times the angular displacement (θ) in radians, which is $2\pi r$ for one turn of the wheel, since $\theta = 2\pi$ radians for each turn.

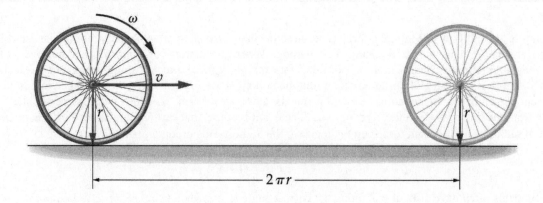

To understand how objects move, it has been important to know the mass of an object, which is the measure of its inertia. For rotating objects, however, mass alone does not describe how it moves. An object's rotational characteristics are dependent upon its **rotational inertia** or **moment of inertia** (I), which depends upon the object's mass and how the mass is distributed around the axis of rotation or pivot point. The table below shows values for some common shapes.

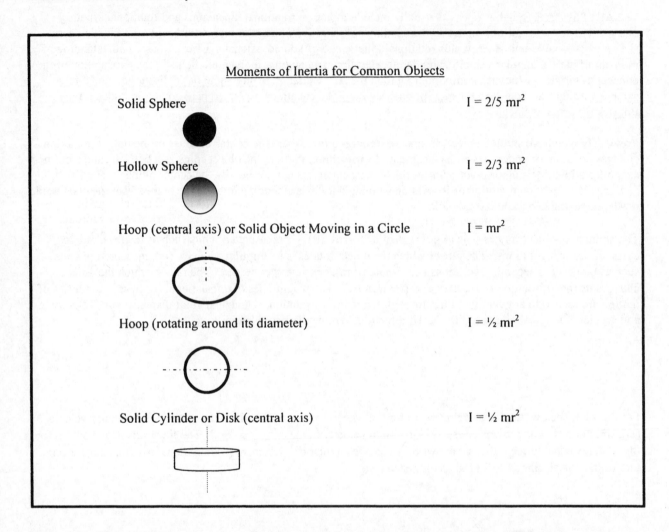

Moments of Inertia for Common Objects

Solid Sphere $I = 2/5\ mr^2$

Hollow Sphere $I = 2/3\ mr^2$

Hoop (central axis) or Solid Object Moving in a Circle $I = mr^2$

Hoop (rotating around its diameter) $I = \frac{1}{2}\ mr^2$

Solid Cylinder or Disk (central axis) $I = \frac{1}{2}\ mr^2$

By Newton's Second Law of Motion, a force is required to change the state of an object's motion, i.e., start it moving if it is not moving, stop it, or change its direction. When considering rotational motion, however, a force may or may not affect the object's motion. Consider, for example, a force directed along the axle of a wheel—which will not start it turning! In order to affect rotational motion, the force must be directed such that is has a component perpendicular to the radius of rotation and also has a "lever arm," r, which is the perpendicular distance from the line of force to the pivot or axle. The quantity, then, that causes angular acceleration is the product of radius of rotation and force perpendicular to that radius. This product is **torque** (τ):

$$\tau = r \mathrm{x} F = F_\perp r = rF\sin\theta$$

[Note: Students often have difficulty defining the correct angle to use when using $rF\sin\theta$, so I advise my students to use the right-hand rule and the cross product, resulting in fewer errors.]

Newton's Second Law for linear motion is $F = ma$, and Newton's Second Law for rotational motion is:

$$\tau = I\alpha$$

In linear motion, momentum depends upon mass and velocity:

$$p = mv$$

In rotational motion, **angular momentum (L)**, depends upon moment of inertia and angular velocity:

$$L = I\omega$$

In the same manner that linear momentum is conserved if there is no external force, angular momentum is conserved if there is no external torque.

Finally, as mentioned earlier, the angular measures of displacement, velocity, acceleration, torque, and momentum are vectors quantities in the same manner as their linear counterparts. Determining direction for these quantities requires a different approach, however. For linear motion, the directions of net force, change in velocity, and change in momentum are the same. Similarly for rotational motion, the directions of net torque, change in angular velocity, and change in angular momentum are the same—and are determined by the right-hand rule. Curling the fingers of the right hand in the direction of rotation, extend the thumb to determine the direction of angular velocity, which is also the direction of the torque that produced the motion and is the direction of angular momentum.

Sample Problems

1. The wheel and axle below have the labeled forces applied tangentially, as shown. There is also a frictional torque of 0.02 N·m on the wheel, once the wheel starts moving. The radius of the axle is 20 cm, and the radius of the wheel is 60 cm. Calculate the net torque on the moving wheel and axle.

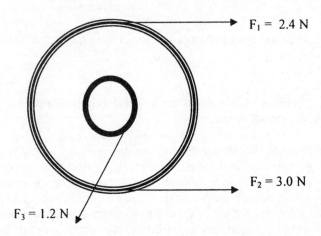

$F_1 = 2.4$ N

$F_2 = 3.0$ N

$F_3 = 1.2$ N

2. The Earth spins toward the east on an axis that extends form the north geographic pole to the south geographic pole. The average radius of Earth is 6.38×10^6 meters. Using this and common knowledge of the planet, calculate:

(a) the angular speed of the planet as it spins on its axis.

(b) the linear speed of a point on the equator.

(c) the linear speed of a point at latitude 39° north.

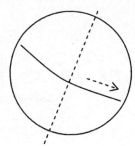

SOLUTIONS TO SAMPLE PROBLEMS

1. (1) Add known torques, with clockwise torques positive and counterclockwise torques negative. (As always, we can select signs for directions.)

$$\tau = rxF = F_\perp r$$
$$(2.4\ N)(0.6\ m) + (1.2\ N)(0.2\ m) - (3.0\ N)(0.6\ m) = -0.12\ N \cdot m$$

This tells us that the applied forces produce a counterclockwise movement, which means the frictional torque opposes this movement and is clockwise.
(2) Add the frictional torque to obtain the net applied torque.

$$\Sigma\tau = -0.12 + 0.02 = -0.10\ N \cdot m\ or\ \textbf{0.10 N} \cdot \textbf{m counterclockwise}$$

2. (a) The angular speed for Earth is angular distance divided by time:

$$\omega = \frac{\theta}{t} = 1\frac{revolution}{day} = \frac{(2\pi)\ radians}{86,400\ sec\ onds} = 7.3 \times 10^5\ rad/s$$

(b) Method 1: $v_{equator} = \dfrac{circumference}{time} = \dfrac{2\pi R}{t} = \dfrac{(2)(\pi)(6.38 \times 10^6 \ m)}{86{,}400 \ s} = 464 \ m/s$

Method 2: Use the angular equation $v = \omega r = (7.3 \times 10^{-5} \ rad/s)(6.38 \times 10^6 \ m) = 466 \ m/s$

(c)

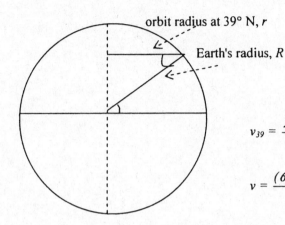

orbit radius at 39° N, r

Earth's radius, R

$v_{39} = \dfrac{2\pi R}{t} = \dfrac{2\pi R \cos 39^\circ}{T}$

$v = \dfrac{(6.38 \times 10^6 \ m)(2\pi)(\cos 39^\circ)}{86{,}400 \ s} = \boldsymbol{360 \ m/s}$

Chapter 11

Rotational Dynamics and Static Equilibrium

Equations

Torque: $\tau = r \times F = F_\perp R = rF\sin\theta$

Net torque: $\Sigma\tau = 0$

The AP* Physics Syllabus includes static equilibrium but does not specifically include topics on rotational dynamics. This review covers portions of rotational dynamics as a subject of interest to the student and also to help create a deeper understanding of torque. However, the AP* Examination is not likely to include angular velocity or angular acceleration. [Note that equations on rotational dynamics are not on the AP* Equations List provided for the exam.] There have been, however, occasional questions on rotational kinetic energy and conservation of angular momentum. The sample questions and problems at the end of this chapter should give you a better idea of where to focus your review. It is very important to review the static equilibrium section of this chapter.

Up to this point, the motions we have studied have been for objects in **translational** motion, where the **center of mass** of the object changes position. **Rotational** motion is that in which the object rotates about an axis or point of balance called a **fulcrum**. There are several differences in the way we will treat rotational motion, compared to how we have previously determined translational motion. The following chart summarizes some similarities and differences:

Translational   **Rotational**

Quantity	Symbol	SI Units	Quantity	Symbol	SI Units
mass	m	kg	moment of inertia	I	$kg \cdot m^2$
linear displacement	s	m	angular displacement	θ	radians
linear velocity	v	m/s	angular velocity	ω	radians per second
linear acceleration	a	m/s^2	angular acceleration	α	radians per second squared
force	F	N	torque	τ	$N \cdot m$
work	W	J or $N \cdot m$	work	W	J or $N \cdot m$
kinetic energy	K	J	kinetic energy	K	J
linear momentum	p	$kg \cdot m/s$	angular momentum	L	$kg \cdot m^2/s$

In some cases, such as work and kinetic energy, the symbols and units are the same for both types of motion, but the differences lie in how these quantities are calculated:

Measurement or Calculation	Linear Equations	Angular Equations
inertia	mass, m	$I = kmr^2$
average velocity	$v = s/t$	$\omega = \theta/t$
average acceleration	$a = \Delta v/\Delta t$	$\alpha = \Delta\omega/\Delta t$
Newton's Second Law	$F = ma$	$\tau = I\alpha = F_\perp r$
work	$W = Fd\cos\theta$	$W = \tau\theta$
kinetic energy	$K = \frac{1}{2}mv^2$	$K = \frac{1}{2}I\omega^2$
momentum	$p = mv$	$L = I\omega$

Torque is the result of a force applied at a distance from the axis or pivot point of an object that is rotating or attempting to rotate. The applied force must have a component perpendicular to the distance from the axis or pivot. (This distance is often called the **lever arm**). An optional method of determining torque is to find the vector cross product of lever arm *(R)* and the force *(F)*.

$$\tau = r \times F = F_{\perp}r$$

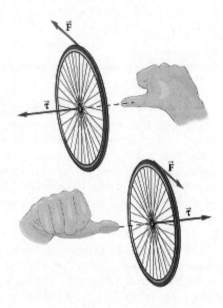

As shown in these diagrams, when a force is applied to start an object into rotational motion, the right-hand rule can be used to determine the direction of torque—with the torque aligned along the axis of rotation. The applied force must have a component perpendicular to the radius at the point of application, with maximum torque when the force is tangent at the point of application. The magnitude of torque is the product of the force component perpendicular to the radius and the radius at the point of application of the force.

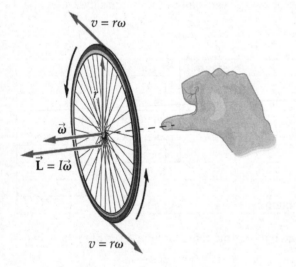

The diagram at left shows the application of the right-hand rule to rotational dynamics. By curling the fingers of your right hand in the direction an object is rotating, the extended thumb indicates the direction of all the following: (a) torque applied to start the motion, (b) direction of angular acceleration, (c) direction of angular velocity, and (d) direction of angular momentum.

For **static equilibrium**, all the net forces and all net torques on any object must add to zero:

$$\Sigma F_x = 0$$
$$\Sigma F_y = 0$$
$$\Sigma F_z = 0$$
$$\Sigma \tau = 0$$

Once you recognize a situation in static equilibrium, follow these steps toward a solution:
1. Draw a free body diagram for all forces on the object in equilibrium.
2. Don't forget friction forces on contact surfaces (wall, floor, etc.), the weight of the object at its center of mass, and forces at hinge points.
3. Determine an appropriate set of coordinate axes (usually x for horizontal and y for vertical).
4. Any forces that are not in positive or negative x or y direction should be split into components in those directions.
5. Write the net force equation for each direction in which there are forces, then substitute values.

$$\Sigma F_x = 0$$
$$\Sigma F_y = 0$$

6. Set a pivot point for torque. It's wise to select a point where one or more forces acts, since a force acting through a pivot exerts no torque. This will eliminate an unknown force from the equation, leading to easier mathematical solutions.
7. Use the torque equation $\tau = F_\perp R$ for each torque about the pivot, remembering that clockwise and counterclockwise torques are opposite in sign.

$$\Sigma \tau = 0$$

8. Solve the equations.

Sample Questions

1. A ball is given an initial force through its center of mass to start it moving across a level floor. What force produces the torque to start the ball rolling?
   A. the gravitational force acting at the ball's center of mass
   B. the friction force of the floor on the ball
   C. the normal force of the floor on the ball
   D. the friction force of the ball on the floor
   E. the initial push on the ball

2. A clock is attached to the west wall of a classroom. What is the direction of the angular velocity of the hands of the clock?
   A. up on the wall
   B. down on the wall
   C. toward the west
   D. toward the east
   E. toward the north

3. What is the direction of the torque the clock motor has to constantly apply to the clock hands in Question 2 in order to keep the clock hands moving?
   A. up on the wall
   B. down on the wall
   C. toward the west
   D. toward the east
   E. toward the north

4. What is the direction of the frictional torque on the clock hands in Question 2?
   A. up on the wall
   B. down on the wall
   C. toward the west
   D. toward the east
   E. toward the north

5. A string is wound around a nearly frictionless wheel, and a 20 N force is applied at a 60° angle, as shown below. The diameter of the wheel is 1.0 meter. What is the magnitude of the torque applied to the wheel?

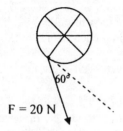

60°

F = 20 N

A. 5.0 N·m
B. 8.7 N·m
C. 10 N·m
D. 20 N·m
E. 40 N·m

Sample Problems

1. A uniform beam of mass 20 kg has a sign of mass 5 kg hanging from its end. (a) Find the tension in the cable (shown above) that helps to support the beam and sign. (b) Find the normal force on the beam from the wall.

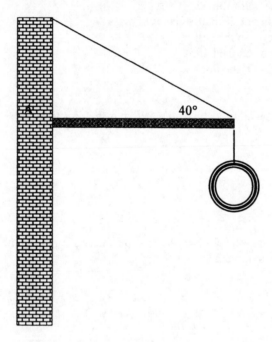

40°

2. This ladder is 3 meters long and has a mass of 4 kg. With a paint bucket of mass 1 kg hanging 0.5 m from the top end, the ladder remains stable against a frictionless wall with its bottom end 2 meters from the base of the wall. Find the coefficient of friction between the ladder and the floor.

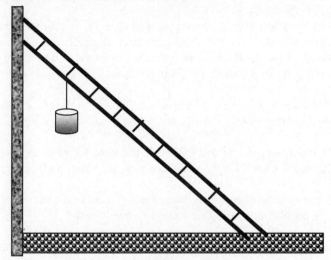

3. The uniform meter stick below has a mass of 700 grams hanging at the 15-cm mark and a mass of 350 grams at the 70-cm mark. It balances on a pivot placed at the 35-cm mark. What is the mass of the meter stick?

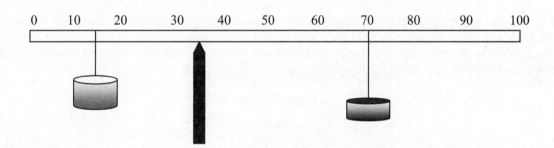

4. Determine the minimum horizontal force that would need to be applied at the axle of the wheel below to roll the wheel up over the curb, as shown below.

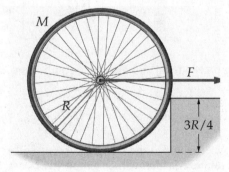

SOLUTIONS TO SAMPLE QUESTIONS AND SAMPLE PROBLEMS

Multiple Choice Questions:

1. B The gravitational force acts at the center of mass of the ball, and for that reason exerts no torque on the ball with respect to the center of mass. Once the initial push starts the ball moving across the floor, it is the torque applied by the friction force from the floor on the ball that causes the ball to rotate around the center of mass, which then results in rolling down the ramp. Without friction, the ball would slide across the floor.

2. C Using the right-hand rule, with curled fingers in the direction the clock hands turn and thumb extended in direction of angular velocity, the angular velocity due to the clock hands is west.

3. C As in linear motion, where the applied force is in the same direction as constant velocity (in the presence of friction), the applied torque must be in the same direction as angular velocity, or west.

4. D Friction forces opposes the direction of linear velocity, and in the same manner frictional torque is in the opposite direction as the angular velocity. The friction torque is east.

5. A Use the component of force tangent to the circle (or perpendicular to the radius).
$$\tau = r \times F = F_\perp r = (20\ N)(cos\ 60°)(0.5\ m) = 5\ N{\cdot}m$$
The problem only asks for magnitude of torque.
[Note: Torque can also be solved using the equation $\tau = rF\ sin\theta$. However, students often have difficulty defining the correct angle to use, so I recommend the use of the right-hand rule using the vector cross product...or using the vector components that are perpendicular.]

Free Response Problems:

1. First, construct a labeled force diagram and split the force at the hinge and the tension force into components. It's easier to just consider the force at the hinge as two individual component forces, F_v and F_H, from the beginning. (If we have drawn F_v in the wrong direction, it will simply turn out negative in our solution!) Notice also that the weight of the beam has been added at its center.

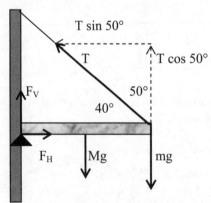

Then write Newton's laws, showing translational and rotational equilibrium. Since we don't know the length of the beam, we'll call it L:

$$\Sigma F_x = 0 \qquad\qquad\qquad \Sigma F_y = 0$$
$$F_H = T\ sin\ 50° \qquad\qquad F_V + T\ cos\ 50° = Mg + mg$$

Place a pivot, preferably at a point where some of the unknown forces will act (in this case F_H and F_v), since those forces will not exert torque and the torque equation will be simplified.

$$\Sigma\tau = 0$$

$$\tau_{clockwise} = \tau_{counterclockwise}$$

$$Mg(\tfrac{1}{2}L) + mg(L) = (T\cos 50°)L$$

[Note: In the torque equation, we have used the component of tension that is perpendicular to the beam times the length of the beam. Notice also that the length of the beam, L, cancels from the equation.]

$$(20\ kg)(9.8\ m/s^2)(\tfrac{1}{2}) + (5\ kg)(9.8\ m/s^2) = T\cos 50°$$

$$T = 230\ N$$

Substituting the value of T and solving for the other forces:

$$F_H = T\sin 50° = 230\sin 50° = 176\ N$$

$$F_V = -T\cos 50° + Mg + mg$$
$$F_v = (20\ kg)(9.8\ m/s^2) + (5\ kg)(9.8\ m/s^2) - 230\ N\cos 50° = 97\ N$$

2. Begin by drawing a free-body diagram for the situation, where mg is the weight of the paint bucket, Mg is the weight of the ladder, N is the normal force from the floor, F_N is the normal force from the wall, and F_f is the friction force at the floor.

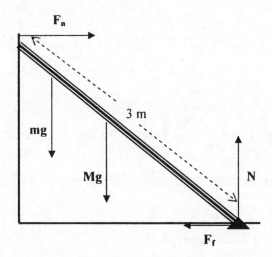

Write the equations for balanced forces in each direction:

$$\Sigma F_x = 0 \qquad\qquad\qquad \Sigma F_y = 0$$
$$F_n = F_f \qquad\qquad\qquad N = mg + Mg$$
$$\qquad\qquad\qquad\qquad N = (5\ kg)(9.8\ m/s^2) = 49\ N$$

Set the pivot at the contact point between the ladder and the floor, since that will eliminate F_f, one of the unknown forces, from the equation. First, we'll do a little trigonometry to find the angle between the ladder and the floor and the height of the top of the ladder at the wall.

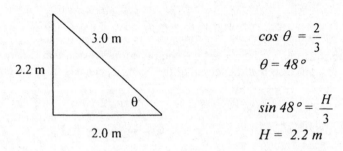

$$cos\ \theta\ =\ \frac{2}{3}$$

$$\theta = 48°$$

$$sin\ 48° =\ \frac{H}{3}$$

$$H =\ 2.2\ m$$

In each case, the lever arm for the force will be the perpendicular distance from the line of force to the pivot:

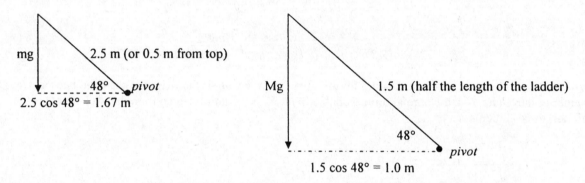

Use these lever arms to write the torque equation:

$$\Sigma\tau = 0$$

$$\tau_{clockwise} = \tau_{counterclockwise}$$

$$F_n(2.2\ m\ ) = Mg(1.0\ m\ ) + mg(1.67\ m)$$

$$F_n(2.2\ m) = (4\ kg)(9.8\ m/s^2)(1.0\ m) + (1\ kg)(9.8\ m/s^2)(1.67\ m)$$

$$F_n = 25\ N$$

Now that we know the friction force and the normal force at the floor, calculate the coefficient of friction. (Checking above, note that $F_n = F_f$.)

$$\mu = \frac{F_f}{N} = \frac{25\ N}{49\ N} = 0.51$$

3. Make a free-body diagram, with m_1g the weight of the large mass, m_2g the weight of the smaller mass, N the normal force on the stick at the pivot, and mg the weight of the meter stick (at the center of the stick).

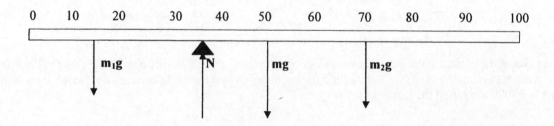

We notice here that with the normal force at the hinge will not produce a torque, so a little insight tells us here that the torque equation alone will solve for the only unknown variable we need.

$$\Sigma \tau = 0$$
$$\tau_{clockwise} = \tau_{counterclockwise}$$
$$mg(15\ cm) + m_2g(35\ cm) = m_1g(20\ cm)$$
$$(m)(15\ cm) + (350\ g)(35\ cm) = (700g)(20\ cm)$$
$$m = 117\ g$$

> Note: If we keep units consistent, there is no need to convert to SI units here.

4. The free body diagram is shown, with the fulcrum at the curb. As the wheel leaves the curb, there is no normal force from the ground, and the normal force from the curb will provide no torque (at the pivot).

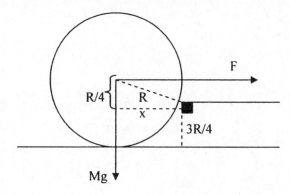

The "known" values that we are able to use are the mass of the wheel, M, the radius of the wheel, R, and the height of the curb, $3R/4$. The value x that is needed as the lever arm for Mg needs to be found first. Using the Pythagorean Theorem:

$$x^2 + (R/4)^2 = R^2$$
$$x^2 = R^2 - R^2/16 = 15R^2/16$$
$$x = R\sqrt{\frac{15}{16}}$$

With only one unknown, F, the torque equation alone will be enough.

$$\Sigma \tau = 0$$
$$\tau_{clockwise} = \tau_{counterclockwise}$$
$$(F)(\frac{R}{4}) = MgR\sqrt{\frac{15}{16}}$$
$$F = \sqrt{15}\ Mg$$

> Note: By retaining the expression $(R\sqrt{\frac{15}{16}})$ and rewriting 4 as $\sqrt{16}$, we get a neat cancellation of both the R and the $\sqrt{16}$. Watch for this common "trick" on the AP*, i.e., setting up numerical values for easy cancellations.

▶ Recommended for further practice (Walker, 3rd ed.):
  • Omit Section 11-2 and Section 11-5 on angular acceleration and moment of inertia.
  • Active Example 11-3 on page 329 (classic ladder problem)
  • Chapter Summary on page 346–348 (Sections 1, 3, 4, and 7 only)
  • Chapter Problems on pages 350–357: 5, 17, 23, 27, 77, 85, 95

√ **Reminders:**
- Any force applied such that the line of force can be extended through the pivot exerts no torque.
- When calculating torque for any applied force, remember that torque is the product of force and lever arm, with the two perpendicular to each other.
- The right-hand rule can be used to determine directions for angular motion vectors. By curling the fingers of the right hand in the direction the object is turning, the extended thumb indicates the direction of torque, angular acceleration, angular velocity, and angular momentum.

Chapter 12

Gravity

Equations

Gravitational force: $F_g = -\dfrac{Gm_1m_2}{r^2}$

Gravitational potential energy: $U_g = -\dfrac{GMm}{r}$

Newton's Law of Universal Gravitation states that every particle or object in the universe attracts every other particle or object with a force that is directly proportional to the product of the two masses and inversely proportional to the square of the distance between their centers of mass. The attractions between two objects are equal in magnitude and opposite in direction, with the forces directed along the line between the centers of the objects.

$$F_g = -\dfrac{Gm_1m_2}{r^2}$$

The constant of proportionality is the universal gravitational constant, G, which is equal to 6.67×10^{-11} N-m²/kg². The negative sign indicates that the gravitational force is always an attractive force, since every other quantity in the formula will always be positive. A more concise explanation of this negative sign comes from the vector expression for gravitational force:

$$F_g = -\dfrac{Gm_1m_2}{r^2}\,\hat{r}$$

The $\hat{r}$ notation indicates a unit vector (magnitude equals one) in a direction radially outward. Thus $-\hat{r}$ on this formula makes all gravitational forces radially inward between the two centers of mass. [This unit vector notation (See Chapter 1) is not used on the AP* Exam, but is, I believe, helpful to understanding the negative sign in the equation. After all, force is a vector.]

The gravitational potential energy of an object of mass M in a gravitational field is:

$$U_g = -\dfrac{GMm}{r}$$

In this case, the gravitational potential energy (in newtons) is negative—not indicating a direction, since energy is not a vector, but indicating a magnitude less than zero. Thus, as the object moves farther away from the source of the field (provided by another object or group of objects), r increases and U decreases until the gravitational potential energy is zero at that theoretical point (infinity) where there is no gravitational field and U is zero.

Important Note: Gravitational potential energy is directly proportional to distance from the center of gravitational pull. In the case of $U = mgh$, the form used in a previous chapter, this is obvious, i.e., U increases as h increases. It's not so obvious for the gravitational potential energy above. As the object of mass m moves farther from the center of gravitational pull, the value of r increases. However, the negative sign means that as r increases, U becomes less negative—or has a larger value.

We can derive a value for g, the gravitational acceleration at the surface of an object by setting the weight of a second object at the surface of the first object equal to the gravitational force exerted by the first object on the second object:

$$mg = \frac{Gm_1 m_2}{r^2}$$

$$g = \frac{GM}{r^2}$$

In the above formula, the mass M is the mass of the object providing the gravitational field, and r is the radius of this object.

The gravitational force between you and the Earth is your weight:

$$mg = \frac{Gm_1 m}{r^2}$$

where m is your mass, and m_1 is the mass of the Earth.

The gravitational acceleration near the surface, g, should not be confused with the universal gravitational constant, G. Though g near Earth's surface has an accepted value of 9.8 m/s^2, it varies with the shape of Earth, magnetic deposits, variations in density, and altitude. The value of g on Mt. Everest is 9.77 m/s^2

For an object held in circular or nearly circular orbit by a gravitational force, the centripetal force is provided by gravity, and radius, r, is constant:

$$F_c = F_G$$

$$\frac{mv^2}{r} = \frac{Gm_1 m_2}{r^2}$$

$$v = \sqrt{\frac{GM}{r}}$$

Be aware that in the above formula for the constant velocity of an object in a circular orbit, M is the mass of the object being orbited, and r is the center-to-center orbital radius. An important observation here is that the velocity of a satellite in circular orbit is inversely proportional to the orbital radius. Thus, for an Earth satellite to move into a "higher orbit," i.e., an orbit farther from Earth, it will actually reduce its speed in orbit. Satellites orbiting closer to Earth must travel faster.

Velocity in circular orbit is also equal to distance divided by time, where the distance is the circumference of a circle and the time for a complete orbit is the period, T:

$$v = \frac{2\pi r}{T}$$

An astronaut aboard a space shuttle will experience what we call weightlessness, only because the astronaut, the shuttle, and everything and everyone on board are all in free fall, i.e., they are accelerating toward Earth. They don't hit Earth, because the tangential velocity of the shuttle is large enough that they fall toward Earth and "miss." In fact, at the altitude the shuttles orbit, g has a value of about 8.7 m/s^2.

A **geosynchronous orbit** is one is which an object orbits Earth such that it maintains the same position above a given point on Earth's surface. For this to be possible, the object's orbital period must be the same as Earth's rotational period, which is one day. To calculate the velocity for such an orbit, set the period equal to the number of seconds in a day and orbital radius equal to the center-to-center distance, i.e., Earth's radius plus satellite's height above the surface. [Note: The orbit must be around the Earth's equator.]

Circular orbits are special cases of elliptical orbits, which are the common orbit for the planets of the solar system, most Earth satellites (including the moon), and other orbits in the universe. Kepler's Laws of Planetary Motion describe these elliptical orbits.

Kepler's Laws of Planetary Motion:
(1) The orbit of every planet is an <u>ellipse</u>, with the Sun at one <u>focus</u>.
(2) A line from the planet to the Sun sweeps equal areas in equal amounts of time.

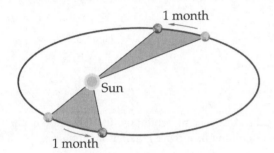

Essentially, this means that the planet or satellite in an elliptical orbit does not travel at constant speed. Rather, it must speed up and slow down—moving faster during the portion of its orbit when it is closer to the orbited body and more slowly when it is farther from the orbited body.

(3) The square of the period of a planet in its orbit is directly proportional to the cube of its orbital radius.

By assuming a nearly circular orbit, one can derive this by first setting the gravitational force between the planet (m_p) and the Sun (M_s) equal to the centripetal force, with R equal to the orbital radius (i.e., center-to-center distance between the Sun and the planet):

$$\frac{Gm_p M_s}{R^2} = \frac{m_p v^2}{R}$$

Then recognize that the velocity of the planet in its orbit (v) is distance divided by time, or circumference of the orbit ($2\pi R$) divided by orbital period (T).

$$v = \frac{2\pi R}{T}$$

Substitute for v in the above expression:

$$\frac{Gm_p M_s}{R^2} = \frac{m_p \left(\frac{2\pi R}{T}\right)^2}{R}$$

$$\frac{T^2}{R^3} = \frac{4\pi^2}{GM_s}$$

For any two planets orbiting the Sun, this relationship between their respective orbital periods and their orbital radii becomes:

$$\frac{T_1^2}{R_1^3} = \frac{T_2^2}{R_2^3}$$

As a matter of fact, this statement is true for any set of satellites orbiting the same central body. This is the statement of Kepler's Third Law that is most useful to us. Again, this only applies to two satellites orbiting the same central body, such as two planets orbiting the Sun—or two moons orbiting Jupiter.

Sample Questions

1. A satellite of mass m is in a stable circular orbit of radius r. A second satellite is to be placed in the same orbit, but the second satellite has twice the mass. The ratio of the speed of the second satellite to the speed of the first satellite must be:
    A. 1:4
    B. 1:2
    C. 1:1
    D. 2:1
    E. 4:1

2. Two satellites, of masses m and $2m$ are placed into circular orbits of the same orbital radius. The ratio of the magnitude of the gravitational potential energy of the second satellite ($2m$) to the gravitational potential energy of the first satellite (m) is:
    A. 1:4
    B. 1:2
    C. 1:1
    D. 2:1
    E. 4:1

3. The Moon moves in an elliptical orbit around Earth. Which of the following is true of this orbit?
    I.   The Moon moves fastest in its orbit when it is farthest from Earth.
    II. The Moon moves slowest in its orbit when it is closest to Earth.
    III. Earth is always positioned at one of the foci of the Moon's orbit.
    A. I only
    B. I and II only
    C. II and III only
    D. I and III only
    E. III only

4. An object with a mass 27 kg has what approximate weight at two Earth radii above Earth's surface?
    A. 10 N
    B. 30 N
    C. 90 N
    D. 135 N
    E. 270 N

5.   Suppose we discover a new planet in a galaxy far, far away that looks as if it has about twice Earth's mass and four times Earth's radius. What might we predict for gravitational acceleration on that planet, compared to g on Earth?

   A. $\frac{1}{16}$

   B. $\frac{1}{8}$

   C. $\frac{1}{4}$

   D. ½

   E. the same

Sample Problems

1. A spacecraft orbits a distant planet at a distance of 6.0×10^7 meters from the center of the planet. The period of the orbit is 1.4 hours. From this information, calculate:

   (a) the speed of the spacecraft in its orbit

   (b) the mass of the planet

2. Calculate the average orbital radius of Pluto, using the fact that it takes Pluto 248 Earth years to make one orbit. [The average Earth-Sun distance is 1.5×10^8 km.]

3. What should the speed of a geosynchronous satellite orbiting at 4 Earth radii above Earth's surface at the equator be for a stable orbit? [Earth's average radius is 6.38×10^6 m.]

SOLUTIONS TO SAMPLE QUESTIONS AND SAMPLE PROBLEMS

Multiple Choice Questions:

1.   **C**   The orbit of a satellite is independent of its mass and depends only on the constant G, the mass of the central body M, and the radius of the satellite's orbit R. Thus, two satellites of different mass orbiting the same center body at the same orbital radius must have the same velocity: $v = \sqrt{\dfrac{GM}{R}}$

2.   **D**   The magnitude of the gravitational potential energy is doubled when mass is doubled: $U_g = \dfrac{GMm}{r}$

3.   **E**   By Kepler's Second Law, the Moon will move fastest in its orbit when it is closest to Earth and slowest in its orbit when it is farthest from Earth, so both **I** and **II** are false. By Kepler's First Law, however, one of the foci of the Moon's orbit is Earth—defining the orbit.

4.   **B**   If the object's mass is 27 kg on Earth's surface, then its weight on Earth's surface, mg, is 270 newtons. Moving the object 2 Earth radii above the surface then triples the distance of the object from the center of Earth. Since the gravitational force is an inverse square law, the weight would be one-ninth as great, or 30 N.

5. B We can set an object's weight equal to the gravitational force, with r equal to the radius of the planet.

$$mg = \frac{Gm_1m_2}{r^2}$$

$$g_{earth} = \frac{GM}{r^2}$$

$$g_{planet} = \frac{G(2M)}{(4R)^2} = \tfrac{1}{8}\frac{GM}{r^2} = \tfrac{1}{8}g$$

Free Response Problems:

1. (a) $v = \dfrac{2\pi r}{T} = \dfrac{2\pi(6 \times 10^7 \ m)}{(1.4)(3600) \ s} = 7.5 \times 10^4 \ m/s$

(b) Centripetal force for the orbit is provided by the gravitational force:

$$F_c = F_G$$

$$\frac{mv^2}{r} = \frac{GMm}{r^2}$$

$$M = \frac{v^2 r}{G} = \frac{(7.5 \times 10^4 \ m/s)^2(6 \times 10^7 \ m)}{6.67 \times 10^{-11} \ N \cdot m^2/kg^2} = 5.1 \times 10^{27} \ kg$$

2. Since Earth and Pluto both orbit the Sun, we can equate their orbital periods (T) and orbital radii (R) using Kepler's Third Law:

$$\frac{T_E^2}{R_E^3} = \frac{T_P^2}{R_P^3}$$

$$\frac{(1 \ year)^2}{(1.5 \times 10^8 \ km)^3} = \frac{(248 \ years)^2}{R_P^3}$$

$R_P = 5.9 \times 10^9 \ km$ (which is almost 6 trillion meters!)

3. Geosynchronous means the satellite's orbital period equals Earth's, so the period of both is one day:

$$T = 24 \ h = 8.64 \times 10^4 \ s$$

Find the radius of the orbit:

$$r_{orbit} = h + r_{earth} = 4r + r = 5(6.38 \times 10^6 \ m) = 3.19 \times 10^7 \ m$$

Determine the velocity of the satellite in terms of its period and orbit radius:

$$v_{satellite} = \frac{2\pi R}{T} = \frac{2\pi(3.19x10^7 \, m)}{8.64x10^4 \, s} = 2320 \, m/s$$

Note: This is the orbital speed for every geosynchronous equatorial Earth satellite, regardless of its mass.

▶ **Recommended for further practice (Walker, 3rd ed.):**
- Cavendish Experiment on page 365
- Orbital maneuvers on page 373–374
- Potential/kinetic energy plot on page 379
- Chapter Summary on pages 386–388
- Chapter Problems on page 389–393: 11, 17, 19, 27, 29, 37, 43, 61, 63

√ **Reminders:**
- When calculating the gravitational force or gravitation potential energy, remember that the units in G demand that when substituting quantities into these equations all masses must be in kilograms and distances must be in meters.
- The gravitational forces between any two masses are equal in magnitude and opposite in direction.
- The gravitational force is always an attractive force.
- The gravitational force follows an "inverse square law," i.e., doubling the distance between two objects cuts gravitational force in fourth, tripling the distance cuts in to one-ninth, etc.
- The gravitational potential energy is directly proportional to distance from center of gravitational pull.
- The mass, m, in the centripetal force formula is always the mass of the object in orbit.
- Centripetal and gravitational forces are both negative, indicating force toward the center.
- Kepler's Third Law relates objects that are orbiting the same central body.
- The radius in the centripetal force and the gravitational force formulas is center-to-center, so if an altitude for a satellite in orbit is given, the radius of the orbited body must be added to the altitude to obtain orbital radius.

Chapter 13

Oscillations About Equilibrium

Equations

Period of a pendulum: $T = 2\pi \sqrt{\dfrac{L}{g}}$

Period of a spring: $T = 2\pi \sqrt{\dfrac{m}{k}}$

Period related to frequency: $T = \dfrac{1}{f}$

When an object in equilibrium is displaced, it may undergo **oscillations,** where the object undergoes repeated motion back and forth past the equilibrium position. The force that returns the object to its equilibrium position is termed a **restoring force (F).** The restoring force is directed toward the equilibrium position, accelerating the object toward the equilibrium position. If the restoring force is directly proportional to the displacement of the object from the equilibrium position, the motion is **simple harmonic motion.** This is a type of **periodic** motion, since the motion repeats at regular intervals. The time it takes for one complete cycle, which is the time from a given displacement and velocity back to the same displacement and velocity is called the **period (T).** The number of complete oscillations per second is called **frequency (f)** of oscillation, measured in cycles per second (sometimes called **hertz**).

$$T = \frac{1}{f}$$

In simple harmonic motion, the maximum displacement of the object from equilibrium is called the **amplitude (A)** of the motion. As displacement increases, the restoring force increases, with maximum restoring force when the object is at the amplitude position. By Newton's Second Law, when the force is a maximum on a given mass, the acceleration is also maximum. At the equilibrium position, there is no net force, so acceleration is zero.

In the absence of friction, mechanical energy is conserved during these oscillations. At maximum amplitude, the potential energy is maximum and kinetic energy is zero. At this point also, the restoring force is maximum, so acceleration is maximum. Then as the oscillating mass passes through the equilibrium position, the restoring force is zero, acceleration is zero, and potential energy is zero. At the equilibrium position, the kinetic energy is maximum.

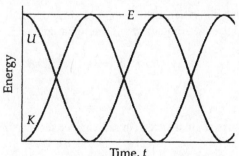

We can expect, then, that since potential energy is a function of position and kinetic energy is a function of velocity, that the plots of position and velocity with respect to time would be **sinusoidal.** Without an extensive derivation of this, consider one example of harmonic motion—an object moving in a circle. The radius of the circle is R, and the displacement of the object at any point is its distance from the equilibrium line. At its beginning point, as you can see in the diagram below, its displacement is zero. After it has moved an angle 90° to the top of the circle, its displacement is R. After it moves 180° to the other side of the circle, its displacement is zero again…and so on. What we're interested in here is a general equation that will work for every point on the circle, so we'll choose point P, where the object has moved an angle θ. We're interested in the displacement of the object, which is its vertical distance from the equilibrium line. Now we've got an equation!

$$x = R \sin\theta$$

In this case, the amplitude is R, so we can generalize an equation for harmonic motion:

$$x = A \sin\theta.$$

From rotational kinematics (Chapter 10), angular displacement is equal to angular velocity multiplied by time:

$$\theta = \omega t \quad \text{and} \quad \omega = 2\pi f$$

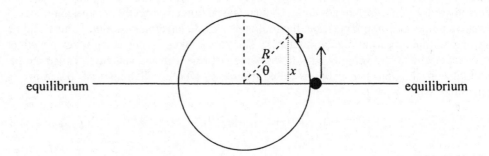

By substitution of the above quantities into the harmonic motion equation:

$$x = A \sin \omega t \quad \text{or} \quad x = A \sin 2\pi f t$$

These are the working equations for position of a harmonic oscillator as a function of time. Alternatively, the cosine function can be used instead of sine. Whether the function used is sine or cosine depends upon the position of the oscillator at $t = 0$. If the oscillator starts its motion at equilibrium, use the sine function. If the oscillator starts its motion at its amplitude (such as a pendulum pulled back and released), use the cosine function.

The AP* Exam will not require such derivation—this is provided for depth of understanding—but will expect the student to be able to recognize and use these equations. To summarize:

$$x = A \sin \omega t \quad \text{or} \quad x = A \sin 2\pi f t$$
$$\text{or}$$
$$x = A \cos \omega t \quad \text{or} \quad x = A \cos 2\pi f t$$

where A is amplitude (in meters), ω is angular speed (in radians per second), f is frequency (in cycles per second or hertz), and t is time (in seconds).

The velocity as a function of time is the first derivative of the position *vs* time function, since $v = \dfrac{\Delta x}{\Delta t}$. Another way to consider this is to think back to Chapter 2, when we found velocity as the slope of the *position vs. time* graph. The equation for velocity can be derived:

$$x(t) = A \sin \omega t$$
$$v(t) = A\omega \cos \omega t$$

And in the same manner, acceleration is the derivative or slope of the velocity *vs.* time:

$$a(t) = -A\omega^2 \sin \omega t$$

In summary:
1. Position, velocity, and acceleration plots are all sinusoidal functions with time.
2. Velocity maxima are shifted by 90°, or by $\frac{1}{4}$ cycle, from the position. This means that if position is a maximum, velocity is a minimum—and will be a maximum $\frac{1}{4}$ cycle later.
3. Acceleration maxima are shifted by 90°, or by $\frac{1}{4}$ cycle, from the velocity. This means that if velocity is a maximum, acceleration is a minimum—and will be a maximum $\frac{1}{4}$ cycle later.
4. Acceleration and position functions are maxima and minima at the same time—but in opposite directions.
5. The velocity amplitude, or maximum velocity, is $A\omega$.
6. The acceleration amplitude, or maximum acceleration, is $A\omega^2$.

A mass oscillating on a **spring** is an example of harmonic motion. The period of oscillation of the spring depends upon the spring constant, k, and the mass, m:

$$T = 2\pi \sqrt{\frac{m}{k}}$$

As a spring oscillates, friction forces may dissipate some of the total mechanical energy (K + U) of the spring so that the amplitude gradually decreases. This decrease in amplitude of a spring is called **damping**. Notice that amplitude is not included in the equation above, so an oscillating spring's period (and frequency) do <u>not</u> change as the amplitude of the spring decreases—eventually to a stop. The restoring force for a spring is, of course, the spring force, $F = -kx$. The potential energy at any point during the motion is $U_s = \frac{1}{2} kx^2$, where k is the spring constant and x is the displacement from equilibrium.

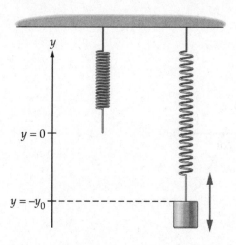

If a mass, m, is added to a relaxed spring, the spring will expand to an equilibrium point, shown here at $-y_0$. The spring constant can be determined by setting the applied weight equal to the restoring force of the spring:

$$mg = ky_0$$

The restoring force is in the opposite direction of the extension of the spring. The spring force and acceleration are in the same direction and are always directed toward the equilibrium position.

A mass oscillating on a **pendulum** is an example of harmonic motion—though the motion of a pendulum is not true simple harmonic motion unless the angle at which the pendulum is released is small (generally less than 10° to 15°). We won't go into the derivation of this, but in the process of deriving the equations for a pendulum, the assumption is made that $sin\theta \approx \theta$. This assumption will only hold true if the angle is small. The period (and frequency) of oscillation of a pendulum depends upon the acceleration due to gravity, g, and on the length of the pendulum, L:

$$T = 2\pi \sqrt{\frac{L}{g}}$$

The restoring force for an oscillating pendulum is gravity. As the pendulum is displaced from equilibrium it develops gravitational potential energy: $U_G = mgh$. [Reminder: The height to which the pendulum bob is raised to develop this potential energy is $h = L - Lcos\theta$. The complete explanation of this is in Chapter 8 of this text.] If the pendulum bob is pulled back so that it is raised to a height h and released, it will begin to oscillate. The pendulum bob's maximum potential energy (and zero velocity) occurs at each instant it reaches a height h, and its maximum kinetic energy (and maximum speed) occurs each time it passes through the equilibrium position.

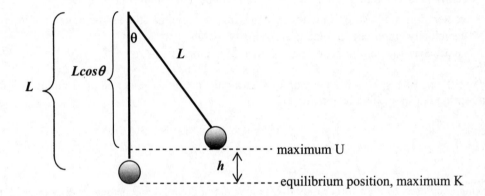

Below is a sample plot for a harmonic oscillator, which is in this case a sine function, since $x = 0$ at $t = 0$. The amplitude of the motion is 0.5 meters, and the period of the motion is 4.0 seconds. We can also conclude that the frequency is equal to $1/T$ or 0.25 hertz, and the equation of the motion is:

$$x(t) = A \ sin \ 2\pi ft = (0.5 \ m) \ sin \ 0.5\pi t$$

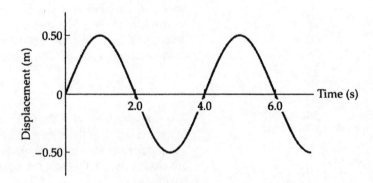

At $t = 0$, the oscillator in the sample on the previous page has a displacement of zero, restoring force of zero, acceleration of zero, potential energy of zero, maximum velocity, and maximum kinetic energy. The same is true at $t = 2.0$ s, $t = 4.0$ s, etc.

At $t = 1.0$ s, the oscillator is at its amplitude and has a displacement of 0.50 m, kinetic energy of zero, maximum restoring force, maximum acceleration, and maximum potential energy.

Energy relationships for the spring and pendulum can be used to find instantaneous velocity and acceleration at various moments during the oscillation. To determine these, remember that the maximum potential energy occurs at the amplitude of the object's motion, where kinetic energy is instantaneously zero. Set that as the sum of potential and kinetic energy at every other point in the object's motion. Thus, at any displacement, x, from equilibrium:

$$K_x + U_x = U_{max}$$

	Kinetic Energy	Potential Energy	Maximum Potential Energy	Velocity $\Delta K = \Delta U$	Acceleration $F = ma$
Spring	$\frac{1}{2}\, mv^2$	$\frac{1}{2}\, kx^2$	$\frac{1}{2}\, kA^2$	$v = x\sqrt{\dfrac{k}{m}}$	$F = -kx$ $-kx = ma$ $a = \dfrac{-kx}{m}$
Pendulum	$\frac{1}{2}\, mv^2$	$mg(L - L\cos\theta)$	mgh_{max}	$v = \sqrt{g(L - L\cos\theta}$	$a = g\sin\theta$

Objects have a **natural frequency** at which they will oscillate when free from external disturbances. If a force is applied at the same frequency as this natural frequency, the object will oscillate at this frequency, or **resonate**.

Sample Questions

1. What would be the approximate length of a pendulum that has a period of one second on Earth?
   A. 0.1 m
   B. 0.3 m
   C. 1 m
   D. 2 m
   E. 3 m

2. The mass on a spring is quadrupled. How will this affect the frequency at which the spring will oscillate?
   A. $\frac{1}{4}$ the original frequency
   B. ½ the original frequency
   C. same frequency
   D. twice the original frequency
   E. four times the original frequency

3. What is the period of an oscillator that has the equation $x(t) = (0.2\ m)\cos \pi t$?
   A. ½ s
   B. 1 s
   C. 2 s
   D. 3 s
   E. π s

4. A 1-kg mass attached to a spring at equilibrium is displaced 10 cm and released and allowed to oscillate. Determine the maximum velocity of the mass if the spring constant is 100 N/m.
    A. 0.5 m/s
    B. 1.0 m/s
    C. π m/s
    D. 10 m/s
    E. 100 m/s

5. A mass, m, on a spring is displaced a distance x from its equilibrium position and released. The spring constant of the spring is k. What is the velocity of the mass when it is at a distance d from equilibrium?
    A. $kx^2 - kd^2$
    B. $\sqrt{kx^2 - kd^2}$
    C. $d\sqrt{\dfrac{k}{m}}$
    D. $\dfrac{k}{m}\sqrt{x^2 - d^2}$
    E. $\sqrt{\dfrac{k}{m}(x^2 - d^2)}$

Sample Problems

1. Below is a plot of *Position vs. Time* for a harmonic oscillator.

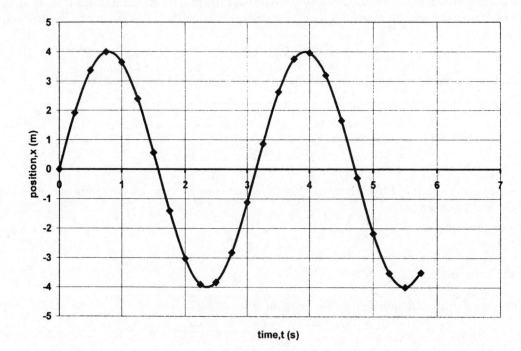

Section II – Reviewing the Physics

(a) What is the amplitude of the motion?

(b) What is the period of the motion?

(c) What is the frequency of the motion?

(d) If this is a bowling ball pendulum, what is the length of the pendulum?

(e) If this is a 2-kg mass oscillating on a spring, what is the spring constant?

(f) Give a time on the graph when the oscillator's acceleration is zero.

2. A pendulum of length 0.50 m with a mass of 0.20 kg is pulled back to a 10° angle and released.

(a) Find the period of the vibration

(b) Find the frequency of the vibration.

(c) Determine the period of the pendulum when it is pulled back 5° and released.

3. When a mass of 1 kg is placed on a vertical spring, the spring stretches a distance of 6 cm. The mass on the spring is then pulled down an additional distance of 10 cm beyond the equilibrium point and allowed to oscillate.

(a) What is the amplitude of the spring's oscillation?

(b) Find the frequency of oscillation of the spring.

(c) Calculate the total energy of the spring

(d) Calculate the maximum velocity of the spring

(e) Calculate the velocity when the mass is 4 cm from equilibrium.

(f) What is the total vertical distance the mass travels during one cycle?

SOLUTIONS TO SAMPLE QUESTIONS AND SAMPLE PROBLEMS

Multiple Choice Questions:

1. **B** Use the pendulum equation, setting period equal to one second:

$$T = 2\pi \sqrt{\frac{L}{g}}$$

$$\frac{T^2 g}{4\pi^2} = L$$

$$\text{estimating:} \quad \frac{10}{36} = L \approx 0.3 \text{ m}$$

2. D Examine the spring equation. When mass is quadrupled, the period will be doubled.

$$T = 2\pi \sqrt{\frac{m}{k}}$$

3. C Using the harmonic motion equation: $x = A \cos 2\pi ft$
The quantity $2\pi f$ in this equation is equal to π in the equation given, so $2f = 1$ and $f = 0.5$ Hz. Period is the reciprocal of frequency, so the period is 2 seconds.

4. B The maximum velocity occurs at equilibrium, when all the potential energy has been converted to kinetic energy. The amplitude is the displacement when the mass is released. Set the kinetic energy at equilibrium equal to the potential energy at amplitude and solve:

$$\frac{1}{2} mv^2 = \frac{1}{2} kA^2$$

$$v = A \sqrt{\frac{k}{m}} = (0.10 \text{ m}) \sqrt{\frac{100 \text{ N/m}}{1 \text{ kg}}} = 1 \text{ m/s}$$

5. E Set the total mechanical energy when the oscillator is at position d equal to the maximum potential energy at amplitude (x in this case), which is the maximum energy of the oscillator:

$$\frac{1}{2} mv^2 + \frac{1}{2} kd^2 = \frac{1}{2} kx^2$$
$$mv^2 = kx^2 - kd^2$$
$$v = \sqrt{\frac{k}{m}(x^2 - d^2)}$$

Free Response Problems:

1. (a) Reading from the plot, the amplitude is the magnitude of maximum displacement from equilibrium, which is **4 meters**.

(b) The period is the time for one full cycle, including one "crest" and one "trough," which is about **3.2 seconds**.

(c) Frequency is the reciprocal of the period: $f = \dfrac{1}{T} = \dfrac{1}{3.2 \text{ s}} = \textbf{\textit{0.31 Hz}}$

(d) Use the pendulum equation with the period we determined in part (b):

$$T = 2\pi \sqrt{\frac{L}{g}}$$

$$\frac{T^2 g}{4\pi^2} = L$$

$$\frac{(3.2 \text{ s})^2 (9.8 \text{ m/s}^2)}{4\pi^2} = \textbf{\textit{2.5 m}}$$

(e) Use the spring equation with the period from (b) and value given for m:

$$T = 2\pi \sqrt{\frac{m}{k}}$$

$$kT^2 = 4\pi^2 m$$

$$k = \frac{4\pi^2(4kg)}{(3.2\ s)^2} = 7.7\ N/m$$

(f) The acceleration is zero when the net force is zero—at equilibrium, when the displacement is zero. That occurs at *0 s, 1.6 s, 3.2 s, 4.8 s*, etc.

2. (a) The period depends only on the length of the pendulum and g.

$$T = 2\pi \sqrt{\frac{L}{g}} = 2\pi \sqrt{\frac{0.5\ m}{9.8\ m/s^2}} = 1.4\ s$$

(b) Frequency is the reciprocal of period, so $f = \dfrac{1}{1.4\ s} = 0.71\ Hz$ (sometimes written as *0.71 s⁻¹*)

(c) As long as angles are small, changing the angle of release of the pendulum will not change its period or frequency, so *T = 1.4 s.*

3. (a) Once the mass is at equilibrium on the spring, the amplitude of oscillation will be equal to the displacement when it is released, or *0.10 m.*

(b) First, find the spring constant of the spring, using Hooke's Law and the applied force. [Note that the applied force, or added weight, is in the same direction as the displacement, so there is no negative sign.]

$$F_{app} = kx$$
$$mg = kx$$
$$(1\ kg)(9.8\ m/s^2) = k(0.06\ m)$$
$$k = 160\ N/m$$

Then use the spring constant and mass in the spring equation to find period and frequency.

$$T = 2\pi \sqrt{\frac{m}{k}} = 2\pi \sqrt{\frac{1\ kg}{160\ N/m}} = 0.5\ s$$

$$f = \frac{1}{T} = 2\ Hz$$

[Note: Sometimes, we see the reciprocal equation for the spring equation—and the same for the pendulum equation—that solves for frequency: $f = \dfrac{1}{2\pi} \sqrt{\dfrac{k}{m}}$. However, I recommend against this only because mistakes are too often made in the calculator when entering the $\dfrac{1}{2\pi}$ and then multiplying. It's your choice.]

(c) The total energy of the spring is the maximum potential energy at amplitude:

$$E_T = U_{max} = \tfrac{1}{2} kA^2 = \tfrac{1}{2} (160 \ N/m)(0.1 \ m)^2 = \textbf{0.8 J}$$

(d) The maximum velocity occurs at equilibrium, when all the potential energy has been converted to kinetic energy:

$$\Delta K = \Delta U$$

[Strictly speaking, one is a loss and one is a gain, so there should be a negative sign, but we're looking for magnitude here.]

$$\tfrac{1}{2} mv^2 = \tfrac{1}{2} kA^2 = E_T$$
$$\tfrac{1}{2} (1 \ kg) \ v^2 = 0.8 \ J$$
$$v = \textbf{1.3 m/s}$$

(e) In this situation, the total energy is split between kinetic and potential energies:

$$E_T = \tfrac{1}{2} mv^2 + \tfrac{1}{2} kx^2$$
$$0.8 \ J = \tfrac{1}{2} (1kg)v^2 + \tfrac{1}{2} (160 \ N/m)(0.04 \ m)^2$$
$$0.8 = \tfrac{1}{2} v^2 + 0.128$$
$$v = \textbf{1.2 m/s}$$

(f) The amplitude of the oscillator is *0.1 m*, so the total distance traveled is *4A*—up, back to equilibrium, down, and back to equilibrium for one cycle—or *0.4 m*.

▶ **Recommended for further practice (Walker, 3rd ed.):**
- Figure 13-10 on page 410, energy as a function of position for an oscillator
- Omit physical pendulum on page 416 and 417
- Omit equations for damped oscillations and resonance in sections 13-7 and 13-8
- Chapter Summary on pages 421–423
- Chapter Problems on pages 425–429: 5, 17, 19,23, 29, 31, 35, 39, 47, 75

√ **Reminders:**
- A pendulum approximates a simple harmonic oscillator at small angles of displacement.
- The length of a pendulum is measured from point of attachment to center of mass of the pendulum bob.
- Mass and angle of release (small) do not affect period and frequency of a pendulum.
- Amplitude and the value of *g* do not affect period and frequency of a spring.

Chapter 14

Waves and Sound

Equation

Wave velocity: $v = f\lambda$

Waves are oscillations that travel from one place to another, transferring energy. **Electromagnetic waves**, which will be studied in more detail beginning in Chapter 25, are produced by electric and magnetic fields and travel fastest through a vacuum, though they can travel through some other materials. In this chapter, we will focus on waves that require a medium to transfer the energy of the wave; i.e., they must travel through a material medium.

Waves transmit energy as disturbances or oscillations from one place to another at various speeds. As you well know, electromagnetic waves in a vacuum transmit energy in various forms (ultraviolet, visible, radio, etc.) at the speed of light—3×10^8 m/s. The energy is transmitted at speeds in other media that depend upon the temperature, elasticity, density, etc., of the material. The **frequency** (*f*, measured in hertz) of a wave is the number of complete oscillations per second, and the **wavelength** (λ, measured in meters) is the distance traveled during one complete oscillation. The product of wavelength and frequency is equal to the velocity of the wave—for any type of wave.

$$v = f\lambda$$

A **longitudinal wave** is one in which the direction of propagation of the wave (i.e., direction the energy travels) is the same direction as the back and forth oscillations of the medium. However, the energy does the traveling—the medium simply oscillates back and forth from an equilibrium position. This might be best compared to a lineup of dominoes, where a push on the first domino sends that push down the line to the last domino, but the dominoes oscillate in position and do not travel along with the energy. An example of a longitudinal wave is sound, where energy is transferred from molecule to molecule by changes in pressure. One complete wavelength for a longitudinal wave such as sound consists of one compression (where molecules are pushed closer together) and one rarefaction (where molecules are expanded farther apart).

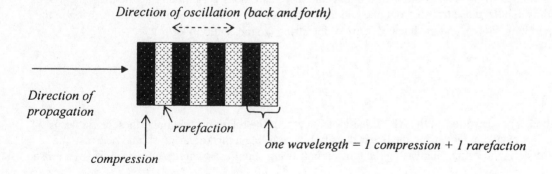

Direction of oscillation (back and forth)

Direction of propagation

rarefaction

compression

one wavelength = 1 compression + 1 rarefaction

Transverse waves may also transfer energy through a medium, but the oscillation of the medium is perpendicular to the direction of propagation of the wave.

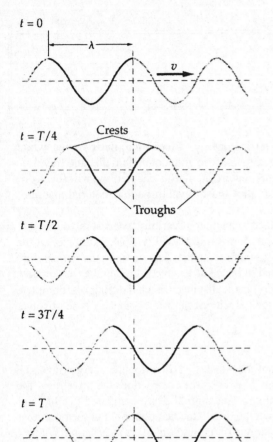

Direction of wave propagation or energy transfer

Wavelength, λ, is measured from crest to crest or trough to trough of a transverse wave.

Direction of oscillation of particles of the medium

In this example, a crest of the transverse pulse moves one complete wavelength (λ), from $t = 0$ to $t = T$. The wave crest moves a distance equal to one wavelength, and the time required is the period (*T*) of the wave.

A pulse traveling along a string is an example of a transverse wave and looks very much like the diagram above. The velocity with which the pulse travels from one end of the string to the other depends upon the tension in the string (*T*, measured in newtons), and the linear density of the string (*μ*, measured in kg/m):

$$v = \sqrt{\frac{T}{\mu}}$$

The above equation is not provided on the AP* Equations Sheet, but the relationship among these variables is helpful to know. For example, increasing the linear density by providing a thicker string should decrease the velocity of a pulse along the string. Increasing the tension in a string should also increase the velocity of a pulse along the string.

Sound is a form of energy that travels as a longitudinal wave through a medium. Thus, sound cannot travel through a vacuum. The speed of sound through any given medium depends on the density of material (*ρ*) and the elasticity of the material (*B*):

$$v = \sqrt{\frac{B}{\rho}}$$

The velocity of sound in air is usually accepted as about 340 m/s at room temperature. This value is generally provided on AP* tests. A useful equation for the calculation of the speed of sound in dry air is:

$$v = 331 \ m/s + 0.6 \ T_{C^\circ}$$

This equation shows us that the speed of sound in dry air at 0° C is accepted as 331 m/s, and the speed of sound increases by 0.6 m/s for each one degree increase in Celsius temperature. Again, this is not an equation required in calculations, but knowledge of the concepts can be useful.

Speed of Sound in Various Materials	
Material	Speed (m/s)
Aluminum	6420
Granite	6000
Steel	5960
Pyrex glass	5640
Copper	5010
Plastic	2680
Fresh water (20 °C)	1482
Fresh water (0 °C)	1402
Hydrogen (0 °C)	1284
Helium (0 °C)	965
Air (20 °C)	343
Air (0 °C)	331

Humans can only hear sounds with frequencies between 20 and 20,000 hertz. The **intensity**, which determines loudness of a sound, is defined by energy transmitted per unit time across a given area (measured in watts per square meter) and is not affected (generally) by the frequency. For example, if a guitar string of a given frequency is pulled back farther when it is struck, it will have a larger amplitude and thus be louder, but it should still have the same frequency, or pitch. Humans do perceive the loudness of sounds differently at different frequencies. It's interesting to note at this point that humans begin to suffer auditory damage at a lower intensity level than the level at which we feel pain! In the table on the next page, we see that sound intensities at a rock concert can reach 0.1 or even 1 W/m², where damage begins, while pain doesn't occur until the intensity reaches 1 W/m². Important to the rock concert enthusiast is the knowledge that sound intensity follows an **inverse square law**; i.e., doubling the distance between observer and source can cut the intensity to one-fourth.

Rather than dealing with the powers and exponents for intensity, the **decibel level** scale has been developed to convert intensities to more manageable numerical values. Since 1×10^{12} W/m² is the threshold of human hearing, a decibel level of 0 is the threshold—or softest sound humans can hear at a given distance.

$$decibel \ level = d\beta = 10 \ log\left(\frac{I}{1x10^{-12} \ W/m^2}\right)$$

Decibel level is not included in the AP* Syllabus, but students should know that sound intensity decreases with the inverse square of the distance from the sound source.

Sound Intensities (W/m^2)	
Loudest sound produced in laboratory	10^9
Saturn V rocket at 50 m	10^8
Rupture of the eardrum	10^4
Jet engine at 50 m	10
Threshold of pain	1
Rock concert	10^{-1}
Jackhammer at 1 m	10^{-3}
Heavy street traffic	10^{-5}
Conversation at 1 m	10^{-6}
Classroom	10^{-7}
Whisper at 1 m	10^{-10}
Normal breathing	10^{-11}
Threshold of hearing	10^{-12}

Some examples are shown in the table below. A decibel level of 120 dB—that rock concert again—is generally considered to be the threshold for pain and beyond the point at which some temporary or permanent damage to hearing has begun.

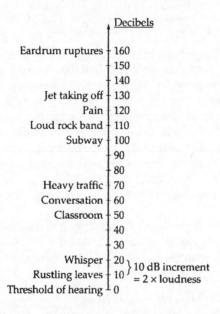

The frequency of a sound wave defines the pitch of the sound we hear; i.e., high frequency sounds are what we call high pitches, and low frequency sounds are low pitches. A change in pitch due to relative motion between a source of sound and the observer is called the **Doppler Effect.** When the source is moving toward the observer, or the observer is moving toward the source—or both—the pitch the observer hears is higher than the actual pitch produced at the source. Likewise, if the source is moving away from the observer, the observer away from the source—or both—the observer hears a lower pitch. The actual pitch change depends on whether the observer or source is moving. The Doppler Effect applies to all types of waves, including electromagnetic waves. So a light source that appears more red is moving away, since a shift to lower frequency (toward the red end of the spectrum) would mean relative motion away. We call this a "red shift."

Waves may interfere with each other when their paths intersect, producing **constructive interference** when they are in the same **phase** (i.e., crest to crest, trough to trough, compression to compression, rarefaction to rarefaction). **Destructive interference** occurs if the waves are not in the same phase as they meet, e.g., a crest of a transverse wave meeting a trough of another will cancel each other as they pass. In the example below, two pulses traveling toward each other will be exactly in the same position, or **superimposed**, in 2.5 seconds from the positions shown here. They are each traveling 1.0 m/s and are each 1.0 meter wide. The leading edge of the pulse on the right will be at 3.5 m, and the trailing edge will be at 4.5 m. For the pulse on the left, in 2.5 seconds the leading edge will be at 4.5 m, and the trailing edge will be at 3.5 m. They will pass each other, since the energy is not destroyed or created, but at that moment their heights will add, creating one pulse that is twice as tall as either of them. This is constructive interference.

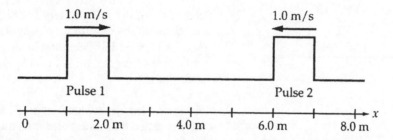

Sound waves, light waves, and other types of waves undergo constructive and destructive interference when they meet, creating patterns of high and low intensity. As waves radiate outward from multiple sources and interfere, they create regions of high intensity (bright light, loud sound) where constructive interference occurs and regions of low intensity (muted sound, no light) where destructive interference occurs. In a later chapter, we will discuss the interference patterns of light in much greater detail. However, keep in mind that sound waves interfere in the same way, as shown in the diagram below.

Consider the **path length** from each source to the point under examination.
- If the path lengths from both sources are the same, then constructive interference will occur (loud sound, bright light, wave of high amplitude).
- If the path lengths from both sources are different, <u>but the difference in the lengths is a whole number of wavelengths,</u> then constructive interference will again occur. In other words, the **path length difference** needs to be a whole number of wavelengths for constructive interference.
- If the path length difference from the sources is ½ λ or any other ½ multiple of wavelengths, then destructive interference will occur (muffled sound, no light, canceled waves).
-

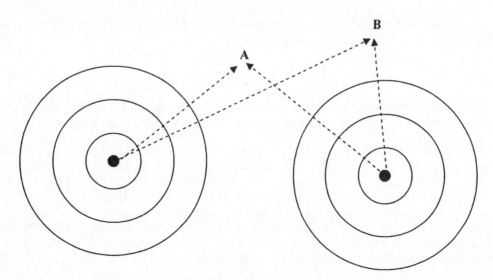

At **A**, the path length difference is zero, so constructive interference occurs.

The distance to **B**, however, is 9 wavelengths from the source on the left and 4 ½ wavelengths from the source on the right. Crests from one will meet troughs from the other, and the waves will cancel at **B**.

A **standing wave** is produced when an oscillation or pulse that is sent into a medium, such as a string or a tube of air, reflects back on itself in such a way that the reflected wave constructively interferes with the ongoing wave. If the initial pulse is of a frequency that matches a natural frequency of the string or tube, the reflection will reinforce. **Harmonics** are the set of frequencies that will naturally vibrate on an oscillator of a given length.

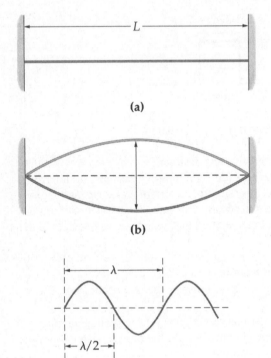

(a)

(b)

(c)

In the case of the string attached at both ends, an oscillation of the right frequency at one end travels to the other end, where it reflects and inverts. Because there is a frequency "match," the reflected pulse reinforces the initial pulse.

The lowest frequency that will produce such a standing wave is called the **fundamental frequency,** and the reinforced oscillation seen here is called the **first harmonic**. This standing wave is ½ λ, so the **fundamental wavelength** is twice the length of the string.

The next higher frequency that will produce a standing wave is the **second harmonic** or **first overtone**, which will oscillate in two loops. The wavelength will be equal to the length of the string.

The frequency above that is the **third harmonic** or **second overtone** and oscillates in three loops. The wavelength for the third harmonic is $\frac{2}{3}$ λ.

We can conclude that the wavelength for a particular numbered harmonic (n) on a fixed string, in terms of the length of the string, can be found by the formula:

$$\lambda_n = \frac{2L}{n}$$

Since the velocity of pulses on the string stays constant for all harmonics and velocity equals wavelength times frequency, we have a general formula for frequencies of the harmonics on a fixed string:

$$v = f\lambda$$
$$f = \frac{nv}{2L}$$

The points of oscillation at maximum amplitude are called **antinodes**, and the points of no amplitude are called **nodes**.

The harmonics for an air column in a tube that is open at both ends are very similar to the fixed string.

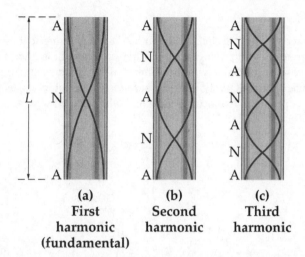

(a)
First
harmonic
(fundamental)

(b)
Second
harmonic

(c)
Third
harmonic

However, in the case of the open tube, there are antinodes at each end. From this, the pattern for harmonics can be developed. For the first harmonic or fundamental, the standing wave in the tube is ½ λ. The second harmonic, or first overtone, has a standing wave of one full wavelength in the tube. The third harmonic is 1.5 λ, and so on:

$$\lambda_n = \frac{2L}{n} \quad \text{and} \quad f = \frac{nv}{2L} \quad \text{(all harmonics: } n = 1, 2, 3, \text{etc.)}$$

For a tube that is open on one end and closed on the other, a node appears at the closed end and an antinode at the open end. The wavelength for the fundamental or first harmonic is 4 times the length of the tube. The wavelength for the next harmonic is $\frac{4}{3}$ L, and then $\frac{4}{5}$ L, and so on, so the general formula is:

$$\lambda_n = \frac{4L}{n.} \quad \text{and} \quad f = \frac{nv}{4L} \quad \text{(odd harmonics only: } n = 1, 3, 5, 7, \text{etc.)}$$

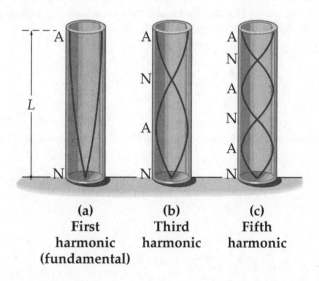

(a)
First
harmonic
(fundamental)

(b)
Third
harmonic

(c)
Fifth
harmonic

Music is often defined as a regular pattern of harmonic sounds. Instruments constructed with strings, open tubes, and other vibrating materials produce sounds that we recognize as having pleasing combinations of frequencies and rhythms.

When notes produced simultaneously have frequencies that have simple numerical ratios, they are called **chords**. Two notes that are close in frequency will produce **beats** if they are played together, as the waves combine. Beats are regular increases and decreases in volume, with the number of beats per second equal to the difference in the two frequencies. The frequencies constructively interfere at regular time intervals, as shown below. For example, if a note with frequency 256 Hz produces two beats per second when played with a second note, the unknown note is 2 Hz different—either 254 Hz or 258 Hz.

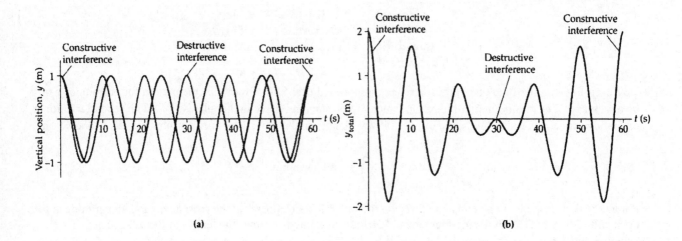

(a)   (b)

Sample Questions

1. A tuning fork with marked frequency 128 Hz has the same pitch as a note produced by blowing across an open pipe. The pipe is shortened slightly, and when the two are played together, a beat frequency of 6 Hz is heard. What is the new frequency of the pipe?
   A. 6 Hz
   B. 122 Hz
   C. 128 Hz
   D. 134 Hz
   E. 736 Hz

2. What is the approximate wavelength produced by middle C on a piano (256 Hz)?
   A. 1 mm
   B. 1 cm
   C. 10 cm
   D. 1 m
   E. 10 m

3. A leaf blower has a sound intensity of 1,000 W/m^2 when operated at a distance of 30 meters from my house. When it is moved to a distance of 60 meters, what is the sound intensity of the leaf blower?
    A. 250 W/m^2
    B. 500 W/m^2
    C. 1000 W/m^2
    D. 2000 W/m^2
    E. 4000 W/m^2

4. A musician playing a pan pipe—a tube open at both ends—covers one end of the pipe. How does the note played when one end of the tube is covered compare to the original note played?
    A. The second note is an octave lower in pitch.
    B. The second note is slightly lower in pitch.
    C. The second note is the same pitch as the first note.
    D. The second note is slightly higher in pitch.
    E. The second note is an octave higher in pitch.

5. A sound (one constant pitch) is produced by two speakers that are set 3 meters apart. At a point that is located 5 meters from one speaker and 7 meters from the other speaker, an antinode, or loud sound, is heard. At another point that is 8 meters from one speaker and 5 meters from the other, the sounds cancel, or produce a node. What is the largest possible wavelength of the sound?
    A. 1 m
    B. 2 m
    C. 3 m
    D. 4 m
    E. 6 m

Sample Problems

1. Calculate the frequencies for the first three harmonics of sound that will resonate in a tube that is 60 cm long and open at both ends. Use 340 m/s for the speed of sound in air.

2. A guitar string is tuned to produce the note B (frequency 288 Hz) in our physics classroom, where the temperature is 20 degrees Celsius. Describe qualitatively what will happen to the note a listener will hear under each of the following conditions. (In each case, compare to the original conditions, and assume the listener doesn't travel with the guitar.) Substantiate each answer with a reason or an equation.

   (a) The tension in the string is increased.

   (b) The temperature in the room is increased.

   (c) The note is played as the guitar is placed into a car speeding at 40 m/s away from the school.

   (d) The air in the room is humidified.

   (e) The string is "fretted" at its half-way point; i.e., its effective length is halved.

   (f) The guitar is somehow played after it is placed into a large vacuum jar and the air is evacuated.

   (g) The guitar is played again in the vacuum jar, but this time we fill the jar with helium.

   (h) The guitar string is replaced with a thicker string that is the same length and at the same tension.

3. A common physics experiment involves lowering an open tube into a cylinder of water and moving the tube up and down to adjust the length of the air column in the tube. A tuning fork of frequency 330 Hz is sounded and held at the upper end as the tube is lifted out of the water until the first resonant sound is heard. The length of tube above water level when the fundamental note sounds is 26 cm.

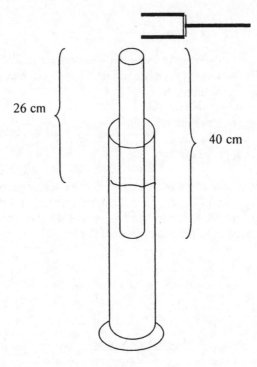

26 cm

40 cm

(a) Calculate the speed of sound in the air column in the tube.

(b) Determine another position for the tube that will result in a resonance with this tuning fork.

(c) Determine the first position (as we again lower the tube into the water) that will resonate with a 256-Hz tuning fork.

SOLUTIONS TO SAMPLE QUESTIONS AND SAMPLE PROBLEMS

Multiple Choice Questions:

1. D A beat frequency of 6 Hz is the difference in frequencies of the two note-producers, so the pipe has a new frequency of 128 ± 6 Hz. Since the tube has been shortened, it should produce a higher-pitched note, or higher frequency, which would be 134 Hz.

2. D Since the answers are spread out in value, we need only a rough estimate of the speed of sound to determine a wavelength. You should remember that the speed of sound in air is somewhat over 300 m/s, so, using $v = f\lambda$, the wavelength is about 1 meter.

3. A Since sound intensity follows an inverse square, doubling the distance would cut the intensity to one-fourth, or 250 W/m^2.

4. A An open tube has wavelength twice the length of the tube, whereas the tube with one end closed has a wavelength 4 times the length of the tube. Doubling the wavelength will cut the frequency to half, which is an octave lower than the original note.

5. B The path length difference for 5 meters and 7 meters is 2 meters—which must be an integral number of wavelengths to produce an antinode. Therefore, the possibilities so far are: $\lambda = 2m$, 1m, 0.5 m, etc. In the second case, the path difference of 3 meters must be multiple of ½ λ, $\frac{3}{2}$ λ, $\frac{5}{2}$ λ, etc., to produce a cancellation. The possibilities here are: $\lambda = 6m$, 2m, 1.2m, etc. The 2-meter quantity fits both situations.

Free Response Problems:

1. If the tube is open at both ends, the resonant tones must have antinodes at each end of the tube. The possible wavelengths are 2L, L, and $\frac{2}{3}$ L, where L is the length of the tube. The wavelengths, then, are 1.2 m, 0.6 m, and 0.4 m. Using $v = f\lambda$ and the speed of sound given, $f = \dfrac{340\ m/s}{1.2\ m}, \dfrac{340\ m/s}{0.6\ m}$, and $\dfrac{340\ m/s}{0.4\ m}$. The frequencies are *283 Hz, 567 Hz*, and *850 Hz*.

2. (a) When tension is increased, the velocity is increased:

$$v = \sqrt{\frac{T}{\mu}}$$

When velocity on the string is increased, assuming string length and thus wavelength are unchanged, the frequency (and pitch) must increase: $v = f\lambda$

(b) If the temperature is increased, the velocity of sound increases, so for the same reasons indicated in (a), the frequency increases. (This is why musicians warm up before a concert—to get the instrument tuned with warm air so the pitch doesn't go up during the concert!)

(c) The Doppler Effect will cause the listener to hear a lower pitch, since the relative velocity between the guitar and listener is lowered.

(d) Humid air is less dense than dry air. Since the velocity of sound is inversely proportional to density of air (assuming humidity doesn't affect the elasticity of air), the velocity will increase. By the same reasoning as in (a), the frequency and pitch will increase.

(e) Fretting the string at its halfway point reduces the fundamental wavelength to half, so the frequency will double. The note heard will go up by one octave.

(f) Sound does not travel through a vacuum (since it is a longitudinal matter wave), so the listener will hear nothing.

(g) Referring to the table for Speed of Sound in Various Materials earlier in this chapter, we find that the speed of sound in helium is almost 3 times the speed of sound in air. If the speed is that much greater, we can expect the pitch or frequency heard to be significantly higher.

(h) If the length and tension are the same but linear density (μ) is greater, the velocity will be lower:

$$v = \sqrt{\frac{T}{\mu}}$$

By $v = f\lambda$, a lower velocity will produce a lower frequency or lower pitch.

3.   (a) Since the water closes one end of the tube, a node forms at that end and an antinode forms at the top end. The wavelength produced is four times the length of the air column:

$$\lambda = (4)(.26m) = 1.04 \; m$$
$$v = f\lambda = (330 \; Hz)(1.04 \; m) = \boldsymbol{343 \; m/s}$$

(b) The next harmonic for a closed tube is the <u>third</u> harmonic, which has a frequency 3 times the fundamental frequency. Using a frequency of (3)(330) or 990 Hz and the velocity determined in part (a):

$$v = f\lambda$$
$$343 \; m/s = (990 \; Hz)\lambda_3$$
$$\lambda_3 = 0.35 \; m$$
[Note: Closed tubes only have the odd harmonics.]

This wavelength, then, will be four times the new air column height, so the new air column height is $\dfrac{0.35 \; m}{4}$ or

$0.09 \; m$ or $\boldsymbol{9 \; cm}$.
[Note: Students doing this experiment have to be careful that they get the fundamental and not an overtone when trying to determine the speed of sound.]

(c) By lowering the tube, the students will find the longest wavelength or lowest frequency first, which will be the fundamental frequency. Using the speed of sound determined earlier:

$$v = f\lambda$$
$$343 \; m/s = (256 \; Hz)\lambda$$
$$\lambda = 1.34 \; m$$

The wavelength is four times the air column height, so the air column height is $0.34 \; m$ or $\boldsymbol{34 \; cm}$.

▶ **Recommended for further practice (Walker, 3rd ed.):**
- Omit the equations presented in Sections 14-3 (wave functions), 14-5 (intensity), and 14-6 (decibels)
- Examine Figure 14-21 on page 453 on interference patterns
- Chapter Summary on page 465–468 (omitting above equations but including concepts)
- Chapter Problems on page 469–475: 19, 23, 47, 49, 55, 57, 63, 65, 67, 77

√ **Reminders:**
- Waves in phase will undergo constructive interference, and waves 180° or ½ λ out of phase will undergo destructive interference.
- An open tube (i.e., open across both ends) will produce a fundamental standing wave that is twice the tube length. Subsequent harmonic frequencies are integral multiples of the fundamental frequency.
- A closed tube (i.e., open at one end and closed across the other) will produce a fundamental standing wave that is four times the tube length. Subsequent harmonic frequencies are integral odd number multiples of the fundamental frequency.
- The speed of sound in air is about 340 m/s at room temperature—and increases with temperature.

Chapter 15

Fluids

Equations

Total fluid pressure: $P = P_o + \rho g h$

Pressure: $P = \dfrac{F}{A}$

Density: $\rho = \dfrac{m}{V}$

Buoyant force: $F_B = \rho V g$

Continuity equation: $A_1 v_1 = A_2 v_2$

Bernoulli's equation: $P + \rho g h + \frac{1}{2}\rho v^2 = constant$

Fluids are defined as states of matter than can take the shape of their containers, which qualifies both **gases** and **liquids**. Although a fourth state of matter, **plasma**, seems to exhibit some of the properties of fluids, plasma is made up of very high temperature charged particles that do not behave according to the equations we will apply to fluids.

Densities of Common Substances	
Substance	Density (kg/m^3)
Gold	19,300
Mercury	13,600
Lead	11,300
Silver	10,500
Iron	7860
Aluminum	2700
Ebony (wood)	1220
Ethylene glycol (antifreeze)	1114
Whole blood (37 °C)	1060
Seawater	1025
Freshwater	1000
Olive oil	920
Ice	917
Ethyl alcohol	806
Cherry (wood)	800
Balsa (wood)	120
Styrofoam	100
Oxygen	1.43
Air	1.29
Helium	0.179

The **density** of any material (solid, liquid, or gas) is mass per unit volume : $\rho = \dfrac{m}{V}$. The density of pure water is 1.00 g/ml, though we are more likely to use SI units, where the density of water is 1000 kg/m^3. [Think about it: a large cubic aquarium that is one meter on a side would hold 1000 kilograms of water, weighing 2200 pounds here on Earth—certainly not easy to move!] That same one cubic meter holds 1.29 kilograms of air. **Specific gravity** of any solid or liquid is mass divided by the mass of an equal volume of water. Another way to think of this is that specific gravity is the density of that material divided by the density of pure water at standard conditions. For example, lead has a density of 11.3 g/cm^3 or 11,300 kg/m^3, so lead has a specific gravity of 11.3, since it is 11.3 times as dense as water.

Fluids exert **hydrostatic pressure** that is dependent only on the density of the fluid, ρ, the gravitational acceleration, g, and the depth of fluid, h :

$$P = \rho gh.$$

The **absolute pressure** or **total pressure** is the sum of atmospheric pressure and **gauge pressure**, which is the pressure of the fluid:

$$P = P_o + \rho gh$$

For example, if you use a tire gauge to take the pressure in a flat tire, the gauge will read zero—yet the pressure in the tire is equalized with the atmosphere. (Certainly, there is not a vacuum in the tire.) Thus, the actual pressure in a flat tire is just one atmosphere. And the absolute pressure in a tire at working pressure is the gauge pressure plus the atmospheric pressure.

Since pressure is force per unit area, the SI units for pressure are newtons per square meter, called **pascals**.

$$P = \frac{F}{A}$$

Standard sea level air pressure is 1.01×10^5 Pa, which is often written as 101 kPa.

Atmospheric Pressure
1 atmosphere $= P_{at}$ $= 760$ mmHg (definition) $= 14.7$ lb/in^2 $= 101$ kPa $= 101$ kN/m^2 ~ 1 bar $= 100$ kPa

For a depth of 10.3 meters of water, for example, $P = \rho gh = (10^3$ kg/m$^3)(9.8$ m/s$^2)(10.3$ m$) = 101$ kPa, or about 1 atm. Thus, the total pressure or absolute pressure at a depth of 10.3 m in fresh water would be 2 atm. This is very helpful to remember, i.e., that each 10 meter depth of fresh water is about one atmosphere.

Pressure is exerted equally in all directions at any depth in a fluid, which is a statement of **Pascal's Principle.**

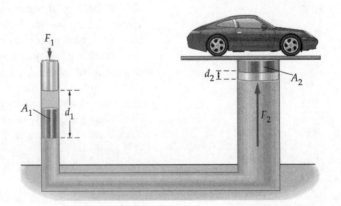

Let's examine the situation in the diagram on the previous page—a hydraulic lift—where a small force, F_1, can produce a large force, F_2, through an incompressible fluid. When the force F_1 is applied to the small piston of area A_1, a pressure is produced:

$$P = \frac{F}{A}$$

That pressure is exerted downward (and all directions) in the fluid. It increases as fluid depth increases, then is transmitted equally in all directions across the horizontal section at the bottom, decreasing with fluid depth under the car. The pressure at the large piston (under the car) is the same as the pressure at the small piston:

$$P_{small\ piston} = P_{large\ piston}$$

$$\frac{F_1}{A_1} = \frac{F_2}{A_2}$$

Thus, a small force over a small area is able to produce a large force over a larger area. However, work output cannot be more than work input, i.e., $F_1 d_1 = F_2 d_2$. Though the force output is much greater than force input, as in any machine, the gain in force means a sacrifice in distance moved. In order to lift the car with such a large force, the input distance must be large.

Any object partially or fully immersed in a fluid experiences a **buoyant force** that is equal to the weight of the fluid displaced by the object. This is a statement of **Archimedes' Principle**. The buoyant force on the object in the fluid is equal to the product of fluid density, ρ, volume of fluid displaced, V, and gravitational acceleration, g.

$$F_B = \rho V g$$

The buoyant force is upward on the object, so a free-body diagram of an object immersed in a fluid would be:

A floating object will only sink into the fluid until enough fluid is displaced so that the weight of the fluid is equal to the object's weight. The object is in equilibrium—or experiences balanced forces. A ping-pong ball, for example, only has to sink into water to about one-tenth of its volume to displace its own weight of water. Thus we conclude that a ping-pong ball has a density of 0.1 g/ml or 100 kg/m³. In fresh water, a golf ball will sink, because it displaces its entire volume of water, which does not weight as much as the golf ball. Thus, the golf ball will sink to the bottom of the container, where the free-body diagram would be:

Even though the object sinks, it still has a buoyant force on it—but the buoyant force is less than the gravitational force on the object. In a fluid, we say the object has an **apparent weight**, which is its actual weight minus the buoyant force. A floating object has an apparent weight of zero.

The **Continuity Equation** is actually a conservation of mass equation that describes motion of fluid through an enclosure of cross-sectional area A.

$$A_1v_1 = A_2v_2$$

If we assume that the fluid is incompressible, density does not change from one point to another. Density is actually included on both sides of the equation, making the units on both sides kg/s, which demonstrates equivalence of rate of mass flow. However, if density doesn't change, it cancels from both sides, leaving the equation in this form.

Bernoulli's Equation describes energy changes in fluid. Since energy must be conserved, the sum of these terms must be constant throughout the fluid. As a fluid moves at greater speed, increasing the $\frac{1}{2}\rho v^2$ term, the pressure of the fluid must decrease. It's interesting here to note that each term applies to a given volume of fluid; if we multiply each term by volume, the terms are, in order: PV (work) + mgh (potential energy) + $\frac{1}{2}$ mv^2 (kinetic energy).

$$P + \rho gh + \frac{1}{2}\rho v^2 = constant$$

Sample Questions

1. What is the force on the outside of a window of area 0.5 m^2 on a submersible at a depth of 20 meters?
   A. 1×10^4 N
   B. 1.5×10^4 N
   C. 2×10^4 N
   D. 1×10^5 N
   E. 1.5×10^5 N

2. A yellow plastic ball with a volume of 50 cm^3 floats in water with half its volume submerged. What is the mass of the ball?
   A. 10 g
   B. 20 g
   C. 25 g
   D. 50 g
   E. 100 g

3. A ball with mass 25 grams displaces 20 cm^3 of water when completely submerged. What is the specific gravity of the ball?
   A. 0.25
   B. 0.50
   B. 0.75
   C. 1.00
   D. 1.25

4. What water pressure is required at a faucet to be able to spray water to a height of 10 meters?
   A. 1×10^4 Pa
   B. 1.5×10^4 Pa
   C. 2×10^4 Pa
   D. 1×10^5 Pa
   E. 1.5×10^5 Pa

5. A ball sinks to a depth of half its volume in water. When the ball is placed in a second liquid, it sinks to a depth of $\frac{3}{4}$ of its volume. What is the density of the second liquid?

   A. 250 kg/m^3
   B. 500 kg/m^3
   C. 667 kg/m^3
   D. 1000 kg/m^3
   E. 1500 kg/m^3

Sample Problems

1. A metal sample has a mass of 63.5 g when measured in air and an apparent mass of 56.4 g when submerged in water.

   (a) What is the apparent weight of the sample in water?

   (b) What is the buoyant force on the sample?

   (c) What is the weight of water displaced by the sample?

   (d) What is the volume of water displaced by the sample?

   (e) What is the volume of the metal sample?

2. Water is poured into a U-shaped tube. Then oil is poured into one end and the liquid levels are allowed to come to equilibrium. From the information given, determine the density of the oil.

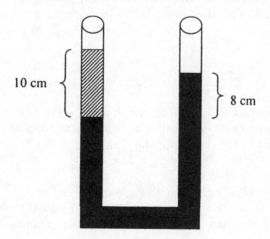

10 cm

8 cm

3. Water flows at 2 m/s through a pipe of diameter 0.8 m into a pipe of diameter 0.2 m and then empties into the bottom of a reservoir that is 20 m deep, as shown below.

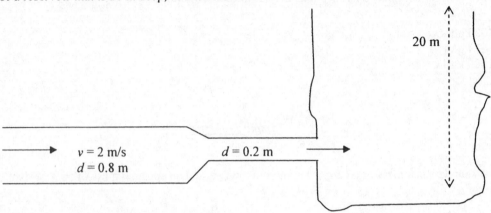

(a) What is the speed of water flow in the smaller pipe?

(b) What is the volume rate of flow of water into the lake?

(c) What is the mass rate of flow of water into the lake?

(d) A small bubble, of volume 10 cm³, flows out of the small pipe into the bottom of the lake. Describe specifically what happens to the bubble as it rises to the surface.

SOLUTIONS TO SAMPLE QUESTIONS AND SAMPLE PROBLEMS

Multiple Choice Questions:

1. **E** Keeping in mind that each 10 meter depth of water creates a pressure of about one atmosphere, the total pressure at 20 meters would be 2 atm of water, plus 1 atmosphere above that: $P = P_o + \rho gh$. Then find the force:

$$P = \frac{F}{A}$$
$$F = PA = (3\ atm)(0.5\ m) = (3 \times 10^5\ Pa)(0.5\ m) = 1.5 \times 10^5\ N$$

2. **C** If the ball floats half submerged, it displaces 25 cm³ of water, which has a mass of 25 grams. By Archimedes' Principle, the buoyant force on the ball is the weight of water displaced, which is the weight of 25 grams of water. Since the ball floats, it has a buoyant force equal to its weight. Thus, the ball's weight is the same as the 25 grams of water. The ball's mass, then, is 25 grams.

3. **D** Since the ball displaces 20 cm³ of water, and we know that 20 cm³ of water has a mass of 20 grams, the buoyant force from the water is not as great as the weight of the ball (which is the weight of 25 grams), so we know the ball sinks. If it sinks, it displaces its volume of water, so the volume of the ball is 20 ml. Thus, the density of the ball is:

$$\rho = \frac{m}{V} = \frac{25\ g}{20\ cm^3} = 1.25\ g/cm^3$$

The ball's specific gravity is its density divided by the density of water (*1 g/cm³*), or *1.25*.

4. D Use Bernoulli's Principle: $P + \rho g h + \frac{1}{2} \rho v^2 = constant$. Inside the faucet, there is only P—height is zero and velocity is zero. When the water reaches its maximum height, velocity is zero and pressure is zero, so there is only $\rho g h$. Therefore:

$$P = \rho g h$$

Without calculating, we have the working estimate that a 10-meter height of water is equal to one atmosphere. (This is the water pressure in addition to atmospheric pressure.)

5. C The ball sinks to half its volume in water, so the ball is half as dense as water, and the weight of that volume of water, $\frac{1}{2}$ V, weighs as much as the ball. In the second liquid, the ball sinks to $\frac{3}{4}$ its volume, so it takes more of the second liquid to weigh the same as the ball. Since the weights are the same, the masses of those amounts of the two fluids are the same. Therefore, the densities of the two fluids should be in inverse proportion to the volumes.

$$\rho = \frac{m}{V}$$
$$\rho_w V_w = \rho_u V_u$$
$$(1 \ g/cm^3)(\tfrac{1}{2} \ V_{ball}) = (\rho_u)(\tfrac{3}{4} \ V_{ball})$$

The unknown fluid's density is $\frac{1}{2}$ divided by $\frac{3}{4}$, or $\frac{2}{3}$ g/cm^3. This means it has a specific gravity of $\frac{2}{3}$ and is $\frac{2}{3}$ as dense as water—or has a density of *667 kg/m^3*.

Free Response Problems:

1. (a) $W = mg = (0.0564 \ kg)(9.8 \ m/s^2) = $ ***0.55 N***

(b) The weight of water displaced is equal to the weight of the object in air minus its apparent weight in water.

$$W_{actual} - W_{apparent} = F_B$$
$$(0.0635 \ kg)(9.8 \ m/s^2) - 0.55 \ N = F_B = \textbf{0.072 N}$$

(c) The weight of water displaced is equal to the buoyant force: ***0.072 N***

(d) Water has density 1 g/cm^3, so we can determine volume, knowing the mass of water displaced. Using $W = mg$, the mass of water displaced is $\dfrac{0.072 \ N}{9.8 \ m/s^2} = 0.007 \ kg$ or *7 grams*. This has a volume of *7 cm^3*.

(e) Since this object obviously sinks (buoyant force less than its weight), the volume of water displaced is equal to the volume of the ball, which is *7 cm^3*.

2. Since the pressure at a point in a fluid only depends on the depth of fluid at that point ($P = P_o + \rho g h$), then:

$$P_A = P_B$$

The pressure at A is due to air (1 atm) plus the column of oil, and the pressure at B is due to air (1 atm) plus the column of water above B. Therefore, the pressure due to the column of oil is the same as the pressure due to the column of water above point B.

$$P_{oil} = P_{water}$$
$$\rho_{oil} \ g \ (10 \ cm) = \rho_{water} \ g \ (8 \ cm)$$
$$\rho_{oil} = (1000 \ kg/m^3) \ (\tfrac{8}{10}) = 800 \ kg/m^3$$

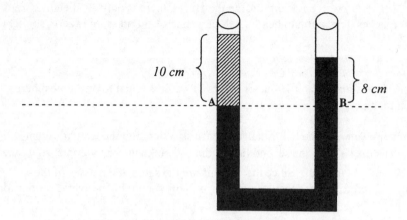

3. (a) Apply the Continuity Equation:

$$A_1 v_1 = A_2 v_2$$
$$\pi r_1^{\,2} v_1 = \pi r_2^{\,2} v_2$$
$$(0.4\ m)^2 (2\ m/s) = (0.1\ m)^2\ (v_2)$$
$$v_2 = 32\ m/s$$

(b) To obtain volume rate of flow (cubic meters per second), multiply cross-sectional area of flow times velocity:

$$\frac{\Delta V}{\Delta t} = Av = \pi (0.1\ m)^2 (32\ m/s) = 1.0\ m^3/s$$

(c) From the density of water, we know that 1.0 m³ of water has a mass of 1000 kg, so the mass rate of flow is **1000 kg/s.**

(d) The total pressure at a depth of 20 meters of water is 2 atm of water pressure plus one atm of air pressure, for a total pressure of 3 atmospheres. (We're using the estimate that each 10-m depth of water is about 1 atm of pressure. The actual calculation is shown earlier in the chapter.) The air bubble moves from a point at the bottom of the lake where the total pressure is 3 atm to the top of the lake where the pressure is only 1 atm. The bubble will expand as it rises under decreasing pressure, with its volume tripling as the pressure is cut to a third. The final volume of the bubble will be 30 cm³.

▶ **Recommended for further practice (Walker, 3rd ed.):**
- Example 15-4 on page 484, on fluid pressure
- Checkpoints 15-5 and 15-6 on page 493 (melting ice cube dilemma)
- Omit equations in section 15-9 on viscosity, fluid flow speed, and surface tension
- Chapter Summary on page 504–506 (omitting above equations but including concepts)
- Chapter Problems on pages 508–513: 9, 19, 21, 27, 29, 33, 39, 41, 47, 53, 55, 81

√ **Reminders:**
- Fluids include both liquids and gases.
- Each ten meters depth of water exerts about one atmosphere of pressure.
- To convert density in g/cm³ to kg/m³, multiply by 1000. The density of pure water is 1000 kg/m³.
- An object that floats has a buoyant force on it equal to its weight, and an object that sinks has a buoyant force on it that is less than its weight.

PART 2

THERMAL PHYSICS

Chapter 16

Temperature and Heat

Equations

Thermal expansion: $\Delta l = \alpha l_o \Delta T$

Rate of heat loss by conduction: $H = \dfrac{Q}{t} = \dfrac{kA\Delta T}{L}$

Thermodynamics is the study of the physical processes by which heat is transferred from one system to another. An important distinction here is that the energy contained by the molecules is called **thermal energy**, but the energy that moves from one system to another is defined as **heat**. If two systems at different temperatures are put into contact, there will be a net heat flow until the two systems are in **thermal equilibrium**. At thermal equilibrium, heat will continue to be transferred between systems, but there will be no net heat exchange once the systems reach the same temperature. The **Zeroth Law of Thermodynamics** states that any two systems that are in thermal equilibrium with a third system must be in thermal equilibrium with each other. The Zeroth Law, then, makes temperature a useful quantity in determining thermal equilibrium.

We will discuss more about the energy contained in systems of molecules in the next chapter, but it's important here to note that **temperature** is the measure of the average translational kinetic energy of molecules. At **absolute zero**, molecules have no kinetic energy; i.e., all molecular motion ceases. Several scales are used to measure temperature:

Temperature Scale	Absolute Zero	Freezing Point of Water	Boiling Point of Water
Fahrenheit	–459°F	32°F	212°F
Celsius	–273°C	0°C	100°C
Kelvin	0 K	273 K	373 K

Note here that the term *degree* is not used for Kelvin temperatures. The Kelvin scale is an **absolute temperature scale**, meaning temperatures on this scale are proportional to the energy of the system. The Kelvin scale is based upon absolute zero, with a temperature change of one Kelvin equal to a temperature change of one Celsius degree. The Kelvin scale will be used exclusively in thermodynamics calculations, as zero and negative temperatures will often confuse calculations (or make them impossible, if a zero temperature is in the denominator).

These formulas for temperature conversion may be helpful, though temperatures will be given in Celsius degrees or Kelvins on the AP* Exam. You do need to be able to convert Celsius to Kelvin temperatures appropriately:

$$F = \tfrac{9}{5} C + 32$$
$$C = (F - 32) \tfrac{5}{9}$$
$$C + 273 = K$$

When heat is added to most substances, the system or object undergoes **thermal expansion** as the molecules undergo an increase in thermal energy. Linear expansion is directly proportional to the increase in temperature:

$$\Delta l = \alpha l_o \Delta T$$

The value of **coefficient of linear expansion**, α, will have units that dictate the units used for ΔT. (However, practically speaking, a ΔT in Kelvins will be the same as a ΔT in Celsius degrees.) The units on original length, l_o, will dictate units for Δl. When determining area and volume expansions, find the linear expansion of each dimension and then calculate the new area. or volume. An interesting result here is that the coefficient for area expansion is about 2α, and the coefficient of volume expansion is about 3α.

Coefficients of Thermal Expansion near 20 °C	
Substance	**Coefficient of linear expansion, $\alpha(K^{-1})$**
Lead	29×10^{-6}
Aluminum	24×10^{-6}
Brass	19×10^{-6}
Copper	17×10^{-6}
Iron (steel)	12×10^{-6}
Concrete	12×10^{-6}
Window glass	11×10^{-6}
Pyrex glass	3.3×10^{-6}
Quartz	0.50×10^{-6}
Substance	**Coefficient of volume expansion, $\beta(K^{-1})$**
Ether	1.51×10^{-3}
Carbon tetrachloride	1.18×10^{-3}
Alcohol	1.01×10^{-3}
Gasoline	0.95×10^{-3}
Olive oil	0.68×10^{-3}
Water	0.21×10^{-3}
Mercury	0.18×10^{-3}

One noteworthy exception to the idea that materials expand when heated is a very common one—water. As expected, water contracts as it is cooled from room temperature (about 20°C) to 4°C. At 4°C, water has its highest density. As it is cooled to its freezing point at 0°C, water expands.

Heat is transferred from one system to another by one or more of three methods—conduction, convection, or radiation. **Conduction** is heat transfer by molecular contact, with materials that transfer heat easily (such as silver, gold, aluminum, steel, and copper) called **conductors** and materials that do not transfer heat well (such as wood, air, wool, glass, and water) called **insulators**. The rate at which heat (Q) can be transferred through an object depends upon the difference in temperatures between two ends of the object (ΔT or temperature gradient), thermal conductivity of the material (k), the cross-sectional area facing the hot and cold ends of the object (A), and the length or thickness through which the heat is transferred (L):

$$H = \frac{Q}{t} = \frac{kA\Delta T}{L}$$

The rate of heat transfer, designated by H in the AP* Equations Sheet, is actually $\frac{Q}{t}$. If Q is measured in joules and t in seconds, the rate of heat transfer will be in J/s or watts.

Convection occurs only in fluids and is the result of differences in density in fluids of varying temperatures. Generally, as a fluid is heated it expands, becomes less dense, and rises. As a fluid cools (or loses heat), it contracts, becomes more dense, and sinks. This movement due to uneven heating and variations in densities results in mixing of the fluid and transfer of heat.

Radiation is the transfer of energy by electromagnetic waves, so it is the only method by which heat can be transferred through space (i.e., a vacuum). The rate at which an object emits or absorbs radiant energy depends on surface area, emissivity, and temperature difference between the object and its surroundings.

[Topics related to calorimetry, specific heat, and latent heat have been removed from the AP* Physics B syllabus in recent years in favor of other added topics.]

Sample Questions

1. A steel rod is used is used to transfer heat from a chamber at 300 K to a chamber at 250 K. Which of the following changes in the setup will result in the greatest increase in the rate of heat transfer?
    A. Replace the steel rod with a glass rod of identical size.
    B. Double the length of the steel rod.
    C. Cut the steel rod in half.
    D. Double the radius of the steel rod.
    E. Double the temperature in the hot chamber.

2. A cubic block of quartz glass measures 0.1 m on a side. What will be the increase in the volume of the block if it is heated from 20°C to 30°C? (Coefficient of linear expansion for this glass is 0.5 x 10^{-6}/K.)
    A. $5.0 \times 10^{-9} \text{ m}^3$
    B. $1.0 \times 10^{-8} \text{ m}^3$
    C. $1.5 \times 10^{-8} \text{ m}^3$
    D. $1.0 \times 10^{-6} \text{ m}^3$
    E. $1.5 \times 10^{-6} \text{ m}^3$

3. How long will it take to transfer an amount of heat Q through a rod of radius r and length L, if the rod has heat conductivity k?
    A. $\dfrac{kQr}{L}$

    B. $\dfrac{QL}{\pi r^2 k \Delta T}$

    C. $\dfrac{QL}{rk\Delta T}$

    D. $\dfrac{Q\Delta T}{\pi r^2 kL}$

    E. $\dfrac{kQ\Delta T}{\pi r^2}$

Sample Problem

We want to set up an experiment to determine the thermal conductivity of a metal rod of unknown composition.

(a) Briefly describe a procedure that might be used to determine this value experimentally. Include any methods that might be used to reduce error.

(b) List materials required.

(c) List measurements you will take and how those measurements will be used to determine the result. Include applicable equations.

(d) List any assumptions made during the experimental procedure.

(e) Discuss one source of error that might affect results and how the value of thermal conductivity will be affected by that error.

SOLUTIONS TO SAMPLE QUESTIONS AND SAMPLE PROBLEM

Multiple Choice Questions:

1. E The formula is $H = \dfrac{Q}{t} = \dfrac{kA\Delta T}{L}$. The ΔT is 50 K in the initial situation, but doubling the high temperature changes the new ΔT to (600-250) or 350 K, which is seven times the original—by far the greatest factor.

2. C The formula for volume expansion is $\Delta V = \beta\, V_o\, \Delta T$, where coefficient of volume expansion is about 3 times the linear coefficient:
$$\Delta V = (1.5 \times 10^{-6}/C^\circ)(0.1\ m)^3(10\ C^\circ) = 1.5 \times 10^{-8}\ m^3$$

3. B Solve the heat rate formula for time, using πr^2 for A:

$$\frac{Q}{t} = \frac{kA\Delta T}{L}$$

$$t = \frac{QL}{\pi r^2 k\Delta T}$$

Free Response Problem:

[Author's note: This is the type of inquiry question students might expect on an AP* Exam. Question writers will often develop experimental questions that are not common to physics courses to assess students' ability to develop experimental method rather than recall actual experiments. Answers are given here as examples of how one might answer such a question—knowing that there may be multiple acceptable answers. Answers to this type of question are scored on feasibility, thoroughness, validity of the calculations, and thought given to sources of error. Keep in mind that calorimetry has been removed from the AP* Syllabus, so this method has been contrived in such a way as to avoid calculations of heat loss and heat gain by the liquids.]

(a) Set up two styrofoam cups with the unknown metal rod inserted into the sides of the cups so it will be in contact with the liquids that will eventually be put into the cups. Seal the openings around the metal rod where it enters the cups so that liquids cannot leak. Take all measurements described below, except temperatures and time, before pouring in liquids. Pour hot liquid into one cup and cold liquid into the other. Quickly take the temperature of the hot liquid and start the stopwatch. After exactly two minutes, take the hot liquid temperature again. For best results, repeat the experiment several times—each time starting with the same hot and cold liquids at the same starting temperatures. Also, be sure to stir the liquids slightly as temperatures are taken (not just next to the rod), and cover the tops of the containers to reduce peripheral heat loss during the two-minute heat transfer time. Repeat the experiment with a rod of the same dimensions as the unknown rod and a known k value, measuring the time for the hot liquid to make the same drop in temperature as recorded for the unknown rod in the two-minute time limit.

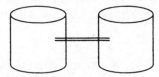

(b) 2 styrofoam cups (or other containers made of insulating material), thermometer, stopwatch, unknown metal rod, known metal rod, hot glue, metric ruler, hot liquid (could be water), cold liquid, electronic or balance scales

(c) Measure the following quantities:

- length of each rod, L, in meters

- cross-section diameter of each rod, d, in meters

- starting and final temperatures of hot liquid, T_H, in Celsius degrees

- change in temperature of hot liquid during the experiment, ΔT_H, in Celsius degrees

- time, t, from the instant liquid is poured into containers until temperatures are taken, in seconds

(1) Calculate the cross-sectional area of the known and unknown rod, using the measurement of d, to assure that cross-sectional areas are equal:

$$A = \pi \left(\frac{d}{2}\right)^2$$

(2) Using the formula $\dfrac{Q}{t} = \dfrac{kA\Delta T}{L}$, solve for thermal conductivity: $k = \dfrac{QL}{At\Delta T}$.

The units on k should be $\dfrac{J}{m \cdot s \cdot C°}$.

(3) Since L, A, Q, and ΔT are kept constant in all trials, set up the proportion:

$$k_{known}\, t_{known} = k_{unknown}\, t_{unknown}$$

(4) Average results from several trials.

(d) This method assumes that the hot liquid loses the same amount of heat through each rod if the change in temperature of the hot liquid is kept the same in both situations.

(e) If some heat is lost by convection to the air by the hot liquid, less heat will actually go through the rod than calculated. Thus, the experimental value for k will be higher than the actual value.

[Note: Time can be saved on a question such as this, which is usually given 10 to 15 minutes, by making lists instead of writing complete sentences and by using a labeled diagram to substitute for a full paragraph explanation of the setup.]

► **Recommended for further practice (Walker, 3rd ed.):**
- Checkpoint 16-2 on page 523 on thermal expansion (expansion of a washer with a hole)
- Chapter Summary on pages 539–540, omitting the radiation equation and Section 16-5
- Chapter Problems on pages 543–547: 13, 17, 23, 39, 41, 59, 71

√ **Reminders:**
- In problem situations calling for ΔT, converting Celsius to Kelvin is unnecessary, since the values would be same for both scales.
- Use the term "heat" for energy being transferred from one system to another and "thermal energy" for the energy contained by molecules.

Chapter 17

Phases and Phase Changes

$$\textit{Equations}$$

$$PV = nRT = Nk_BT$$

$$K_{ave} = \tfrac{3}{2}k_BT$$

$$v_{rms} = \sqrt{\frac{3RT}{M}} = \sqrt{\frac{3k_BT}{\mu}}$$

An **ideal gas** is one in which: (a) the particles of the gas are considered to be point particles (with no motion except translational), (b) all collisions are perfectly elastic, (c) the particles are spaced far apart, (d) the particles exert no attractive or repulsive forces on each other except upon impact, and (d) the system contains a large number of particles. Though gases are assumed to be ideal in calculations using the equations of thermodynamics, real gases are certainly not ideal. The gases that come closest to assuming ideal behavior are the inert gases, such as helium and argon.

The **ideal gas equation**, $PV = nRT$, describes the relationships among pressure (P), volume (V), Kelvin temperature (T), and number of moles of gas (n), in terms of an ideal gas constant (R). The value of the constant depends upon the units used for the other variables. [Note: The only value for R given for the AP* Exam is 8.30 J/(mol-K), so it's fair to assume that pressures will be in pascals and volumes in cubic meters in any situation where a gas constant is required for calculation.] From this equation, we can conclude that in any process where temperature is not changed (called **isothermal**), PV is constant. This is a statement of Boyle's Law:

$$P_1V_1 = P_2V_2$$

From the ideal gas equation, we can also conclude that if pressure is kept constant, then P, n, and R are all constant and $\dfrac{V}{T}$ is constant. This is a statement of Charles' Law:

$$\frac{V_1}{T_1} = \frac{V_2}{T_2}$$

The combined ideal gas law is often helpful:

$$\frac{P_1V_1}{T_1} = \frac{P_2V_2}{T_2}$$

Another form of the ideal gas equation is $PV = Nk_BT$, where N is the number of molecules of gas and k_B is Boltzmann's Constant.

The **average translational kinetic energy** of the molecules in an ideal gas is directly proportional to the absolute temperature of the gas, by the equation:

$$K_{ave} = \tfrac{3}{2}k_BT$$

Since kinetic energy is $\frac{1}{2}mv^2$, we can solve for an average translational velocity for the molecules, called the **root mean square** or **rms velocity,** using the above equation and the ideal gas equations:

$$v_{rms} = \sqrt{\frac{3RT}{M}} = \sqrt{\frac{3k_BT}{\mu}}$$

In these equations, R is the ideal gas constant, T is the absolute (Kelvin) temperature, M is molar mass, k_B is Boltzmann's Constant, and μ is the molecular mass. The rms velocity for a given system of molecules is, as we see here, dependent upon temperature. The value calculated for this average velocity is only an average—there are many molecules in that system with velocities higher and lower than that average. Increasing the absolute temperature of the gas increases the average velocity, or shifts what is called the **Maxwell distribution** of molecular speeds to a higher value.

Ideal gas molecules possess kinetic energy, so collisions among these molecules or with the walls of their container will produce forces on the molecules and on the walls. Remember, from Newton's Second Law, that force is the rate of change in momentum. Since forces, then, are produced when gas molecules collide with their container, **pressure** is exerted on the walls during these collisions:

$$P = \frac{F}{A}$$

If gas temperature is increased, the average velocity of molecules increases, causing larger momentum changes upon collision and larger forces. As a result, an increase in temperature produces an increase in gas pressure, since gas molecules are moving faster, colliding more often, and exerting more force per area on the walls. Likewise, decreasing the volume of the container increases the rate of collisions with the walls, increasing the pressure.

The **internal energy**, U, of a gas is its total kinetic energy. (If the gas is ideal, there are no interactions among molecules and thus no potential energy.) Internal energy is proportional to the temperature of the gas:

$$U = \tfrac{3}{2}Nk_BT$$

where N is number of molecules, k_B is Boltzmann's Constant, and T is the absolute temperature. The internal energy can also be written in terms of the number of moles, $m,$ and the ideal gas constant, R:

$$U = \tfrac{3}{2}nRT$$

Molecules of an ideal gas are considered to be point particles, so the equations that relate these quantities do not take into account the rotational, vibrational, and other types of energy of real gas molecules.

The **mechanical equivalent of heat**, or the **Joule equivalent**, is the amount of **work** that must be done on a system to transfer an equivalent amount of heat into that system. For example, if 4.186 joules of mechanical work are done on a system, 1 calorie of heat will be transferred into the system, so:

$$4.186\ J = 1\ cal$$

A nutritionist's Calorie is actually 1 kilocalorie, by the definition above. Much more discussion on work is included in the next chapter.

[Topics related to calorimetry, specific heat, and latent heat have been removed from the AP* Physics B Syllabus in recent years in favor of other added topics.]

Sample Questions

1. Doubling the absolute temperature of a system of ideal gas will have what effect on the root-mean-square velocity of its molecules?
    A. Cuts to one-fourth
    B. Cuts to one-half
    C. Does not affect *rms* velocity
    D. Multiplies by square root of two
    E. Multiplies by two

2. Doubling the absolute temperature of a system of ideal gas will have what effect on the average pressure exerted by the gas, assuming constant volume?
    A. Cuts to one-fourth
    B. Cuts to one-half
    C. Does not affect *rms* velocity
    D. Multiplies by square root of two
    E. Multiplies by two

3. The temperature of a gas is decreased while volume is kept constant. Which of the following is true?
    - **I.** Pressure will decrease, because molecules do not strike the container walls as often.
    - **II.** Pressure will increase, because the molecules will have higher average velocity.
    - **III.** Pressure will decrease, because molecular collisions result in less force.
    A. **I** only
    B. **II** only
    C. **III** only
    D. **I** and **III** only
    E. **I** and **II** only

4. An ideal gas at 1 atmosphere and 200 K has a volume of 400 cm^3. The gas is warmed to 300 K and pressure increased to 2 atm. What is the new volume of the gas?
    A. 100 cm^3
    B. 200 cm^3
    C. 300 cm^3
    D. 400 cm^3
    E. 500 cm^3

5. An ideal gas has absolute temperature *T*, pressure *P*, and volume *V*. Under what new conditions of pressure and volume could a constant temperature be maintained?

	new pressure	new volume
A.	*3P*	*V/3*
B.	*2P*	*2V*
C.	*4P*	*V/2*
D.	*P*	*2V*
E.	*3P*	*3V*

SOLUTIONS TO SAMPLE QUESTIONS

Multiple Choice Questions:

1. D Root-mean-square velocity is proportional to the square root of absolute temperature, so doubling the temperature increase the rms velocity by a factor of square root of two.

$$v_{rms} = \sqrt{\frac{3RT}{M}} = \sqrt{\frac{3k_B T}{\mu}}$$

2. E If volume is constant, pressure is directly proportional to absolute temperature, so doubling temperature will double the pressure:

$$\frac{P_1 V_1}{T_1} = \frac{P_2 V_2}{T_2}$$

3. D Lowering the temperature of molecules causes a reduction in root-mean-square velocity, so the molecules are not exerting as much force when they strike each other or the walls of the container, resulting in reduced pressure. At a lowered speed in the same size container, they also do not strike the walls as often, again resulting in reduced pressure.

4. C Use the combined gas law equation:

$$\frac{P_1 V_1}{T_1} = \frac{P_2 V_2}{T_2}$$

$$\frac{(1\,atm)(400\,cm^3)}{200\,K} = \frac{(2\,atm)V}{300\,K}$$

$$V = 300\,cm^3$$

5. A Since temperature does not change, the product of the new P and V needs to be equal to PV.

$$PV = (3P)(P/3)$$

▶ **Recommended for further practice (Walker, 3rd ed.):**
- Omit section 17-3 on deformations and section 17-5 on latent heats.
- Chapter Summary on pages 576–578
- Chapter Problems on pages 579–584: 1, 3, 9, 15, 19

√ **Reminders:**
- Use absolute or Kelvin temperatures in gas law equations.
- When using any form of the gas laws that does not contain a constant, such as Boyle's Law or Charles' Law, any units will work for P and V, as long as they are the same on both sides of the equation.
- The units on any constant, such as R, used in an equation will define the units on other variables in the equation.

Chapter 18

The Laws of Thermodynamics

Equations

Work on/by a thermodynamic system: $W = -P\Delta V$

First Law of Thermodynamics: $\Delta U = Q + W$

Efficiency of an engine: $e = \left| \dfrac{W}{Q_H} \right|$

Carnot efficiency: $e_c = \dfrac{T_H - T_C}{T_H}$

Many common devices, such as refrigerators and automobile engines, use thermodynamic processes in their operation. These processes can be described by the laws of thermodynamics. The **First Law of Thermodynamics** is a conservation law; i.e., heat added to a system is used by the system to increase its **internal energy** or to do **work** in expanding:

$$\Delta U = Q + W$$

This form, as shown on the AP* equation sheet, defines an increase in internal energy due to heat added to the system (positive) or work done on the system (also positive). Work done on a system, according to this convention, would result in a decrease in volume:

$$W = -P\Delta V$$

Temperature is our only external measure of changes in internal energy, so in an **isothermal** process where there is not change in temperature, we assume also no change in internal energy of the system. An **adiabatic** process is one in which no heat is allowed to enter or leave the system. An **isochoric** or **isovolumetric** process is one in which there is no change in volume—and thus no work done on or by the system. The following summary may provide some insights into how the First Law of Thermodynamics appears during certain types of processes:

Type of Process or Step	Definition	Result in First Law
isothermal process	$\Delta T = 0 \rightarrow \Delta U = 0$	$Q = -W$
adiabatic process	$Q = 0$	$\Delta U = W$
isochoric or isovolumetric process	$\Delta V = 0 \rightarrow W = 0$	$\Delta U = Q$

IMPORTANT NOTE

This is an article written by the author to explain to AP* physics teachers and students the changes made in the conventions used for the exam.

A "Hot Topic"

Several years ago, the A.P. Physics Test Development Committee voted to make a sign convention change for the First Law of Thermodynamics equation on the A.P. Physics B Examinations, beginning with the year 2001 test.

Many physics textbooks now give the equation for the First Law: $\Delta U = Q - W$. The equation listed on the AP*Equation Sheet is: $\Delta U = Q + W$. This is consistent with most chemistry texts and with the convention wherein <u>work done on a system is positive</u>. In consideration of this difference in sign convention, it is important for teachers and students to review the concept of **WORK** *and the consistency of sign convention that this difference represents overall.*

WORK

Mechanical work done against a gravitational force:
- *Work done against gravity, e.g., in lifting an object, is positive work.*
- *Work done with gravity, e.g., in lowering an object, is negative work.*
- *Positive work done on a system increases the potential energy of that system.*
- *$W = F\, s\, \cos\theta$, where maximum work is done when the external force doing the work and the displacement are in the same direction.*

Mechanical work done against a spring force:
- *Work done in stretching or compressing a spring, i.e., work done against the spring force, is positive.*
- *Positive work done on a spring-mass system increases the potential energy of that system.*
- *$W = \Delta U = \frac{1}{2}\, k\, x^2$*

Mechanical work done against an electrical force:
- *Work done in moving a positively charged particle toward another positively charged particle, i.e., against the electric fields lines and against the electric force on that particle, is positive work. Likewise, work done in moving a negatively charged particle toward another negatively charged particle is positive work.*
- *Positive work done in each case increases the potential energy of the system.*
- *$W = \Delta U = q\, \Delta V$ [If q is positive, positive work is done when ΔV is positive; i.e., the particle is moved from lower potential to higher potential, as is the case when moving toward another positive charge. If q is negative, positive work is done when ΔV is negative; i.e., the particle is moved from higher potential to lower potential, as is the case when moving toward a negative particle.]*

Work done on a thermodynamic system:
- *Work done in compressing a system of ideal gas particles is positive, since it increases the potential energy of the system of particles.*
- *Since $W = -P\Delta V$, at constant pressure, if volume decreases, ΔV is negative and work done is positive.*
- *$\Delta U = Q + W$, where +W is work done on the system, so it produces a positive ΔU, and +Q is heat added to the system, so it also produces a positive ΔU.*

Plots of *Pressure vs. Volume*, often called **P-V diagrams**, are used to analyze thermodynamic processes. One such diagram showing a complete cycle is shown on the next page, with the arrows indicating the direction of change during each stage of the cycle. In step AB, the pressure and volume both decrease, and work is done <u>on</u> the gas, since the volume decreases. In step BC, volume increases at constant pressure, and work is done <u>by</u> the gas, since the volume increases. In step CA, the gas is brought back to its initial conditions of pressure, volume, and temperature. (By the ideal gas law, $PV = nRT$, if P and V are back to initial conditions, then T *is* also unchanged, since n and R are constant.) Also in step CA, pressure increases as volume decreases, and work is done on the gas. In each step, the amount of work is the area between the graph line and the x-axis, by $W = -P\Delta V$. We can conclude from all this that, for the entire cycle, the net work for the cycle is the area enclosed by the cycle, as shown by the shaded area below. Additionally, since temperature is back in its initial state, there is no ΔT and thus no change in internal energy for the cycle. Thus, any net heat loss or heat gain during a complete cycle can be found by determining the work done during the cycle (area enclosed) and setting internal energy equal to zero, with the result:

$$Q = -W$$

In the situation shown below, the net work for the cycle is positive, since there was more work done in the compression than in the expansion of the gas. More work was done <u>on</u> the gas than by the gas. From the equation above, we see that the net value of Q must be negative, indicating a net heat loss for the cycle.

$$\Delta T_{cycle} = 0$$
$$therefore: \quad \Delta U_{cycle} = 0$$
$$therefore: \quad Q = -W$$

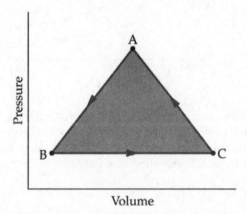

One of the special cases for a thermodynamic cycle is shown in the diagram below, where a process is isothermal. At each point along a given curve below, the temperature is the same. If we consider the ideal gas equation $PV = nRT$, constant T along with constants n and R means that the product PV must also be constant. An isothermal curve can easily be identified by determining that at each point along the curve the product of pressure and volume is the same constant value. Along the 300 K curve below, for example, multiplying P and V gives a value of 2.5 all along the curve. [You may recognize this as the general form for a hyperbolic curve.]

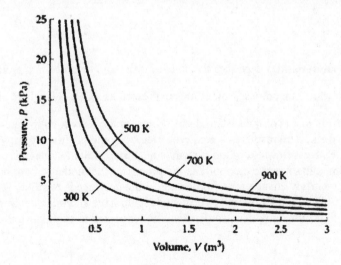

An adiabatic curve ($Q = 0$) looks much like an isothermal curve. Two isotherms and an adiabat are shown for comparison below. These can be distinguished visually, since the adiabatic curve is not hyperbolic; i.e., multiplying P and V values along the adiabatic curve will not produce a constant value.

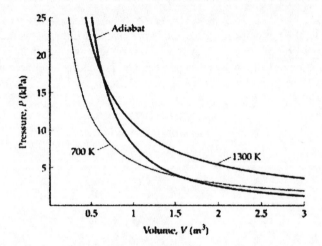

As mentioned earlier, common devices involve thermodynamics processes. In the situations shown on the next page, heat is moved between hot and cold reservoirs, with net work done by the process or net work added to cause the process to run. In a refrigerator, for example, input work (W) is required to move heat from food inside the cooler refrigerator into the warmer room. "Cooling" the food is actually a process of removing heat from it.

Efficiency is the absolute value of the ratio of work to heat flow:

$$e = \left| \frac{W}{Q_H} \right|$$

For an ideal engine, or Carnot engine, the efficiency can be calculated from the ratio of the difference of temperatures in the hot and cold reservoirs and the temperature in the hot reservoir:

$$e_c = \frac{T_H - T_C}{T_H}$$

The **Second Law of Thermodynamics** describes the state of order and disorder in the universe, or entropy.

Entropy is the tendency toward randomness, sometimes expressed as $\Delta S = \dfrac{Q}{T}$, where change in entropy for a system is equal to heat flow in or out of the system divided by average Kelvin temperature during the heat exchange. Heat flow into the system results in a positive value of Q and positive entropy change, i.e., greater entropy and greater disorder. Heat flow out of the system is negative, yielding a negative entropy change and less disorder in the system. Although there are thermodynamic processes that undergo both positive and negative changes in entropy, the net entropy change for all processes in the universe is positive, i.e., toward greater disorder and more entropy. The AP* Exam will expect students to have an understanding of entropy, direction of heat flow, and thermal equilibrium. However, students are not expected to calculate entropy changes.

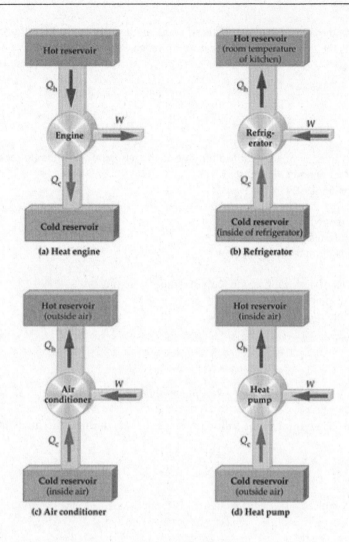

(a) Heat engine   (b) Refrigerator

(c) Air conditioner   (d) Heat pump

Sample Questions

1. In a sealed glass container, an ideal gas is heated so that its pressure increases without breaking the glass or the seal. Which of the following is true?

    A. The process is adiabatic.
    B. The process is isothermal.
    C. No work is done on the gas.
    D. Positive work is done by the gas.
    E. The process is isobaric.

2. Two hundred joules of heat are added to an ideal gas during a process in which there is no change in volume. That heat is used by the gas to:

    A. Do positive work.
    B. Do negative work.
    C. Increase its internal energy.
    D. Expand.
    E. Decrease its total potential energy.

3. At one point in a thermodynamic cycle, one mole of an ideal gas is under 100 Pa of pressure and has a volume of 2 cubic meters. What is the approximate temperature of the gas?
   A. 25 K
   B. 50 K
   C. 100 K
   D. 200 K
   E. 300 K

4. What happens to the efficiency of an ideal heat engine as the temperature in the hotter chamber decreases and the temperature in the colder chamber increases?
   A. Efficiency approaches 100%.
   B. Efficiency decreases.
   C. Efficiency is unchanged.
   D. Efficiency levels off at 50%.
   E. Efficiency depends upon rate of heat flow.

5. To double the *rms* speed of an ideal gas, the Kelvin temperature must:
   A. be one-fourth the original value
   B. be one-half the original value
   C. stay the same
   D. be doubled
   E. be quadrupled

Sample Problems

1. Two moles of an ideal gas go through the following steps (I-II-II) during a thermodynamic process.

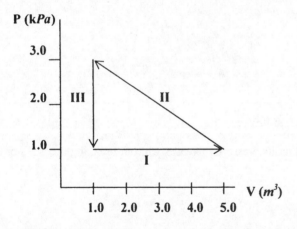

(a) What is the temperature of the gas at the end of step I?

(b) What is the temperature of the gas at the end of step II?

(c) Complete the following table: [Note: Positive work is done <u>on</u> the gas.]

	Work	Change in Pressure	Change in Volume	Change in Temperature
Step I				
Step II				
Step III				
Entire cycle				

2. The diagram below describes several thermodynamic processes for one mole of an ideal gas.

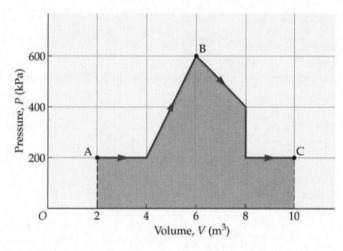

(a) How much work is done from A to C?

(b) Is the work for steps A to C done on the gas or by the gas? Justify your answer.

(c) What happens to the internal energy of the gas from A to C? Justify your answer.

(d) Does a net amount of heat enter or leave the system during the steps from A to C? Justify your answer.

SOLUTIONS TO SAMPLE QUESTIONS AND SAMPLE PROBLEMS

Multiple Choice Questions:

1. C We assume no change in volume for the sealed glass container, so no work is done. Further, if the pressure increased without a change in volume, then the temperature also had to increase. Thus the process cannot be isothermal.

2. C If heat is added, then Q is positive. No change in volume would mean that no work is done. Therefore, the First Law equation becomes: $Q = \Delta U$. The heat is used to increase internal energy.

3. A Use the ideal gas equation to solve for temperature: $T = \dfrac{PV}{nR} = \dfrac{(100 \, Pa)(2 \, m^3)}{(1 \, mole)(8.3 \, J/mol \cdot K)}$

A quick estimate shows 25 K to be the best answer.

4. B Refer to the formula $e_c = \left| \dfrac{W}{Q_H} \right|$, which can also be written: $(1 - \dfrac{T_c}{T_H})$. As heat flows, T_c increases and T_H decreases, so $\dfrac{T_c}{T_H}$ increases and $(1 - \dfrac{T_c}{T_H})$ decreases. Thus, the engine is more efficient when the temperature difference, or temperature gradient, is greater.

5. E Quadrupling the temperature (and taking the square root) will double the *rms* velocity. (Reviewed in Chapter 17.)

$$v_{rms} = \sqrt{\frac{3RT}{M}} = \sqrt{\frac{3k_BT}{\mu}}$$

Free Response Problems:

1. (a) At the end of step I, as indicated by the arrow, pressure is 1000 Pa and volume is 5.0 m³.

$$PV = nRT$$

$$T = \frac{PV}{nR} = \frac{(1000\ Pa)(5.0\ m^3)}{(2\ mol)(8.31\ J/mol \cdot K)} = 300\ K$$

(b) At the end of step II, pressure is 3000 Pa and volume is 1.0 m³.

$$T = \frac{PV}{nR} = \frac{(3000\ Pa)(1.0\ m^3)}{(2\ mol)(8.31\ J/mol \cdot K)} = 180\ K$$

(c)

	Work	Change in Pressure	Change in Volume	Change in Temperature
Step I	–4.0 J	0	4.0 m³	240 K
Step II	+8.0 J	2.0 kPa	–4.0 m³	–120 K
Step III	0	–2.0 kPa	0	–120 K
Entire cycle	+4.0 J	0	0	0

Once the temperature at the beginning of step I is determined by the same formula used in parts (a) and (b), which is 60 K, the construction of the chart become simple. Remember that the "change" in each situation is *final minus original*, so we obtain some negative values. Negative changes in volume are compressions. Negative values for work occur when work is done by the gas in expanding. Note that the net changes in pressure, volume, and temperature are zero for the cycle; thus, the net work for the cycle is equal to net heat removed during the cycle.

2. (a) The work done from points A to C is the area under the graph, or area between graph and x-axis. We can estimate this by finding the value of each block and then counting numbers of blocks or by calculating the areas of individual shapes and adding them. We'll count blocks. Each block has a value of 400 kJ. Using 6 ½ blocks as our estimate, the work is (400 J/block)(6.5 blocks), or **2600 J**.

(b) The work is done **by** the gas, since the gas is increasing its volume, or expanding.

(c) If we use the ideal gas law to determine the temperature at points A and C, we realize right away that P, n, and R remain constant, so the temperature change is directly proportional to the volume change. The temperature at C will be five times the temperature at A. Since temperature is a measure of the internal energy of the gas, the internal energy also **increases**.

(d) $Q = \Delta U - W$, so the amount of heat added or lost is the sum of the increase in internal energy and the energy used <u>by</u> the gas to do 2600 joules of work [from our answer to question (a)]. The internal energy increases, according to the answer to question (c). In this case, both changes require energy that must be **added** in the form of heat.

► **Recommended for further practice (Walker, 3rd ed.):**
- Checkpoint 18-3 on page 597
- Section 18-4 on molar specific heats (optional; not on exam)
- Section 18-6 on heat engines and Carnot cycle
- Chapter Summary on pages 615–617
- Chapter Problems on pages 619–624: 3, 9, 13, 17, 21, 29, 39, 43, 53, 81, 91

√ **Reminders:**
- All temperatures should be converted to Kelvins in ideal gas equations.
- For the AP* Exam, work done <u>on</u> a system is positive (decrease in gas volume) and work done <u>by</u> a system is negative (increase in gas volume).
- On a P-V diagram, the work done for any step in a process is the area between the P-V curve and the x-axis. The work done for any process described by a set of steps in a closed loop is the area enclosed by the loop.

PART 3

ELECTROMAGNETISM

Chapter 19

Electric Charges, Forces, and Fields

Equations

Electric force between two charges: $F = \dfrac{1}{4\pi\varepsilon_o} \dfrac{q_1 q_2}{r^2}$

Electric field around a charge: $E = \dfrac{1}{4\pi\varepsilon_o} \dfrac{q}{r^2}$

Electric field: $E = \dfrac{F}{q}$

The basic unit of charge is the magnitude of charge on one electron, which is e or 1.6×10^{-19} coulombs. Although there are smaller quantities of identified charge (such as the $+2/3\ e$ charge on an "up" quark), it is believed that the electron carries the smallest charge that exists on an isolated particle. The **coulomb**, symbol C, is the SI unit for charge. A proton carries a charge of $+e$, or $+1.6 \times 10^{-19}$ coulombs. An electron carries a charge of $-e$, or -1.6×10^{-19} coulombs.

Objects that contain equal numbers of positive and negative charges are called electrically neutral. However, friction between electrically neutral materials may result in transfer of electrons from one to the other, resulting in a net positive charge on the material that lost electrons and a net negative charge on the material that gained electrons. The extent of this **triboelectric charging** depends upon the materials used.

Triboelectric charging	
Material	Relative charging with rubbing
Rabbit fur	+++++
Glass	+++++
Human hair	++++
Nylon	+++
Silk	++
Paper	+
Cotton	−
Wood	−−
Amber	−−−
Rubber	−−−−
PVC	−−−−−
Teflon	−−−−−−

A material near the top of the table, such as rabbit fur, loses electrons easily when in contact with a material near the bottom of the table, such as Teflon. Once an object obtains a net charge, it will attract an object of the opposite charge and repel an object with the same charge.

Once objects obtain a charge, they may cause charge changes in other objects of the same charge, opposite charge, or zero net charge.

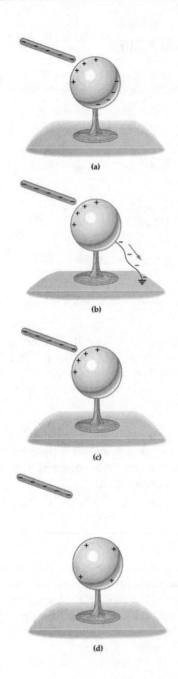

(a)

(b)

(c)

(d)

When the negatively charged rod is brought near the sphere (diagram a), which has zero net charge, the charge on the sphere separates, or **polarizes**. The negative charge on the rod repels negative charges, which move away, leaving the region near the rod negative. If the rod were moved away without touching the sphere, the charge would resume its previous unpolarized arrangement.

However, if a wire were connected to the sphere and to the ground while the rod was in position (b), negative charges would be repelled to the ground. If the conducting wire is removed while the rod is still in place, the sphere is left with a positive charge. This is charging by **induction**. Once the rod is removed—without ever having touched the sphere—the sphere keeps its positive net charge, which distributes evenly through the sphere.

If the wire were left connected to the sphere as the rod was removed, negative charge would move back onto the sphere to equalize the charge. The sphere would then be left with no net charge.

Another way to charge the sphere would be to touch the sphere with the rod, which would be charging by **conduction**. In this case, the sphere would be left with a negative charge when the rod is removed.

If the sphere is made of conducting material, the charge will move to the outside of the sphere.

Materials that transfer electric charges easily (most metals) are called **conductors**. Materials such as wood and glass that do not transfer charges easily are called **insulators**.

Charged particles or objects exert **electrical forces** on each other. The force between two charged point particles, for example, is directly proportional to the product of the magnitudes of the charges and inversely proportional to the square of the distance between the charges:

$$F = \frac{1}{4\pi\varepsilon_o} \frac{q_1 q_2}{r^2}$$

This is a statement of **Coulomb's Law.** The force exerted by charge q_1 on charge q_2 is equal in magnitude and opposite in direction to the force exerted by charge q_2 on charge q_1—directed along a line between the centers of the charges. The quantity $\dfrac{1}{4\pi\varepsilon_o}$, where ε_o is the permittivity constant of free space, has the value 9×10^9 N-m^2/C^2. This is called **Coulomb's constant** (k) and is sometimes used in calculations instead of $\dfrac{1}{4\pi\varepsilon_o}$. Thus, the equation can be used in the form:

$$F = k\frac{q_1 q_2}{r^2}$$

Either form for the constant in Coulomb's Law is acceptable on the AP* Exam.

Although Coulomb's Law is given in the form shown above on the AP* Equations Sheet, it is sometimes helpful to see the force equation in vector form:

$$\boldsymbol{F} = \frac{1}{4\pi\varepsilon_o}\frac{q_1 q_2}{r^2}\,\hat{r}$$

The force $\boldsymbol{F}$ is a vector, and the symbol $\hat{r}$ gives the vector the direction "radially outward". Thus, if both charges are positive or both charges are negative, the force is outward—or a repulsive force. If one charge is positive and the other negative, the direction is then $-\hat{r}$, which the opposite of radially outward (radially inward)—or an attractive force.

An isolated charge has an **electric field** around it that is directed radially outward in all directions around a positive charge and is directed radially inward in all directions around a negative charge, as shown in the diagrams below. Electric field is a vector quantity with units N/C or V/m. The magnitude of the electric field is proportional to the charge and inversely proportional to the square of the distance from the charge:

$$E = \frac{1}{4\pi\varepsilon_o}\frac{q}{r^2}$$

Again, Coulomb's constant can be used for the quantity $\dfrac{1}{4\pi\varepsilon_o}$, so the equation becomes: $E = k\dfrac{q}{r^2}$

The electric field equation can be written as a vector equation: $\boldsymbol{E} = \dfrac{1}{4\pi\varepsilon_o}\dfrac{q}{r^2}\,\hat{r}$

If the charge q is positive, the direction of the electric field is $\hat{r}$, or radially outward. If the charge q is negative, the field direction is $-\hat{r}$, or radially inward.

The electric field $\boldsymbol{E}$ produced by one charge results in an electric force $\boldsymbol{F}$ on a second charge q brought into the field:

$$\boldsymbol{F} = q\boldsymbol{E}.$$

The force and field are vector quantities in the same direction if the charge q is positive and in the opposite direction if the charge is negative.

In the diagram on the next page, we can see the electric field lines radiating outward (in three dimensions, actually) from the positive charge in diagram (a). These field lines never touch or cross each other. In diagram (b), we can see electric field lines radiating inward toward the negative charge. Further, the number of field lines or density of field lines double, since the quantity of charge doubles.

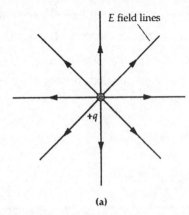

(a)

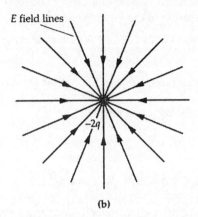

(b)

The diagrams below show the complexity of field lines around systems of charges. Again, the field line densities are proportional to the sizes of the charges. Diagram (a) also shows that the electric field vector is tangent to the field lines at every point. It can further be pointed out that in diagram (b) the field lines are even more dense (i.e., a large **flux density**) between the two charges where the electric field vectors add. In diagram (c), there is a point between the two charges where there is no net electric field, since the electric field vectors from each charge are equal and opposite—and cancel.

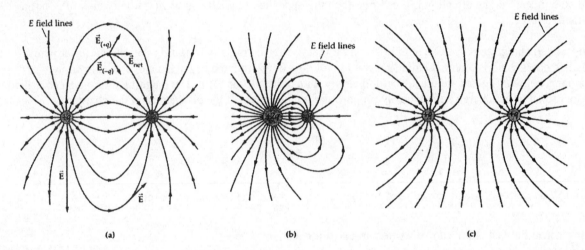

(a) (b) (c)

Two oppositely charged parallel metal plates have an electric field between them that is directed from the positive plate to toward the negative plate. The electric field is uniform between the plates; there is no field outside the plate.

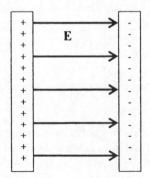

This arrangement, called a **parallel plate capacitor**, can store energy by charge separation.

Excess charge on any object made of conducting material will collect at the surface of the object, leaving no electric field inside. Electric field lines are perpendicular to a tangent at the surface.

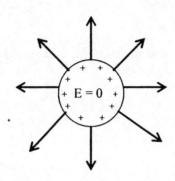

Sample Questions

Questions 1-2. Consider the two charges positioned below.

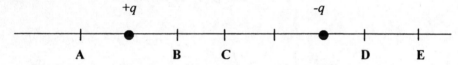

1. At which of the labeled points does the electric field have greatest magnitude?
    A. A
    B. B
    C. C
    D. D
    E. E

2. At which of the labeled points will a third charge, +q, experience the greatest magnitude of force?
    A. A
    B. B
    C. C
    D. D
    E. E

3. What is the magnitude of the force between two protons at a distance of 1 nm?
    A. 2.3×10^{-54} N
    B. 2.3×10^{-44} N
    C. 2.3×10^{-27} N
    D. 2.3×10^{-26} N
    E. 2.3×10^{-10} N

<u>Questions 4-5</u>. An electric field of magnitude E is set up between two horizontal plates so that an oil droplet of mass m is in equilibrium when it is given a charge and suspended between the plates.

4.   What would be a correct expression for the magnitude of the charge on the droplet?
      A. mgE
      B. $\dfrac{mg}{E}$
      C. $\dfrac{E}{mg}$
      D. mgE^2
      E. ma

5.   Assuming the charge on the droplet is negative, what are the directions of the electric field between the plates and the force on the charge that will keep the charge suspended?

<u>Direction of Electric Field</u>   <u>Direction of Force on Droplet</u>

A.   ↓   ↓

B.   ↓   ↑

C.   ↑   ↑

D.   ↑   ↓

E.   →   →

Sample Problems

1. Three charges are held in position at the corners of an equilateral triangle, as shown. Express all answers in terms of given quantities and fundamental constants. Assume the charges are all of equal magnitude, q.

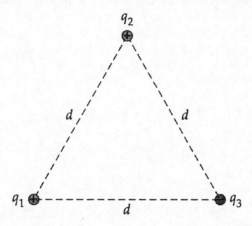

(a) What is the strength of the electric field at the point where q_1 resides, due to the other two charges?

(b) What is the magnitude of the electric force on q_1 due to the other two charges?

2. Two charged parallel plates are a distance $d = 3\ mm$ apart, with each plate holding a charge of magnitude $Q = 10\ \mu C$. A constant electric field of strength $E = 100\ V/m$ exists in the area between the plates.

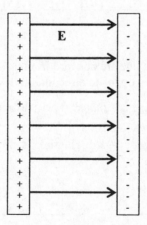

(a) Calculate the magnitude of the electric force on an electron at the instant it is released halfway between the plates.

(b) Calculate the acceleration of an electron at the instant it is released halfway between the plates.

(c) If the electron were released from that point halfway between the plates, how long would it take the electron to strike the positive plate?

3.   Two charged objects are suspended at equilibrium by thin threads, as shown below. Each has a charge of magnitude 0.03 μC and a mass of 5.4 g.

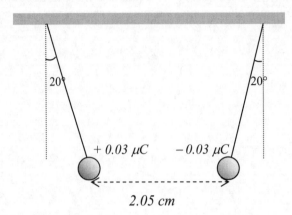

2.05 cm

(a) Calculate the magnitude of the electric force of the positive charge on the negative charge.

(b) What is the magnitude of the electric force of the negative charge on the positive charge?

(c) What is the tension in each of the threads?

(d) What, if anything, will happen to the angles if the positive charge is doubled while its mass stays the same? Explain.

SOLUTIONS TO SAMPLE QUESTIONS AND SAMPLE PROBLEMS

Multiple Choice Questions:

1.   **B**   The electric field vectors along the line are outward from $+q$ and inward toward $-q$. At points A, D, and E, the field vectors from each charge are in opposite directions and will cancel. So we consider either point B or point C. Let's assume each mark on the line is 1 meter. The field at B is: $E = \dfrac{kq}{1^2}\ right + \dfrac{kq}{3^2}\ right = \frac{10}{9}\ kq.$

The field at C is: $E = \dfrac{kq}{2^2}\ right + \dfrac{kq}{2^2}\ right = \frac{1}{2}\ kq.$ The field is stronger at B.

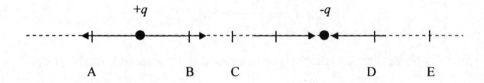

2.   **B**   Since $F = qE$, the force is strongest on a charge where the field is strongest.

3.   **E**   The base number is the same on all the answers, so we simply need to determine the exponent:

$$F = k\frac{q_1 q_2}{r^2} = (9 \times 10^9)\frac{(1.6 \times 10^{-19})^2}{(1 \times 10^{-9})^2} = 23 \times 10^{-11} = 2.3 \times 10^{-10}\, N$$

4. B For the forces to be balanced, $mg = qE$, so $q = \dfrac{mg}{E}$

5. B There must be an electrical force upward to balance the gravitational force downward on the droplet. Using $F = qE$, the force and field must be opposite in direction on a negative charge. Thus the field is downward.

Free Response Problems:

1. (a) One field vector points from q_2, toward q_1, equal to $\dfrac{kq}{d^2}$. The second field vector points from q_1, toward q_3, equal to $\dfrac{kq}{d^2}$, since the distances are the same and the charges are the same. We recognize that the triangle is equilateral, so each angle is 60°. Then, the electric field vectors must be separated into x and y components to add them:

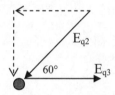

x-direction $\;E_x = E_{q3} - E_{q2x} = \dfrac{kq}{d^2} - \dfrac{kq}{d^2} \cos 60° = \dfrac{kq}{2d^2}$ *(to the right)*

y-direction: $\;E_y = E_{q2y} = \dfrac{kq}{d^2} \sin 60° = \dfrac{\sqrt{3}}{2} \dfrac{kq}{d^2}$ *(downward)*

Resultant Field $= [E_x^2 + E_y^2]^{1/2} = [\tfrac{1}{4}(\dfrac{kq}{r^2})^2 + \tfrac{3}{4}(\dfrac{kq}{r^2})^2]^{\frac{1}{2}} = \dfrac{kq}{d^2}$

(b) Use Coulomb's Law: $\;F = qE = (q)(\dfrac{kq}{d^2}) = \dfrac{kq^2}{d^2}$

2. (a) The force is $qE = (1.6 \times 10^{-19}\ C)(100\ V/m) = 1.6 \times 10^{-17}\ N$

(b) Using $F = ma$, $a = \dfrac{F}{m} = \dfrac{1.6 \times 10^{-17}\ N}{9.11 \times 10^{-31}\ kg} = 1.8 \times 10^{13}\ m/s^2$

(c) This is just a kinematics problem: $s = v_o t + \tfrac{1}{2} at^2$

$$1.5 \times 10^3\ m = 0 + \tfrac{1}{2}(1.8 \times 10^{13}\ m/s^2)t^2$$

$$t = 1.4 \times 10^{-8}\ s$$

3. (a) Use Coulomb's Law: $F_E = k\dfrac{q_1 q_2}{r^2} = \dfrac{(9x10^9 \ N \cdot m^2/C^2)(0.03x10^{-6} \ C)^2}{(0.0205 \ m)^2} = \mathbf{1.9 \times 10^{-2} \ N}$

(b) The forces are equal in magnitude and opposite in direction: $F_E = \textbf{\textit{1.9 x 10^{-2} N}}$

(c) Start with a free-body diagram, recognizing that if force and angles are equal on both sides of the setup, the tensions will be equal.

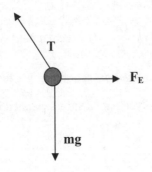

Since the net force in each direction must be zero:

x-direction: $F_E = T \sin 20°$

$1.9 \times 10^{-2} \ N = T \sin 20°$

$T = 0.056 \ N$

(d) If the positive charge is doubled, the force between them would double. Now that the electrical force is larger, the *x*-component of the tension must be larger to balance it (see free body diagram on part c). Since the weight of the particle remains the same, the *y*-component of the tension remains the same. This will increase the angle, moving the particle closer together and also increasing the tension in each thread.

▶ **Recommended for further practice (Walker, 3rd ed.):**
- Example 19-5 on superposition of electric fields
- Example 19-6
- Chapter Summary on pages 653–654
- Chapter Problems on page 657–661: 7, 9, 15, 21, 25, 33, 39, 41, 69, 71

√ **Reminders:**
- Electric forces and electric fields are vectors, so vector components must be used to add them.
- Watch for symmetry when working with electric forces and fields; i.e., situations where components cancel.
- Magnitudes of electric forces and electric fields follow an inverse square law.
- No electric field exists inside a conductor.
- Excess charge placed on a conductor will move to the conductor's exterior surface.

Chapter 20

Electric Potential and Electric Potential Energy

> ### *Equations*
>
> Electric potential energy: $U_E = qV = \dfrac{1}{4\pi\varepsilon_o} \dfrac{q_1 q_2}{r}$
>
> Electric potential due to a system of charges: $V = \dfrac{1}{4\pi\varepsilon_o} \sum_i \dfrac{q_i}{r_i}$
>
> Electric field between charged plates: $E_{\mathrm{avg}} = -\dfrac{V}{d}$

Consider moving a very small, positive **test charge** toward a positive "source" charge. The positive source charge has an electric field around it, so moving a positive test charge toward the source charge requires force. Since positive charges repel, moving a positive test charge toward the positive source charge is going to require **work**. The work required is the change in the test charge's **potential energy**. The change in potential energy per unit of charge is defined as **absolute potential,** V:

$$V = \frac{\Delta U}{q}$$

Absolute potential, or potential, V, is measured in **volts**, where: $1 \text{ volt} = 1 \dfrac{\text{joule}}{\text{coulomb}}$

Positive work is required to move a positive test charge toward a positive source charge—and the closer it is moved, the more work required. Thus, the potential is higher close to the positive charge and lower farther away. The absolute potential around any charge depends on the charge, q, the distance from the charge, r, and the permittivity of free space, ε_o:

$$V = \frac{1}{4\pi\varepsilon_o} \frac{q}{r} \quad \text{or} \quad V = \frac{kq}{r}$$

Another unit commonly used for energy—particularly in the study of electricity and again in the modern physics section—is the **electron volt**. One electron volt (eV) is the change in potential energy of one electron when it moves through a potential difference of 1 volt.

As in the cases of the formulas for electric force and electric field, **Coulomb's constant,** k, can be used interchangeably with $\dfrac{1}{4\pi\varepsilon_o}$, where $k = 9 \times 10^9 \text{ N·m}^2/\text{C}^2$.

Electric potential is a scalar quantity, so potentials can be added for a collection of source charges:

$$V = \frac{1}{4\pi\varepsilon_o} \sum_i \frac{q_i}{r_i}$$

The work required to move a charge, q, to a point where a set of charges creates a potential, V, is equal to the electric potential energy acquired by the charges:

$$W = U_E = qV = q\left(\frac{1}{4\pi\varepsilon_o} \sum_i \frac{q_i}{r_i}\right)$$

[Note: The terms *electric potential*, *potential*, and *absolute potential* are all used in various contexts to mean the same thing, and are all measured in volts. Do not confuse these terms with *electric potential energy*, which is measured in joules.]

The absolute potential around a charge is the same at every point that is equidistant from that charge. All the points connecting these points of equal potential are called **equipotentials**. The positive charge shown below has equipotentials that form three-dimensional patterns—all the same distance from the charge. Equipotential **A** is closer to the charge, so the potential is higher at **A** than it is at **B**. Thus, another positive charge positioned anywhere along equipotential A will have higher potential energy than if it were positioned at **B**. Since positive charges repel, a positive charge released at equipotential **A** will move away from **A** toward **B**. Likewise, a negative charge placed at **B** would move toward **A**. Positive charges tend to move from higher potential to lower potential, and negative charge move from lower potential to higher potential.

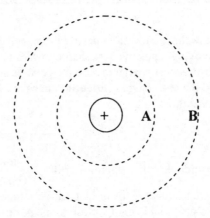

Since the potential at **A** and the potential at **B** are different in value, we can calculate a **potential difference**, ΔV.

Another way to think of this is in terms of the electric field produced by the positive source charge. The work done by the electric field on a charge is the negative of the change in potential energy of the charge. In the situation above, the electric field would exert a force outward on another positive charge, displacing it outward and decreasing its potential energy. We can derive a useful expression that relates electric field to electric potential:

(1) $\Delta U = -W = q\Delta V$
(2) $W = F_{ave}d = qE_{ave}d$
(3) $q\Delta V = -qEd$

Therefore: $E_{ave} = -\dfrac{V}{d}$

Around a positive charge, the electric field, which is outward, is the opposite direction of the increase in potential, which is inward (thus the negative sign).

<u>Example</u>: The charged metal plates below have an electric field that extends from the positive plate to the negative plate, in the x direction. The potential at the positive plate is considered to be 40 volts in this case, and the potential at the negative plate is 0 volts, so there is a potential difference between the plates of 40 volts. The equipotential lines are drawn in the y direction. Along these equipotential lines, the absolute voltage is constant. It would require <u>no work</u> to move a charge along one of these equipotential lines, and the charge would undergo <u>no change in potential energy</u>. A positive 1 μC charge positioned at the 40-V equipotential would have a potential energy of:

$$U = qV = (1\,\mu C)(40\ V) = 40\ \mu J$$

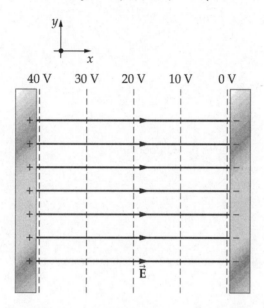

Suppose the charge above is released from the 40 V equipotential. It will experience an electric force in the same direction as the electric field lines that will accelerate it toward the negative plate. As it accelerates, its electric potential energy is converted to kinetic energy, so its velocity at the moment it reaches the negative plate can be calculated (with the charge starting at rest):

$$\Delta U = \Delta K$$
$$q\Delta V = \tfrac{1}{2}\,mv^2$$

If we know the mass of the charge, we can calculate its velocity.

In summary:
1. Positive charges move from high potential to low potential.
2. Negative charges move from low potential to high potential.
3. Positive charges experience an accelerating force in an electric field that is in the same direction as the field.
4. Negative charges experience an accelerating force in an electric field that is the in the opposite direction as the field lines.

A set of charged plates, such as the example above, is called a **capacitor.** Capacitors are examined in much greater detail in Chapter 21.

Questions 1-2. A positive 6 µC charge, shown below, produces equipotentials of 60,000 V at point **A** and 40,000 V at point **B**.

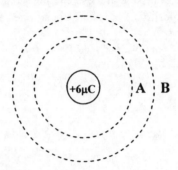

1. What is the distance from the charge to the equipotential **A**?
   A. 0.06 m
   B. 0.09 m
   C. 0.6 m
   D. 0.9 m
   E. 1.5 m

2. What would be the work required to move a +10 µC charge from **A** to **B**?
   A. −0.2 J
   B. +0.2 J
   C. −2.0 J
   D. +2.0 J
   E. +20 J

3. What would be the work required to assemble three charges—two of them positive and one of them negative—at the corners of an equilateral triangle of length d on a side?

   A. $+\dfrac{kq}{d}$

   B. $-\dfrac{kq}{d}$

   C. $+\dfrac{kq^2}{d}$

   D. $-\dfrac{kq^2}{d}$

   E. $\dfrac{2kq^2}{d}$

4. Two equal charges, q, are separated by a distance, d. The charges are moved to a distance $d/2$ apart. What is the work required to do this?

A. $+\dfrac{kq}{d}$

B. $-\dfrac{kq}{d}$

C. $+\dfrac{kq^2}{d}$

D. $-\dfrac{kq^2}{d}$

E. $+kqd$

5. On a plot of *Potential vs. Distance* for a given point charge, the slope of the plot would give:
A. Potential difference
B. Absolute potential
C. Work
D. Potential energy
E. Electric field

Sample Problems

1. A proton is positioned between the charged metal plates below, near the positive plate. The potential difference between the plates is 100 V, and the distance between the plates is 0.1 mm.

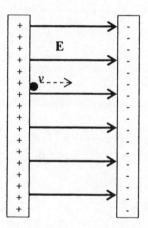

(a) Determine the strength of the electric field between the plates.

(b) Calculate the velocity of the proton as it reaches the negative plate, if it is released at the positive plate.

(c) If the same procedures were performed, except with an electron held at the negative plate, how would the electron's final velocity vary? Justify your answer.

2. Four charges are held at the corners of a square configuration as shown below. The length of each side is 2 mm.

(a) Determine the electric potential in the center of the square.

(b) Determine the potential energy of a positive charge placed at the center of the square.

(c) Determine the net electric field at the center of the square.

3. Two charges, each +3 μC, are positioned on coordinate axes, as shown below, with one charge located 3 meters along the x-axis from the origin and the second charge located 4 meters along the y-axis from the origin.

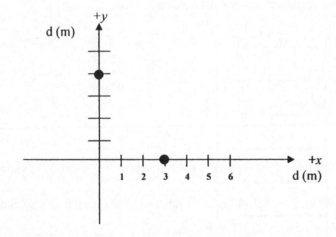

(a) What is the electric potential at the origin due to the two charges?

(b) What is the magnitude of the electric field at the origin due to the two charges?

(c) What would be the magnitude of the force on an electron positioned at the origin?

(d) Draw and label the electric force vector at the origin for the electron.

4. A parallel plate capacitor is connected to a cell with potential difference 36 V and allowed to charge.

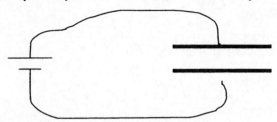

(a) On the diagram, label the positive capacitor plate and the negative capacitor plate.

(b) On the diagram, draw arrows to show the electric field produced in the capacitor.

(c) If an electric field of 500 V/m is produced, how far apart are the capacitor plates positioned?

SOLUTIONS TO SAMPLE QUESTIONS AND SAMPLE PROBLEMS

Multiple Choice Questions:

1. D
$$V = \frac{kq}{d}$$
$$d = \frac{(9 \times 10^9 \ N \cdot m^2/C^2)(6 \times 10^{-6} \ C)}{60,000 \ V} = 0.9 \ m$$

2. A $W = \Delta U = q(V_f - V_o) = (10 \times 10^{-6} \ C)(40000 \ V - 60000 \ V) = -0.2 \ J$

3. D The work is the sum of the potential energies for each combination of charges. Calculate with the two positives, then one positive with the negative, then the other positive with the negative:

$$W = U = (+q)(+\frac{kq}{d}) + (+q)(-\frac{kq}{d}) + (+q)(-\frac{kq}{d}) = -\frac{kq^2}{d}$$

4. C The original potential energy of the two charges is the potential due to one charge $\frac{kq}{d}$ times the second charge: $U = qV = q\frac{kq}{d}$. If the distance between the two is cut in half, d is replaced by $d/2$, so the new potential energy is : $U = \frac{2kq^2}{d}$. The difference between the two is $\frac{kq^2}{d}$. Since the potential energy is increased, the work is positive.

5. E Electric field is change in voltage divided by distance, which would be slope: $E_{avg} = -\frac{V}{d}$

Free Response Problems:

1. (a) The question asks for strength of field, so magnitude only is necessary—not direction.

$$E = \frac{V}{d} = \frac{100\,v}{0.00001\,m} = 1 \times 10^6\ V/m$$

(b) The loss in potential energy of the proton is equal to its gain in kinetic energy:

$$qV = \tfrac{1}{2}\,mv^2$$
$$(1.6 \times 10^{-19}\ C)(100\ V) = \tfrac{1}{2}\,(1.67 \times 10^{-27}\ kg)\,v^2$$
$$v = 1.4 \times 10^5\ m/s$$

(c) The charges of the two are the same, but the proton's mass is almost 2000 times the electron's mass. Thus, the electron's velocity would be $\sqrt{2000}$ or about **45 times** as great.

2. (a) This is a case where examining the symmetry of the configuration can shorten the time involved in determining the answer. Potentials are scalar quantities that simply add. Two of the charges are positive, two are negative, they are all equal in magnitude, and they are all equidistant from the center, so they add to **zero**.

(b) $U = qV$, so in this case the size of the charge placed there is irrelevant. If V in the center is zero, then U is **zero**.

(d) Again, watch for symmetry. Draw the electric field vectors for each charge. Since the magnitudes of the charges and distances to the center are the same, the magnitudes of the vectors are equal. The components of these vectors in the y direction will cancel, so we will only add the four x components—all in the same direction, and all equal. Each component is:

(e)

$$E = \frac{kq}{r^2}\ cos\ 45° = \frac{(9x10^9\ N \cdot m^2/C^2)(2 \times 10^{-6}\ C)}{(0.001\,m)^2} = 6.4 \times 10^9\ N/C$$

The electric field from all four charges is four times that, or **2.5×10^{10} N/C to the right.**

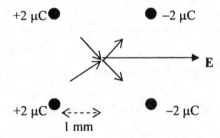

+2 μC   –2 μC

E

+2 μC <--->   –2 μC
        1 mm

3. (a) Add the potentials due to the two charges:

$$V = \frac{1}{4\pi\varepsilon_o}\ \sum_i \frac{q_i}{r_i} = (9 \times 10^9\ N \cdot m^2/C^2)\left(\frac{3 \times 10^{-6}\ C}{4\,m}\right) + (9 \times 10^9\ N \cdot m^2/C^2)\left(\frac{3 \times 10^{-6}\ C}{3\,m}\right) = 16{,}000\ V$$

(b) The electric field is a vector and cannot be added directly. However, since each charge lies on an axis, the electric field from each charge at the origin becomes a component of the resultant electric field vector.

$$E_x = \frac{kq}{r^2} = \frac{(9x10^9)(3x10^{-6})}{3^2} = 3000\ N/C$$

$$E_y = \frac{(9x10^9)(3x10^{-6})}{4^2} = 1700 \ N/C$$

$$E = \sqrt{E_x^2 + E_y^2} = 3400 \ N/C$$

(c) $F = qE$, so $F = (1.6 \ x \ 10^{-19} \ C)(3400 \ N/C) = 5.4 \ x \ 10^{-16} \ N$

(d)

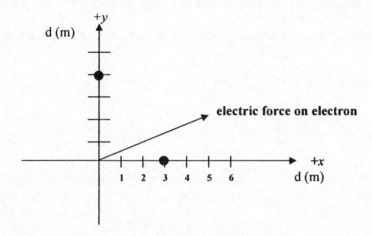

[Note: The electric force on an electron is in the opposite direction of the net electric field at the origin. The question did not ask for the angle, but the direction of the force should clearly be at an angle that shows the larger contribution of the field in the x direction, i.e., a small angle with the negative x axis.]

4. (a)(b)

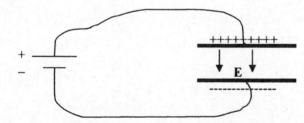

(c) $E_{avg} = \dfrac{V}{d}$ $\qquad\qquad d = \dfrac{36 \ V}{500 \ V/m} = 0.072 \ m$

▶ **Recommended for further practice (Walker, 3rd ed.):**
- Example 20-2 on page 668
- Equipotential surfaces on pages 674–675
- Chapter Summary on pages 685–687
- Chapter Problems on pages 689–694: 7, 9, 11, 19, 17, 29, 31, 35, 47(a), 59, 69, 83 [Note: You may want to review more about capacitors and DC circuits in Chapter 21 before this assignment.]

√ **Reminders:**
- Positive charges move from high potential to low potential, and negative charges move from low potential to high potential.
- Positive charges experience an electric force in the same direction as the electric field, while negative charges experience an electric force opposite the electric field.
- Positive work is done while moving a positive charge to higher potential, and negative work is done in moving a positive charge to lower potential.
- No work is done moving a charge along an equipotential line.
- One volt is a change in potential energy of one joule per coulomb of charge, or, alternately, one volt is the change a potential energy of one electron-volt per electron.
- Parallel plate capacitors are examined in detail in the next chapter, but dielectrics are not included on the AP* Syllabus.

Chapter 21
Electric Current and Direct Current Circuits

<u>*Equations*</u>

Electric current: $I_{avg} = \dfrac{\Delta Q}{\Delta t}$

Ohm's Law: $V = IR$

Electrical Power: $P = VI$

Resistance: $R = \dfrac{\rho L}{A}$

Total resistance in series: $R_s = \sum_i R_i$

Total resistance in parallel: $\dfrac{1}{R_p} = \sum_i \dfrac{1}{R_i}$

Charge on a capacitor: $Q = CV$

Capacitance: $C = \dfrac{\varepsilon_o A}{d}$

Total capacitance in series: $\dfrac{1}{C_s} = \sum_i \dfrac{1}{C_i}$

Total capacitance in parallel: $C_p = \sum_i C_i$

Energy stored in a capacitor: $U_c = \frac{1}{2} Q V = \frac{1}{2} C V^2$

Electrical **current** is the flow of positive electrical charge from high potential to low potential in a **DC** (direct current) circuit. The current, I, in amps, is equal to the rate of flow of charge, measured in coulombs per second:

$$I = \frac{\Delta q}{\Delta t} \qquad 1\,A = \frac{1\,C}{1\,s}$$

One amp (ampere, A) is equal to one coulomb per second. As charges flow through a resistor, the potential energy of each charge decreases due to work done on it. This work per charge is called **voltage**, or change in potential, or potential difference, V, measured in volts. Thus, one volt is equal to one joule per coulomb.

$$1\ volt = \frac{1\ joule}{1\ coulomb}$$

Ohm's Law describes the relationship between voltage, current, and resistance in a circuit:

$$V = IR$$

Remember that, although Ohm's Law describes a general relationship among these three variables, not all circuits are "Ohmic;" i.e., values taken for these variables in the laboratory will not always produce results confirming this law. However, unless told otherwise, you should assume simple DC circuits to be Ohmic.

A **resistor** is any device through which electrical charges (i.e., current) flows and uses energy, such as light bulbs, buzzers, or even pieces of wire. In most cases, however, we will assume connecting wires to have such small **resistance** that the resistance is negligible. The resistance of a piece of wire is dependent upon its length L, its cross-sectional area A, and its resistivity ρ, where resistivity is dependent upon the material of which the wire is made:

$$R = \frac{\rho L}{A}$$

Resistance is measured in ohms, abbreviated with the Greek symbol Ω. Although we assume resistance of a resistor to be constant, you should be aware that the resistivity of most materials increases with temperature. Thus, the actual resistance of a resistor increases as the resistor uses power and heats up. On the AP* Exam, assume constant resistance for an element, unless told otherwise.

Though it is not necessary for the AP* Exam, some students find it helpful to know the colors used on resistors—particularly when working in the laboratory:

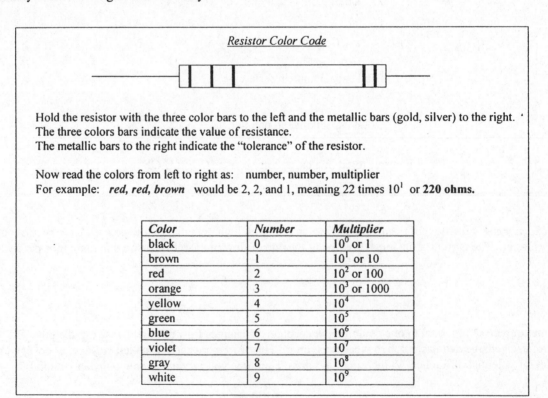

Resistor Color Code

Hold the resistor with the three color bars to the left and the metallic bars (gold, silver) to the right. ·
The three colors bars indicate the value of resistance.
The metallic bars to the right indicate the "tolerance" of the resistor.

Now read the colors from left to right as: number, number, multiplier
For example: *red, red, brown*   would be 2, 2, and 1, meaning 22 times 10^1 or **220 ohms.**

Color	Number	Multiplier
black	0	10^0 or 1
brown	1	10^1 or 10
red	2	10^2 or 100
orange	3	10^3 or 1000
yellow	4	10^4
green	5	10^5
blue	6	10^6
violet	7	10^7
gray	8	10^8
white	9	10^9

Power is the rate at which energy is produced by a power supply (or battery) or the rate at which energy is used by a resistor or circuit to do its work, such as lighting a bulb, getting hot, etc. Power is measured in joules per second, or watts:

$$P = VI$$

Substitute for V or I from Ohm's Law to get other forms of the power equation: $P = VI = I^2R = \dfrac{V^2}{R}$

Since heat produced is proportional to current, Joule's Heating Law is:

$$P = I^2R$$

Questions often arise regarding the notations V and ε, which are both measured in volts. The symbol ε stands for **emf** (which once stood for *electromotive force*—but is not a force). This creates unnecessary confusion, but we have held onto the term emf. I run into situations every day—in text problem sets, reviews, and contests—where the two are used rather interchangeably without clarification. I like to compare it to all those situations we have encountered in mechanics where we neglect friction and come up with an approximation for an answer. Then when we include friction, we discover that it affects our result! In rather the same way, emf is a theoretical cell or battery voltage that neglects any internal resistance in the power supply itself. In reality, the power supply has internal resistance that produces a drop in voltage. For example, a new 9-volt cell might register 10.2 volts on a voltmeter when it is not connected to a circuit. When it's put into a working circuit, however, the current running through the circuit—and through the cell—causes a voltage drop within the cell itself. The cell has an operating **potential difference** (V) that supplies 9 volts to the external circuit. An example is provided in the Sample Problems section. Unless you are given information about internal resistance, use V and ε interchangeably in solving a circuit. Given an internal resistance (r) for a battery or cell, however, use:

$$V = \varepsilon - Ir$$

where ε is the emf, I is the current delivered to the external circuit, and V is the voltage difference across the external circuit.

An electrical circuit consists of several circuit elements connected to each other. A very simple **series** circuit is shown here:

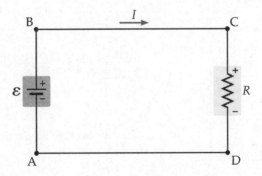

Let's examine two different possibilities for this circuit—with and without internal resistance in the cell:

(1) If the potential difference ε is 12 volts and the resistance R is 4 ohms, then the current I can be determined by Ohm's Law: $V = IR$. The current, which flows from high potential (+) to low potential (-), will be 3 A.

(2) Suppose we are told instead that the cell has an internal resistance of 1 ohm. We now have a total resistance of $(4+1)$ or 5 ohms. The current in this case is $\frac{12}{5}$ or 2.4 A. Now let's look at potential difference, or "voltage drop", as the current flows in this circuit. The potential difference between AB is:

$$V_{AB} = \varepsilon - Ir = 12\ V - (2.4\ A)(1\ \Omega) = 9.6\ V$$

We can then check the potential difference from C to D:

$$V_{CD} = (2.4\ A)(4\Omega) = 9.6\ V$$

The two answers are the same, as they should be, since the potential difference in the external circuit should be the same as the potential difference in the battery, cell, or power supply—assuming, as we must do unless told otherwise, that there is negligible resistance in the connecting wires. [This is really a manifestation of Kirchoff's Law, which we will discuss later.]

Now, let's examine a series circuit with more than one resistor, as shown below.

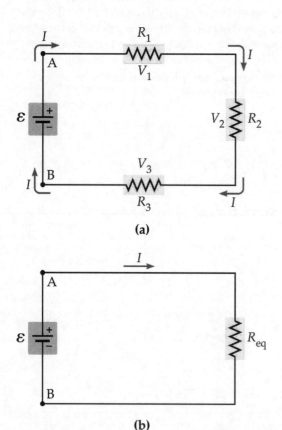

(a)

(b)

In diagram (a), a voltage supply ε is connected to three resistors in series. The total resistance, or **equivalent resistance**, R_{eq}, is:

$$R_s = \sum_i R_i = R_1 + R_2 + R_3$$

The current, I, can be determined from Ohm's Law, using the equivalent resistance as if it were one resistance [see diagram (b)]:

$$I = \frac{\varepsilon}{R_{eq}}$$

The voltage drop or potential difference across each resistor is:

$$V = IR$$
$$V_1 = IR_1$$
$$V_2 = IR_2$$
$$V_3 = IR_3$$

All the current flows through each resistor, so I for each resistor in the series circuit is the same:

$$I_1 = I_2 = I_3$$

The total voltage across the external circuit is equal to the voltage supplied:

$$\varepsilon = V_1 + V_2 + V_3$$

The power used by each of the resistors is:

$$P = VI$$
$$P_1 = V_1 I$$
$$P_2 = V_2 I$$
$$P_3 = V_3 I$$

The sum of these individual power usages is equal to the power supplied: $\quad \mathcal{E}R_{eq} = P_1 + P_2 + P_3$

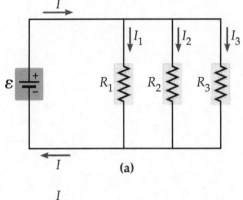

(a)

In a **parallel** circuit, components are connected such that the current has more than one path for travel and must split at branching points called **junctions** or **nodes**. The three resistors in this circuit are connected in parallel to the supplied voltage, $\mathcal{E}$. To solve for the current, I, in the circuit, first find the equivalent resistance for the resistors R_1, R_2, and R_3.

$$\frac{1}{R_p} = \sum_i \frac{1}{R_i}$$

[*Note: One common source of error in using this formula comes in forgetting to take the reciprocal after adding the repicrocals of the resistor values. One way to avoid this is to remind yourself that the equivalent resistance in parallel is going to be less than any of the individual resistors.*]

The current, I, can be determined from Ohm's Law, using the equivalent resistance as if it were one resistance [see diagram (b)]:

$$I = \frac{\mathcal{E}}{R_{eq}}$$

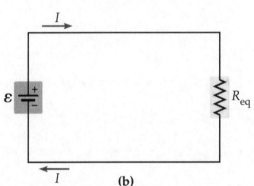

(b)

The current that flows from the high potential end of the power supply will then split at the junction where the three resistors are connected. If the three resistors are equal in value, the current will split equally in all three branches, with $\frac{1}{3}I$ in each branch. However, if the resistors are not equal, the current will split in inverse proportion to the resistance—i.e., more current through the lower resistance branch and less current through the higher resistance. Ultimately, the product of current and resistance in each branch must be such that <u>the voltage across each branch in parallel is the same.</u>

$$V_1 = V_2 = V_3$$
$$I_1 R_1 = I_2 R_2 = I_3 R_3$$

<u>Helpful Note:</u> When two—and only two—resistors are connected in parallel, it is quicker to use the "product over sum" rule to determine equivalent resistance. Be aware, however, that this method is not mathematically valid for more than two resistors:

$$R_P = \frac{R_1 R_2}{R_1 + R_2}$$

Although the current and equivalent resistance values are determined differently for series and parallel circuits, finding total power for a parallel circuit compared to series circuit is much the same. The total power for a parallel circuit is still simply the sum of the power values for the individual components.

$$\mathcal{E}R_{eq} = P_1 + P_2 + P_3$$

The circuit on the next page consists of a combination of series and parallel connections with three equal resistors. A set of simple steps can make solving such a circuit easier:

(1) Find the equivalent resistance, starting with the parallel branches. Here, we can apply the "product over sum" rule, since there are only two resistors in parallel:

$$R_P = \frac{R_1 R_2}{R_1 + R_2} = \frac{R^2}{2R} = \frac{R}{2}$$

(2) Add the equivalent parallel resistance to the one resistor that is in series:

$$R_{total} = R + \frac{R}{2} = \frac{3R}{2}$$

(3) Find the current from the cell, I_1, using Ohm's Law:

$$I_1 = \frac{\mathcal{E}}{R} = \frac{2\mathcal{E}}{3R}$$

(4) Since the resistors in the parallel branches are equal, the current I_1 will split evenly between the two branches:

$$I_2 = I_3 = \frac{1}{2} I_1 = \frac{\mathcal{E}}{3R}$$

(5) The voltage across each of the parallel resistors is the same:

$$V = IR = \frac{\mathcal{E}}{3R} R = \frac{\mathcal{E}}{3}$$

(6) The voltage across the series resistor at the bottom uses the circuit current:

$$V = IR = \frac{2\mathcal{E}}{3R} R = \frac{2\mathcal{E}}{3}$$

(7) The power used by each of the parallel resistors should be the same:

$$P = VI = \frac{\mathcal{E}}{3} \frac{\mathcal{E}}{3R} = \frac{\mathcal{E}^2}{9R}$$

(8) The power used by the series resistor at the bottom:

$$P = VI = \frac{2\mathcal{E}}{3} \frac{2\mathcal{E}}{3R} = \frac{4\mathcal{E}^2}{9R}$$

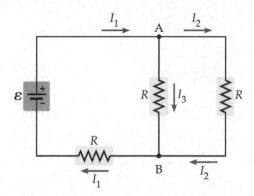

Though **Kirchoff's Laws** are not specifically tested on the AP* Exam, the concepts in these two very important laws are essential—and can make solving or checking solutions for circuits easier.

1. **Kirchoff's Loop Rule** states that the sum of all voltage changes around any complete loop in a circuit is zero. This is <u>conservation of energy</u>, since voltage has been previously defined as change in energy per charge.
    (a) Voltage change going with the current through a resistor is negative.
    (b) Voltage change going against the current through a resistor is positive.
    (c) Voltage change from low potential side of a battery, cell, or capacitor to the high potential side is positive.
    (d) Voltage change from high potential side of a battery, cell, or capacitor to the low potential side is negative.
2. **Kirchoff's Junction Rule** states that the sum of currents flowing toward a junction (or node) is equal to the sum of all currents flowing out of that junction. This is a statement of <u>conservation of charge</u>, since current is rate of flow of charge.

We can now apply these rules to the circuit above.
A. For the small loop on the left, moving clockwise:	$+\varepsilon - I_3R - I_1R = 0$	(loop rule)
B. For the small loop on the right, moving clockwise:	$- I_2R + I_3R = 0$	(loop rule)
C. For the large loop, moving clockwise:	$- I_2R - I_1R + \varepsilon = 0$	(loop rule)
D. For the junction at the top:	$I_1 = I_2 + I_3$	(junction rule)

The circuit on the next page includes both a resistor and a **capacitor**. A circuit such as this is often called an **RC circuit**. A parallel plate **capacitor**, C, is a circuit element that stores charge on parallel metal plates.
In the circuit, the capacitor is connected is series with a resistor and a switch. Before the switch is closed, the capacitor has no charge. After the switch is closed, charge begins to flow from the voltage source, through the resistor, to one side of the capacitor. However, <u>no charge flows through the capacitor</u>. A **dielectric** material between the metal plates physically holds the plates apart and keeps charge from flowing from one plate to another. As positive charge builds up on one plate, an equal amount of positive charge flows off of the other plate, leaving the second metal plate of the capacitor with an equal amount of negative charge. Thus, the current flowing toward the capacitor is equal to the current flowing away from the capacitor.

As charge builds up on the positive plate of the capacitor and negative charge builds up on the negative plate, the potential difference across the capacitor increases. Since the emf is constant, the potential difference across the resistor decreases and the current decreases. During the charging process, the current through the resistor will decrease exponentially with time. The voltage on the capacitor will increase exponentially with time, approaching the power supply voltage as an asymptote. <u>After a period of time, current will be zero in this circuit</u>. The time it takes to charge the capacitor depends on the size of the resistor in the circuit; i.e., a larger resistor slows the charging process. .

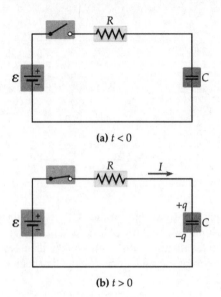

(a) $t < 0$

(b) $t > 0$

The **capacitance** of a capacitor depends on its construction. For a parallel plate capacitor:

$$C = \frac{\varepsilon_o A}{d}$$

where A is the area of the plates, d is the distance between the plates, and ε_0 is the permittivity of free space. [A dielectric material, with dielectric constant κ, placed between the plates can affect its capacitance, but the AP* Physics B Syllabus does not include dielectrics.]

The amount of charge a capacitor stores is proportional to the charging voltage: $\quad Q = CV$
The unit of capacitance is the **farad**:

$$1 \text{ farad } = \frac{1 \text{ coulomb}}{1 \text{ volt}}$$

Assume the power supply is removed after a capacitor is charged. Once the switch is closed, the charge on the capacitor flows from the positive side of the capacitor through the resistor—reversing the direction of current flow from the charging process. The positive charge flows through the circuit (<u>not</u> through the capacitor) to balance the negative charge on the other capacitor plate. As time passes, the charge, and thus the difference in potential, between the capacitor plates decreases, so the current decreases. Thus, the current through the resistor decreases exponentially as a function of time. The voltage on the capacitor also decreases exponentially as a function of time as it discharges.

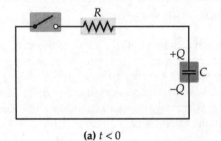

(a) $t < 0$

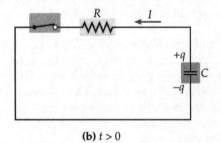

(b) $t > 0$

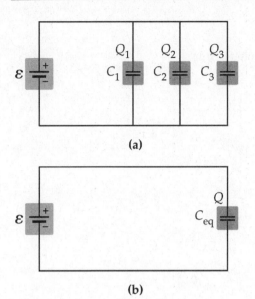

(a)

(b)

Capacitors connected in <u>parallel</u> have a larger equivalent capacitance: $C_p = \sum_i C_i$

The equivalent capacitance of the three capacitors in the diagram is the sum of the three capacitors. This larger capacitance means that more charge can be stored at the same charging voltage.

As in a parallel resistor circuit, the charge that flows from the power supply splits into the three branches. If the capacitors are all of equal size, the charge will split equally among the three capacitors. However, since the equivalent capacitance is three times as great, each of these capacitors will store just as much charge as a single capacitor would store.

Capacitors connected in series have an equivalent capacitance determined by the formula: $\dfrac{1}{C_s} = \sum_i \dfrac{1}{C_i}$

The equivalent capacitance will be less than any of the individual capacitors. In this case, as with parallel resistors, we can use the "product over sum" rule for two capacitors in series:

$$C_s = \frac{C_1 C_2}{C_1 + C_2}$$

[Note: As you have noticed by now, capacitors and resistors add in reverse manner in series and parallel.]

The energy stored on a capacitor (in joules) is: $U_c = \frac{1}{2} Q V = \frac{1}{2} C V^2$
with charge measured in coulombs, voltage measured in volts, and capacitance measured in farads.

An **ammeter** is an instrument connected <u>in series</u> to read the current flowing in that portion of the circuit. Ammeters are constructed with very low internal resistance, so they can be added to the circuit, allowing current through the meter without affecting the total resistance and current in the circuit.

A **voltmeter** is connected <u>in parallel</u> with a circuit to read the potential difference between the two points in the circuit to which the meter is connected. Voltmeters are constructed with very high internal resistance, so they can be added as a parallel branch without allowing an appreciable amount of current to flow in that branch—thus having little effect on the circuit. The instrument below is connected to read the voltage between points C and D.

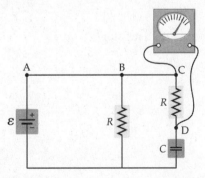

Questions 1-2. Consider this RC circuit, with a capacitor and light bulb resistor.

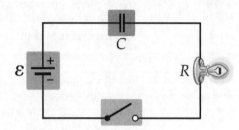

1. Which of the following will occur when the switch is closed?
    I. The light bulb will get brighter as time passes.
    II. Charge will build up on the capacitor.
    III. The voltage on the capacitor will increase with time.
    A. **I** only
    B. **II** only
    C. **III** only
    D. **I** and **II** only
    E. **II** and **III** only

2. The current through the bulb after a long period of time is:
    A. $\dfrac{\mathcal{E}}{R}$

    B. $\mathcal{E}R$

    C. $C\mathcal{E}$

    D. $\frac{1}{2}\,C\mathcal{E}^2$
    E. zero

Questions 3-4. Two 20-Ω resistors are connected in parallel with a power supply, $V = 5\ V$.

3. What is the current in each resistor?
    A. $\frac{1}{4}$ A
    B. $\frac{1}{3}$ A
    C. $\frac{1}{2}$ A
    D. 2 A
    E. 3 A

4. What is the potential difference across each resistor?
    A. 1 V
    B. 2 V
    C. 3 V
    D. 4 V
    E. 5 V

5.   Two 40-watt bulbs are connected in parallel to a 120-volt circuit. What is the current in each bulb?

A. $\frac{1}{4}$ A

B. $\frac{1}{3}$ A

C. $\frac{1}{2}$ A

D. 2 A

E. 3 A

Sample Problems

1. Use the diagram below to answer the questions that follow.

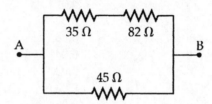

(a) Find the equivalent resistance of the three resistors.

A potential difference of 100 volts is supplied between points A and B.

(b) What is the current through the 45-Ω resistor?

(c) Determine the voltage drop across the 35-Ω resistor.

2. Given: $\varepsilon = 120$ V, $R = 10$ Ω.

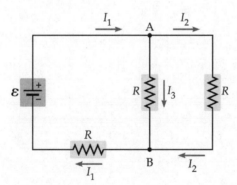

(a) Determine I_1.

(b) Determine V_{AB}.

(c) What happens to the value of I_3 if the branch with current I_2 is removed completely? Justify your answer.

3. A group of AP* physics students recorded the following data for the charging of a capacitor. The circuit included a power supply set at 1.5 volts, a resistor, and an uncharged capacitor at t = 0. The students recorded the voltage across the resistor as the capacitor charged.

Time, t (s)	Resistor voltage, V_r (V)
0	1.41
10	0.92
20	0.58
30	0.38
40	0.26
50	0.18
60	0.11
70	0.08
80	0.07
90	0.06
100	0.04
110	0.03
120	0.03
130	0.03
140	0.03
150	0.03

(a) Plot the data on the axes provided, and draw a best-fit curve. Label it **"Resistor Voltage."**

Capacitor Charging

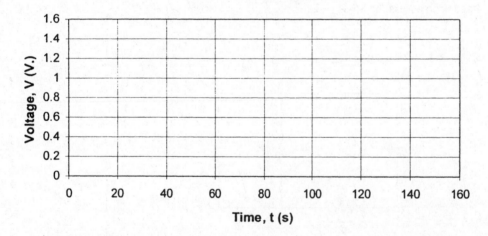

(b) On the same set of axes, sketch the expected curve for the charging voltage on the capacitor. Label it **"Capacitor Voltage."**

(c) Which of the two curves **A** or **B** would be most similar to a plot of the current through the resistor as the capacitor charges? Explain.

Now the power supply is disconnected and the capacitor is discharged through the resistor.

(d) Which of the two curves **A** or **B** would be most similar to a plot of the voltage across the resistor as the capacitor discharges? Explain.

SOLUTIONS TO SAMPLE QUESTIONS AND SAMPLE PROBLEMS

Multiple Choice Questions:

1. E When the switch is closed, the current will decrease with time as the voltage on the capacitor increases with time. The bulb will get dimmer as current decreases.

2. E After a long time, the capacitor is charged, so no charges flow. Thus, current in the bulb is zero.

3. A Each branch will be at the same voltage—5 volts. Use Ohm's Law to find the current in each branch:

$$I = \frac{V}{R} = \frac{5\,V}{20\,\Omega} = 0.25\,A$$

4. E The voltages across the two resistors are equal to each other and to the power supply voltage.

5. B Since the bulbs are connected in parallel with 120 V, they each are supplied with 120 V. Using the power formula:

$$P = VI$$
$$40\,W = (120\,V)(I)$$
$$I = 0.33\,A$$

Free Response Problems:

1. (a) Add the two resistors in series: $R_s = 35\,\Omega + 82\,\Omega = 117\,\Omega$ Then use the "product over sum" rule to combine that parallel branch total with the other parallel resistor: $R_P = \dfrac{R_1 R_2}{R_1 + R_2} = \dfrac{(117)(45)}{117 + 45} = 32.5\,\Omega$

(b) If the potential difference between A and B is 100 V, then each branch has a potential difference of 100 V. Use Ohm's Law to determine the current in the lower branch:

$$I = \frac{V}{R} = \frac{100\,V}{45\,\Omega} = 2.2\,A.$$

(c) The current in the upper branch is: $\quad I = \dfrac{V}{R} = \dfrac{100\,V}{117\,\Omega} = 0.85\,A.$

Use that current with the 35-Ω resistance to find the voltage: $\quad V = IR = (0.85\,A)(35\,\Omega) = 30\,V$

2. (a) The equivalent resistance is the "product over sum" for the parallel resistors, plus the resistor in series:

$$R_{eq} = 10\,\Omega + \frac{10^2}{20} = 15\,\Omega$$

Use Ohm's Law to determine the current: $I_1 = \dfrac{\varepsilon}{R_{eq}} = \dfrac{120\,V}{15\,\Omega} = 8.0\,A.$

(b) The current will split equally at the junction, with 4.0 amps moving through the resistor between A and B. Use Ohm's Law: $\qquad V_{AB} = (4.0\,A)(10\,\Omega) = 40\,V$

(c) The new equivalent resistance for the circuit (which is now two resistors in series) is 20 ohms, so the current is $\frac{120\,V}{6\,\Omega}$ or *6 A*—which is the same through both resistors. Therefore, the current through that resistor **increases** from *4.0 A* to *6.0 A*.

3. (a)(b)

Capacitor Charging

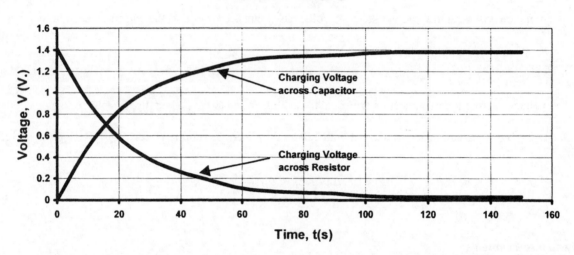

(c) The curve for current through the resistor as the capacitor charges would look most like the voltage across the resistor, since the resistance is constant, and $V = IR$. Current in the circuit decreases exponentially as the capacitor charges.

(d) The curve for voltage across the resistor as the capacitor discharges would look like the voltage across the resistor as it charges. The current during discharge decreases exponentially as the voltage on the capacitor decreases.

▶ **Recommended for further practice (Walker, 3rd ed.):**
- Conceptual Checkpoint 27-1 on page 700 (resistance)
- Kirchoff's Rules, Section 21-5 on page 711 (helpful but not specifically on exam)
- Section 21-8, ammeters and voltmeters
- Internal resistance, page 707
- Chapter Summary on pages 721–723
- Chapter Problems on page 726–731: 5, 11, 21, 29, 33, 39, 43, 47(optional), 53, 55, 57, 85

√ **Reminders:**
- Conventional electrical current represents positive charge flow from high potential (+) to low potential (-) in a DC circuit.
- Unless told otherwise, assume that voltage, current, and resistance in a circuit will
- Unless told otherwise, assume resistance of elements to be constant, though we realize that resistance increases with temperature in most cases.
- Current in a series circuit is the same at every point in the circuit.
- Voltages for resistors in series add up to the total voltage supplied to the external circuit.
- Voltages in parallel branches are equal.

- Adding more resistors in series increases the equivalent resistance, while adding more resistors in parallel reduces the equivalent resistance.
- For two resistors in parallel, use the "product over sum" technique.
- For two capacitors in series, use the "product over sum" technique.
- Circuits with parallel plate capacitors are on the exam—but not dielectrics or RC circuits with time constants.
- Ammeters are connected in series, and voltmeters are connected in parallel.

Chapter 22

Magnetism

Equations

Force on a charge moving in a magnetic field: $F_B = qvB \sin\theta$

Magnetic force on a current-carrying wire: $F_B = BIl \sin\theta$

Magnetic field around a current-carrying wire: $B = \dfrac{\mu_o I}{2\pi r}$

Some objects, such as the Earth, are naturally magnetic. Others can be induced to be magnetic. In this chapter, we will review the magnetic properties of materials, how magnetic materials affect each other, and how electricity and magnetism are inextricably linked.

A **magnet**, whether it's as small as a molecule or as large as the Earth, has two poles—north and south. Two north poles or two south poles repel each other, and a north and south pole will attract. Every magnetic object has around it a **magnetic field,** a vector quantity with symbol **B,** measured in teslas. Magnetic field lines extend outward from the object's north pole and inward to the south pole. These field lines extend in three dimensions through space and do not cross. The density of field lines is proportional to the strength of field, as shown below for the Earth. The magnetic field is strongest near the poles, where field lines are most dense.

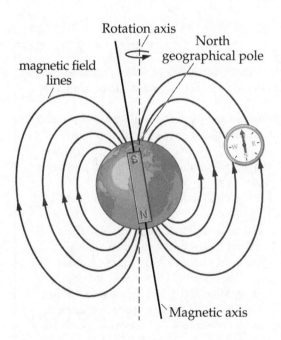

Rotation axis

North geographical pole

magnetic field lines

Magnetic axis

Clarifying a couple of common misunderstandings:

1. Earth's magnetic poles are not at the same locations as the geographic poles. As a matter of fact, they are hundreds of miles from each other at this time. There is evidence in the fossil record that the magnetic poles have shifted over time.

2. What we call the "north pole" is actually near the south magnetic pole. Since the north end of a compass needle points toward the vicinity of the north geographic pole—and opposite magnetic poles attract—the magnetic pole near the north geographic pole must be a south magnetic pole. (Notice the directions of the magnetic field lines on the diagram.)

The strength of Earth's magnetic field is about 0.5 gauss, which is 5×10^{-5} tesla.

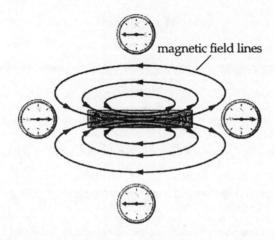

magnetic field lines

The magnetic field lines around any magnetic object, such as the bar magnet above, make continuous loops that extend out from north, inward to the south pole, and through the magnet itself. This is different from electric fields, which begin or end on the surfaces of charged particles. Magnetic field lines are continuous and never cross. A magnetic **compass** is itself a magnet that is free to align along magnetic field lines, with the north pole of the compass pointing in the direction of the magnetic field lines.

Charged particles that move into magnetic fields will experience a force proportional to the strength of the field **B**, the magnitude of the charge, q, and the velocity of the charge, v. The direction of that force on the charge depends on the type of charge and direction of velocity. The **right-hand rule** or a **vector cross product** rule will determine the direction of the force:

$$F_B = qv\textbf{x}B$$

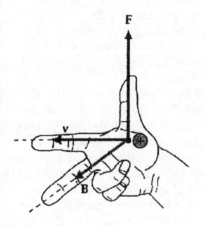

Important Notes:
1. The velocity and magnetic field vectors must be cross multiplied in proper order to get the correct direction for force.
2. The magnitude of the force uses only the components of velocity and field that are perpendicular to each other.
3. Any charged particle motion parallel or antiparallel to the field produces <u>no force</u>.
4. A charged particle motionless in a magnetic field experiences <u>no force</u>.
5. When the particle is negative, the force is in the opposite direction to that of the force on a positive charge, so you must remember to switch the force direction from that obtained from the right-hand rule when using a negative particle. [This author has her students use left hand for negative particles, but many physicists disagree with this—so use what works for you.]

In the situation below, a charged particle with velocity *v* enters a magnetic field. The magnetic field is directed into the page, perpendicular to the plane of the page, as indicated by the symbol ⊗ (like seeing the tail-end of an arrow). (The symbol • indicates a magnetic field out of the page—like the tip of an arrow.) The particle is deflected downward on the page, as shown in the figure. We can determine, using the right-hand rule, that the charge must be negative. The force on the particle initially turns it downward. Then, as the particle turns, the velocity direction changes, so the direction of the force is continually changing. If the force is large enough, the particle turns in a small enough circle to keep the particle in the field—constantly turning in a circle. The magnetic force is providing the centripetal force. However, since the magnetic force is always perpendicular to the direction of motion, the <u>magnetic force does no work</u> on a charged particle.

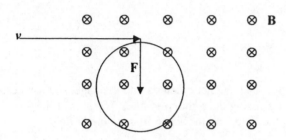

$$F_B = F_C$$

$$qvB = \frac{mv^2}{r}$$

In the case on the right, a charged particle with velocity *v* moves at an angle into a magnetic field, **B** [Figure (a)]. Only the component of the velocity perpendicular to the field produces a force on the particle. From Figure (b) and using the right-hand rule, we can tell that the particle is positive; the magnetic force provides the centripetal force for the circular motion produced.

If the velocity were entirely perpendicular to the field, the particle would just move in a circle in the field. However, the other component of the velocity—the parallel component—maintains the object's motion along the field lines. There is no force exerted on the object in the parallel direction; it simply maintains its velocity in that direction.

The combination of these two types of motion is a helical path along field lines. Charged particles that enter Earth's magnetic field at angles often take this type of path, following field lines to Earth's magnetic poles.

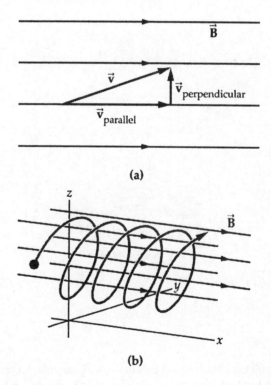

(a)

(b)

A current-carrying wire is placed in a magnetic field. The moving charges in the wire behave in the field in the same way as moving positive charges. When using the cross-product form, the length of wire in the field l, becomes the vector, with the direction of positive charge flow as the direction of the vector.

$$F_B = Il \times B$$

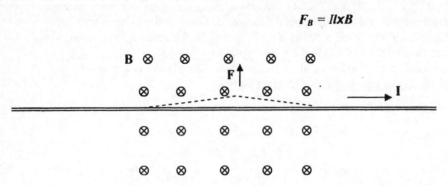

In the case above, the wire is carrying current to the right. The magnetic field is into the page, so the force on the length of the wire in the field is toward the top of the page, using the right-hand rule. The size of the force depends on the size of the current, the length of wire in the field, and the size of the magnetic field.

A current-carrying wire has a magnetic field around it, as can be demonstrated by the following simple experiment.

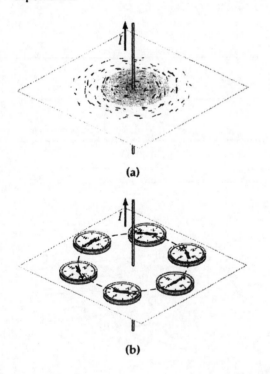

(a)

(b)

(a) Extend the current-carrying wire vertically through a piece of cardboard held horizontally. Sprinkle iron filings on the cardboard to demonstrate the circular pattern of magnetic field around the wire. More filings will collect closer to the wire, showing that the field is stronger near the wire.

(b) Replace the iron filings with several small compasses. Since the compass needles will align in the direction of magnetic field, the direction of field lines can be determined. If the current direction is switched, the direction of magnetic lines will switch, and the compasses will align in the opposite direction around the wire.

The strength of the magnetic field around a current-carrying wire is proportional to the current, I, and the permeability of free space, μ_o, and inversely proportional to the distance from the wire, r.

$$B = \frac{\mu_o I}{2\pi r}$$

This is a statement of **Ampere's Law.**

The direction of the magnetic field around a current-carrying wire can be determined with a variation of the right-hand rule, as shown below:

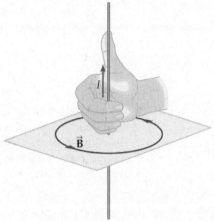

If a current carrying wire is formed into a loop—or a series of loops called a **solenoid**—a similar right-hand rule can determine the direction of magnetic field. This time, curl the fingers in the direction of current flow. Your extended thumb will be in the direction of magnetic field; i.e., the thumb will point to the north pole of the magnetic field.

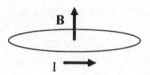

Two current-carrying wires can exert a force on each other, as shown below, since each wire has a magnetic field around it.

wire 1 ═══════════════════════════ ⟶ I_1

wire 2 ═══════════════════════════ ⟶ I_2

Let's first consider wire 2, which has a magnetic field around it due to the current I_2 flowing through it. Using the right-hand rule again for the bottom wire (with thumb in direction of current), the curled fingers come out of the page at a point on the top wire. Using the right-hand rule again for the charges flowing through wire 1 and the magnetic field out of the page (index finger pointing in direction of current I_1, fingers in direction of magnetic field from wire 2 out of the page), we conclude that wire 1 experiences a force <u>toward</u> wire 2 due to the magnetic field created by the current in wire 2. Repeat this process using wire 1. Wire 1 has a magnetic field around it due to the current I_1. Use the right-hand rule (with thumb in direction of charge flow and fingers curled in direction of magnetic field). The magnetic field on wire 2 due to the charge flow in wire 1 is into the page. Determine the force on the charge in wire 2 using the right-hand rule. The result is that the charge in wire 2 (and the wire) experience a force <u>toward</u> wire 1 due to the magnetic field created by the current in wire 1.

Conclusion: Two wires carrying with current flow in the same direction will exert attractive forces on each other.

Now, consider the two wires again, but this time the currents are in opposite directions. Wire 1 creates a magnetic field in the region of wire 2 that is into the page. The force this field creates on the charges flowing in wire 2 is away from wire 1. Likewise, wire 2 creates a magnetic field that is into the page in the region of wire 1. This magnetic field exerts a force on the charges in wire 1 that is <u>away</u> from wire 2. <u>Two wires carrying currents in the opposite direction will exert magnetic forces on each other that cause the wires to repel.</u>

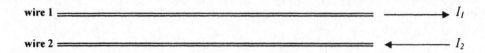

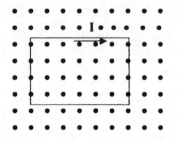

The loop of wire on the left is immersed in a uniform magnetic field directed out of the page. An electrical current, I, flows in the wire. The wire will not experience a torque. Using the right-hand rule, we find that the forces in opposite sides of the wire will cancel each other

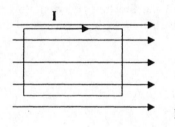

The same loop is now placed in a magnetic field directed to the right on the page. There are no magnetic forces on the top and bottom segments, since the current is in the same direction as the field. However, using the right-hand rule, the right side of the loop will experience a force out of the page, and the left side of the loop will experience a force into the page. Both of these forces exert **torques** to rotate the loop.

<u>**Sample Questions**</u>

1. A proton moves toward the west as it enters a magnetic field directed to the north. What is the direction of the magnetic force on the proton as it enters the field?
   A. no force
   B. south
   C. east
   D. up, away from the center of Earth
   E. down, toward the center of Earth

2. A proton moves toward the west as it enters an electric field directed to the north. What is the direction of the electric force on the proton as it enters the field?
   A. north
   B. south
   C. east
   D. up, away from the center of Earth
   E. down, toward the center of Earth

3.

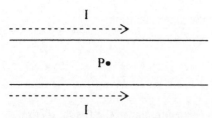

A current is flowing to the right in the above wire, as indicated. What is the direction of the magnetic field at point P due to the current in the wire?

A. to the right
B. to the left
C. into the page
D. out of the page
E. no magnetic field due to the current

$$I$$
$$---------------->$$

P•

$$---------------->$$
$$I$$

4. Refer to the situation in Problem 3. A second wire is added, at the same distance below point P as the first wire is above point P, with the same current in the same direction (to the right), as indicated above. How does the total magnetic field due to the two wires compare to that in Problem 3?

A. It is in the same direction, with the same value as before.
B. It is in the same direction, with twice the value as before.
C. It is now equal to zero.
D. It is in the same direction, with half the value as before.
E. It is in the same direction, with one-fourth the value as before.

5. A current of 0.2 A flows through a magnetic field of strength 100 T, with one meter of the wire enclosed by the field. What is the magnetic force on the wire?

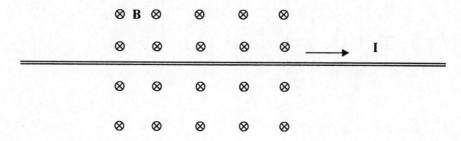

A. 20 N to the left
B. 20 N to the right
C. 20 N toward the top of the page
D. 20 N toward the bottom of the page
E. zero

Sample Problems

1. An electron moving with velocity $v = 2 \times 10^6$ m/s moves into a uniform magnetic field directed out of the page of strength $\mathbf{B} = 30$ T as shown below.

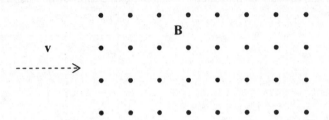

(a) Determine the direction of the force on the electron as it enters the magnetic field.

(b) Determine the magnitude of the force on the electron as it enters the magnetic field.

(c) Describe the subsequent motion of the electron.

(d) Calculate the radius of the electron's orbit in the field.

(e) Suppose the electron had entered the field at an angle other than perpendicular to the field direction. Describe its subsequent motion.

2. An electron is shot between two parallel charged plates at 2×10^6 m/s, as shown. The electron moves a vertical distance of 0.618 cm in the field as it traverses a horizontal distance of 2.25 cm. Neglect fringing effects and gravitation.

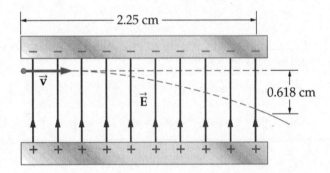

(a) What is the strength of the electric field?

(b) Suppose we want to set up a magnetic field in the same region so that the electron travels horizontally between the plates without any "vertical drop," as shown. Determine the strength and direction of the magnetic field.

SOLUTIONS TO SAMPLE QUESTIONS AND SAMPLE PROBLEMS

Multiple Choice Questions:

1. E Using the right-hand rule, with index finger pointing west and extended fingers to the north, the extended thumb (force) points down.

2. A The electric force on a positive charge is in the same direction as the electric field: $F = qE$

3. C Using the right-hand rule with thumb in direction of current and curled fingers indicating direction of magnetic field. As it curls around the wire, the field goes into the page at P.

4. C The two field vectors are of the same magnitude but opposite direction—one into the page and one out of the page, so the vectors will cancel at point P.

5. C The magnitude of the force must be 20 N, since that is the only magnitude provided:

$$F_B = BIl = (100\ T)(0.2\ A)(1\ m) = 20\ N$$

The direction is determined with the right-hand rule—index finger in direction of current flow, extended fingers in direction of magnetic field (into the page), and extended thumb the direction of force. The force is up on the page, in the plane of the page.

Free Response Problems:

1. (a) Use the right-hand rule for the force on a charge moving through a magnetic field, $F = q\ vxB$. The index finger is direction of velocity, extended fingers are direction of magnetic field, and extended thumb is direction of force. Thus, the force is directed **upward** on the page, in the plane of the page. [Note: The direction of the force must be switched for a negative particle—or use the left hand.]

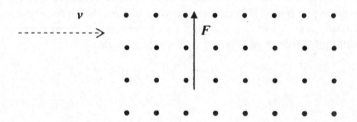

(b) The magnitude of the force can be calculated:

$$F = qvB = (1.6 \times 10^{-19})(2 \times 10^6\ m/s)(30\ T) = 9.6 \times 10^{-12}\ N$$

(c) As the magnetic force acts on the charge, the direction of the velocity changes—and so does the direction of the force (the magnetic force is always perpendicular to the velocity). The electron subsequently moves in a **circle** in the plane of the page, with the magnetic force providing the centripetal force. If, however, the charge's velocity is large enough, it will move in an arc and then exit the field, moving in a tangential linear path as it leaves the field.

(d) The magnetic force provides the centripetal force:

$$F_B = F_C$$

$$qvB = \frac{mv^2}{r}$$

$$r = \frac{mv}{qB} = \frac{(9.11 \times 10^{-31} \text{ kg})(2 \times 10^6 \text{ m/s})}{(1.6 \times 10^{-19} \text{ C})(30 \text{ T})} = 3.8 \times 10^{-7} m$$

(e) If the electron enters the field at an angle other than strictly perpendicular to the field, the velocity component perpendicular to the field will produce a force causing a circular motion. Though the velocity component parallel or antiparallel to the field lines produces no force, it does keep the electron in its inertial motion in that direction, expanding the circular motion to a **helical** motion.

2. (a) The electric force produces acceleration on the particle in one direction only (vertical on the page) as the particle moves in constant velocity in the other direction (horizontal on the page). This defines a parabola, so we can use the same equations used earlier for projectile motion:

horizontal motion: $s_x = v_{ox}t$

$$0.0225 \text{ m} = (2 \times 10^6 \text{ m/s})(t)$$

$$t = 1.13 \times 10^{-8} s$$

vertical motion: $s_y = v_{oy}t + \frac{1}{2}at^2 = 0 + \frac{1}{2}\left(\frac{qE}{m}\right)t^2$ [Note: Combine $F = ma$ and $F = qE$]

$$0.0618 \text{ m} = 0 + (\tfrac{1}{2}) \frac{(1.6 \times 10^{-19} \text{ C}) E}{9.11 \times 10^{-31} \text{ kg}} (1.13 \times 10^{-8} s)^2$$

$$E = 5500 \text{ V/m or N/C}$$

(b) By the vector equation $F = qE$, the electric force is the opposite direction from the electric field if the particle is negative. Thus, the electric force on the electron is down on the page. To balance this force, resulting in no net force on the electron, a magnetic force of equal magnitude needs to be added that acts on the electron upward on the page. Using the right-hand rule, a force upward on the page (extended thumb) and velocity to the right on the page (extended forefinger) would require a magnetic field into the page. However, this is a negative particle, so the field must be reversed—and is thus **out of the page.** [Note: Not everyone agrees, but I encourage my students to use the left hand for negative particles—which works—and avoids that inevitable problem of forgetting to take the opposite of your right hand rule answer when the particle is negative.]

To calculate the magnitude of **B:**

$$|F_B| = |F_E|$$

$$qvB = qE$$

$$B = \frac{E}{v} = \frac{5500 \text{ N/C}}{2 \times 10^6 \text{ m/s}} = 2.8 \times 10^{-3} \text{ T}$$

▶ **Recommended for further practice (Walker, 3rd ed.):**
  - Conceptual Checkpoint 22-2 on page 738
  - Example 22-5, torque on a coil
  - Chapter Summary on pages 757–760 (equations up to section 22-4 and measuring field around a current-carrying wire
  - Chapter Problems on pages 762–767: 3, 11, 13, 19, 23, 29, 43, 45, 47, 65, 67

√ **Reminders:**
- A stationary charged particle in an electric field will experience a force, but a charged particle in a magnetic field must be moving to experience a force.
- For positive particles, the electric force is in the same direction as the electric field.
- Use the right-hand rule to determine the magnetic force on a charged particle in a magnetic field— reversing your answer if the particle is negative—or using the left hand for negative particles.
- Charged particles moving in the same or opposite direction as magnetic field lines will experience no magnetic force.
- The magnetic force does no work on charged particles.

Chapter 23
Magnetic Flux and Faraday's Law of Induction

Equations

Magnetic flux: $\Phi = \mathbf{B} \cdot \mathbf{A} = BA\cos\theta$

Induced EMF: $\varepsilon_{ave} = -\dfrac{\Delta\Phi}{\Delta t}$

Induced EMF: $\varepsilon = Blv$

Magnetic flux, Φ, describes the number of magnetic field lines that pass through a given area. It is the scalar or dot product of magnetic field, **B**, and area, **A**, and is measured in webers (Wb) if the field is in teslas and the area is in square meters:

$$\Phi = \mathbf{B} \cdot \mathbf{A} = BA\cos\theta$$

(a)

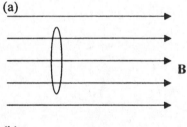

In case (a), the loop of area A is aligned so the plane of the loop is perpendicular to the magnetic field **B**, so the flux is maximum:

$$\Phi = BA$$

(b)

In case (b), the loop of area A is aligned so the plane of the loop is parallel to the magnetic field lines, so none of the field passes through the plane of the loop. Thus, the flux is zero.

In case (c), the loop is aligned at an angle θ, so $B\cos\theta$ is the component of the field that passes through the loop:

$$\Phi = BA\cos\theta$$

(c)

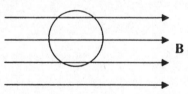

Magnetic flux through a loop of area A, then, is the product of magnetic field and area, times the cosine of the angle between the field lines and a normal to the plane of the loop.

It is particularly useful, once magnetic flux is determined, to examine changes in magnetic flux. It is these changes in flux, $\Delta\Phi$, that will produce effects on materials that conduct electrical current and on other magnetic fields.

Previously, we have examined the Oersted Effect, i.e., that current-carrying wires generate magnetic fields around them. **Faraday's Law of Induction** states that changes in magnetic flux can induce an electric field, causing charges to flow. The rate of change of flux will determine the size of emf induced and thus the amount of current that flows:

$$\varepsilon_{ave} = -\frac{\Delta\Phi}{\Delta t}$$

The emf, ε (volts), is proportional to the rate of change of flux, $\frac{\Delta\Phi}{\Delta t}$. The negative sign indicates that the induced emf will be in a direction that opposed the change in flux. [Note: This is another of nature's ways of assuring that changes in motion don't accelerate things to infinity. Friction is also an example; i.e., the friction force opposes the direction of motion of an object or direction of attempted motion.]

In case (a) below, the magnet has magnetic lines radiating outward from the north pole. As the magnet is moved to the right through a conducting metal loop, the magnetic flux increases in the loop as the magnet passes through the loop. An emf will be induced in the loop such that the current produces a magnetic field that opposes the increasing magnetic flux from the magnet. Use the right-hand rule (fingers curled in direction of current and thumb pointing direction of magnetic field) to assure yourself that the magnetic field created in the loop is in the opposite direction of the magnet's increasing field, therefore decreasing the total flux. In case (b), the magnet is moved away from the loop, which decreases the magnetic flux through the loop. The current in the loop will reverse direction, creating a magnetic field to the right. **Lenz's Law** states that current will be induced in such a direction to oppose the change that produced it.

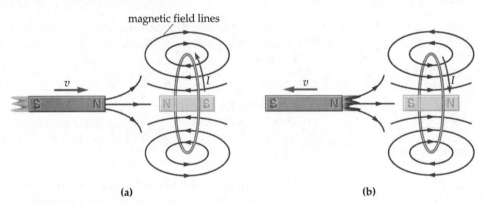

(a)   (b)

The faster these changes are made, the larger the emf and currents induced. If the motion of the magnet above is alternated to the left and to the right at regular intervals, a current will be induced in the loop that also alternates. The emf alternates in strength and direction, and so does the current.

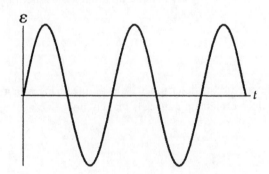

Another way to induce a current in a wire loop is to move the loop in a magnetic field instead of moving the magnetic field inside the loop. In the diagram below, a loop of wire is rotated in a magnetic field so that the magnetic flux through the loop changes as the angle of the loop with the field changes. This change in magnetic flux induces an emf in the loop, causing a current to flow. In this case, the loop makes a complete circuit with a light bulb, so the bulb lights—brighter when the current is maximum and dimmer when the current is minimum. Turned fast enough, you might not notice the flickering of the bulb—which is what we see every day in our homes when we plug a lamp into an alternating current (AC) outlet. [Alternating circuits are not tested on the AP* Exam, but a basic idea is helpful. Some discussion is provided in Chapter 24.] What we see operating here—a mechanical input and electrical output—is an electric **generator**. A similar device that operates on the same principle is the **electric motor**, which converts electrical energy input to mechanical energy output.

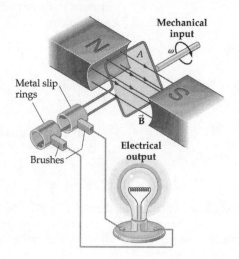

In the situation above, the mechanical work input should equal the electrical energy output—and total energy is conserved. In the following example, we can see how mechanical work is required to produce electrical energy.

A metal rod, below, is attached to a loop of wire. A force, F, pulls the rod into a magnetic field directed into the page. As the rod is pulled into the field, a current is induced in the rod-wire loop circuit. As the rod is pulled into the magnetic field, the magnetic flux is <u>increasing into the page</u> as more of the field appears in the loop. By Lenz's Law, a current will flow in the loop to oppose this change. Thus, the current will flow in a direction that creates an <u>increasing magnetic field out of the page</u> inside the loop to oppose the change in flux. Using the right-hand rule, curling the fingers in direction of current flow, the extended thumb must point out of the page, so the current is induced counter-clockwise in the loop.

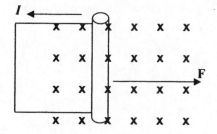

The work done by the force, F, in moving the bar is equal to the electrical energy produced in the circuit—i.e., energy must be conserved. Another way to think of this is in terms of power. If we know the velocity the bar is moving, the product of force and velocity is input power:

$$P = Fv$$

The output power is electrical:

$$P = VI \ \text{ or } P = \varepsilon I$$

To keep the rod moving at constant velocity, the pulling force, **F**, must be equal in magnitude to the magnetic force induced in the loop—which is in the opposite direction.

The emf induced in each portion of the loop on the previous page is proportional to the strength of the magnetic field, the length of loop in the field, and the velocity:

$$\mathcal{E} = Blv$$

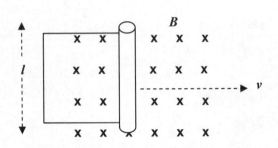

Here's an alternate way to find direction of current in the loop: The only net force is on charges in the rod, with each positive charge in the rod experiencing a force as the rod moves to the right:

$$F = qv\times B$$

This creates a force upward on positive charges in the rod, starting a current flow counter-clockwise.

There are lengths of wire in the field at the top and bottom of the loop, but the forces set up in these two segments will be equal and opposite—effectively canceling.

When the entire loop is immersed in the magnetic field, there is no net force on the loop—and no current in the loop. As the loop moves within the field, there is no change in the flux in the loop, so induced EMF is zero. Current would be induced again as the loop exits the field—in the opposite direction. Sample Problem 1, below, will provide further practice with this.

Sample Questions

1. A 10 cm diameter circular loop of conducting metal is immersed in a uniform magnetic field of strength 2×10^{-5} T, with the plane of the loop perpendicular to the direction of field lines. What is the magnetic flux through the loop?
    A. 0
    B. $2.5\pi \times 10^{-5}$ Wb
    C. $5\pi \times 10^{-8}$ Wb
    D. $\pi \times 10^{-5}$ Wb
    E. $2\pi \times 10^{-1}$ Wb

2. The loop above is held stationary in the magnetic field. What is the emf induced in the loop?
    A. 0
    B. $0.25\pi \times 10^{-5}$ V
    C. $0.5\pi \times 10^{-5}$ V
    D. $\pi \times 10^{-5}$ V
    E. $2\pi \times 10^{-5}$ V

3. "An induced current always flows in a direction that opposes the change that caused it." is a statement of:
   A. Oersted's Law
   B. Faraday's Law
   C. Gauss's Law
   D. Lenz's Law
   E. Ampere's Law

Questions 4-5. The magnetic flux in a coil is changed from 0.4 Wb to 0.2 Wb in one second.

4. What is the emf induced in the coil?
   A. zero
   B. 0.2 V
   C. 0.4 V
   D. 0.6 V
   E. 2.0 V

5. The magnetic flux in the coil is changed from 0.2 Wb to 0.4 Wb in the next second. What is the difference in what happens in the coil in this case?
   A. There is no difference.
   B. The emf is doubled.
   C. The current is doubled.
   D. The current in the coil switches direction.
   E. The current is half is great.

Sample Problems

1.
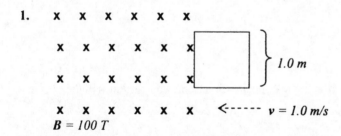
$B = 100\ T$

The square loop of conducting wire shown above measures 1.0 m on a side and is moving at a constant velocity of 1.0 m/s to the left. At $t = 0$, the left edge of the square just begins to enter the uniform magnetic field, which has a field strength of 100 T. The field is 1.5 meters wide.

    (a) What is the magnitude of the emf induced in the wire loop at $t = 0.5$ s?

    (b) What is the emf induced in the wire loop at $t = 1.0$ s?

    (c) If the loop has a resistance of 200 Ω, determine the magnitude and direction of current in the loop at $t = 0.5$ s.

    (d) Determine the magnitude and direction of current in the loop at $t = 2.0$ s.

2.

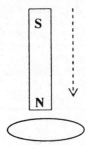

A magnet is dropped from a height of 2.0 m above a metal ring. As the magnet passes through the center of the ring, it is aligned with the north pole of the magnet downward. The magnet has a magnetic field strength of 100 T at its poles, and the diameter of the ring is 10 cm. The resistance of the ring is 100 Ω.

(a) What is the maximum emf induced in the ring?

(b) What is the maximum current induced in the right?

(c) What is the direction of current induced in the ring? (Looking down at the ring from above.)

SOLUTIONS TO SAMPLE QUESTIONS AND SAMPLE PROBLEMS

Multiple Choice Questions:

1. C Since the plane of the loop is perpendicular to field lines, the flux is maximum:

$$\Phi = BA = B(\pi r^2) = (2 \times 10^{-5}\ T)\pi(5 \times 10^{-2}\ m)^2 = 50\pi \times 10^{-9} = 5\pi \times 10^{-10}\ Wb$$

2. A No emf is induced unless the flux is changing.

3. D Though the discoveries of Oersted, Ampere, and Faraday are related, this is a statement of Lenz's Law.

4. B $\varepsilon_{ave} = \dfrac{\Delta\Phi}{\Delta t} = \dfrac{0.4\ T - 0.2\ T}{1\ s} = 0.2\ V$

5. D The change in flux is opposite, so the induced emf is in the opposite direction. The current will then be induced in the opposite direction.

Free Response Problems:

1. (a) Use the equation $\varepsilon = Blv$ for the length of wire that is in the field. After 0.5 seconds, the loop has moved 0.5 meter, so half the loop is in the field as the loop moves to the left at that instant. The only emf induced is in the section of the loop on the left, since emf induced in the upper and lower sections of the loop in the field would be equal and opposite each other and would cancel. Calculate the emf:

$$\varepsilon = (100\ T)(1.0\ m)(1.0\ m/s) = 100\ V$$

(b) After 1.0 second, the loop has moved 1.0 meter, so the loop has completely entered the field and no part of it has yet left the field. However, due to the symmetry of the square loop, emf induced in opposite side of the loop cancels, so there is no emf induced in the loop while it is positioned entirely within the magnetic field. Another way of seeing this is that since the loop is completely immersed in the field, the flux through the loop does not change as the loop moves, and therefore induced emf is zero.

(c) At 0.5 seconds, we use the emf calculated in part (a) and Ohm's Law:

$$I = \frac{\varepsilon}{R} = \frac{100\,V}{200\,\Omega} = 0.5\,A$$

To determine direction, use the right-hand rule for $v \times B$, with v to the left on the page and B into the page. The charge in the wire will experience a force downward on the page, resulting in a **counter-clockwise** current in the loop.

(d) After 2.0 seconds, the loop has moved 2.0 meters from its original position, leaving only the right side of the loop in the field. The emf induced has the same magnitude as in part (a) and the current has the same magnitude as in part (b). However, calculating the direction of current as in part (c) results in a current in the opposite direction, since a force downward on the page in the right side of the loop would result in a **clockwise 0.5 A** current in the loop.

2. (a) The flux is induced as the magnet falls to the ring. The time for the flux change is the time it takes the magnet to fall the 2.0 meter distance:

$$s = v_0 t + \tfrac{1}{2}\,at^2$$
$$2\,m = 0 + \tfrac{1}{2}\,(9.8\,m/s^2)(t^2)$$
$$t = 0.64\,s$$

The flux goes from zero to a flux of BA: $\Phi = (100\,T)(\pi)(0.05\,m)^2 = 0.79\,Wb$

Now calculate the emf: $\varepsilon_{ave} = \dfrac{\Delta\Phi}{\Delta t} = \dfrac{0.79\,Wb}{0.64\,s} = 1.23\,V$

(b) Use Ohm's Law to find the current: $V = IR$
$$1.23\,V = (I)(100\,\Omega)$$
$$I = 0.012\,A$$

(c) The induced current will be counterclockwise, looking down on the ring. As the north pole of the magnet approaches, it increased the flux downward in the ring. The current will be induced in a direction to produce an increased magnetic field upward. By the right-hand rule, curling the fingers in the direction of current, the extended thumb points upward, in the direction of the increased field.

▶ **Recommended for further practice (Walker, 3rd ed.):**
 • Figure 23-3 and Example 23-1 on magnetic flux, pages 770–771
 • Omit inductance and sections 23-7, 23-8, and 23-9
 • Chapter Summary on pages 793–795, sections 1-6 only
 • Chapter Problems on pages 797–802: 3, 11, 13, 15, 19, 21, 25, 31, 79

√ **Reminders:**
 • Review the right-hand rules:
  (a) If curled fingers are direction of current, extended thumb is direction of magnetic field.
  (b) If thumb is direction of current in a wire, curled fingers are direction of magnetic field.
  (c) If index finger points direction of positive charge movement, extended fingers are magnetic field direction, and extended thumb is direction of force.
 • Remember that direction of conventional current is same as direction of positive charge flow.
 • No emf or current are induced if magnetic flux is unchanging.

Chapter 24

Alternating Current Circuits

Equations

Magnetic flux: $\Phi = \boldsymbol{B} \cdot \boldsymbol{A} = BA\cos\theta$

Induced emf: $\varepsilon_{ave} = -\dfrac{\Delta\Phi}{\Delta t}$

Induced emf: $\varepsilon = Blv$

Power: $P = VI = I^2R$

Alternating current circuits are not included on the AP* Physics B Exam, but it is helpful and interesting for students to know why alternating circuits are used in our homes. The idea of electromagnetic induction has already been presented in Chapter 23, so students should have an understanding of flux and induced emf as a function of change in flux. It's not difficult, then, to understand that a coil of wire turning in a magnetic field would have a changing flux, depending upon the alignment of the face of the coil with the field direction:

$$\Phi = \boldsymbol{B} \cdot \boldsymbol{A} = BA\cos\theta$$

The coil turning in a magnetic field then also has an induced emf or voltage in it that is a sinusoidal function, as shown below. This is the basis for understanding of how alternating current can be produced on a very large scale by the relative movements of coils of wire and magnetic fields in electrical power plants.

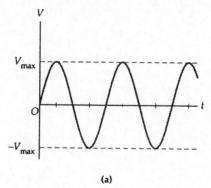

(a)

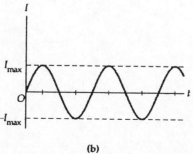

(b)

In transmitting this power long distances from power plants to residences, heat is lost if the power is transmitted as high current:

$$P = VI = I^2 R$$

Thus, it seems a good idea to transmit the power as low current and high voltage. This is where the idea of a **transformer** comes in. A transformer is basically two sets of adjacent coils of wire. When an alternating current as seen above is set up in one set of coils, the variable magnetic field produced by that coil produces a change in flux in the second coil and thus induces an alternating current in that coil. The ratio of numbers of loops of wire in each coil is equal to the ratio of voltages in the two coils. Since the power in equals the power out (assuming some loss as heat in the process):

$$P_{in} = P_{out}$$
$$V_{in} I_{in} = V_{out} I_{out}$$

At the power station end, the transformer is a **step up** transformer, i.e., one with more coils on the outgoing end. The electricity leaves the power station at high voltage and low current, reducing heat loss ($P = I^2 R$). At the consumer end, another transformer is a **step down**, transforming the electricity from high voltage to low voltage and thus low current to high current to meet the needs for the consumer. An examination of small wall outlet transformers supplied with many electronic devices reveals many wraps of wire at the plug end and few wraps of wire at the end connecting to the device, i.e., a step down transformer.

Walker's text has more on this topic in Chapter 23 (page 790), which, again, is not within the scope of the AP* Physics B curriculum but is interesting to know.

PART 4

LIGHT AND OPTICS

Chapter 25

Electromagnetic Waves

Equations

Speed of light in a vacuum: $c = f\lambda$

Momentum of light: $p = \dfrac{E}{c}$

Electromagnetic radiation is the transfer of energy through space by means of electric and magnetic field oscillations, or waves. The electric and magnetic fields are perpendicular to each other and to the direction of propagation of the waves. Using the right hand rule, the vector cross product **ExB** give the direction the wave travels. Electromagnetic waves are produced by accelerating charges, but the specifics of this are outside the realm of the AP* Examination. An interesting example of this, however, is the change in velocity of charged particles as they enter Earth's atmosphere and are accelerated toward the poles. The accelerations of the particles causes them to give off electromagnetic radiation—most notably the visible light patterns of the aurorae.

Electromagnetic radiation—often called generically "light" by physicists—travels through a vacuum at a speed of 3×10^8 m/s. This speed is given its own symbol, c, called "the speed of light." All forms of electromagnetic radiation—called the **electromagnetic spectrum**—travel at this speed through space. The various ranges within the spectrum have common properties and are distinguished only by their differences in frequency and wavelength, which are inversely proportional to each other:

$$c = f\lambda$$

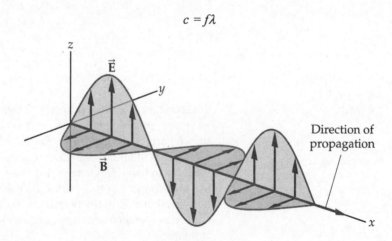

The electromagnetic spectrum includes a range of frequencies from zero to infinity. We are only able to perceive visually, however, a very small range of frequencies called **visible light**. We see these frequencies—in the range of about 4.3×10^{14} Hz (700 nm at the red end of the spectrum) to 7.5×10^{14} Hz (400 nm at the violet end of the spectrum)—as colors on the visible spectrum. In order, from lowest frequency (longest wavelength) to highest frequency (shortest wavelength), they are: red, orange, yellow, green, blue, and violet. The **energy** of light is proportional to its frequency.

The Electromagnetic Spectrum

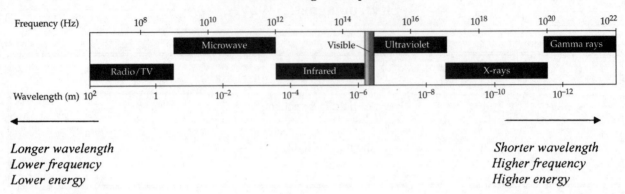

Longer wavelength
Lower frequency
Lower energy

Shorter wavelength
Higher frequency
Higher energy

What we perceive as **white light** is actually a mixture of all visible frequencies. Black is the absence of visible frequencies, so a truly black object would not be visible to us. Other colors are mixtures of the **primary colors** of light—red, blue, and green. (Do not confuse these with the primary colors of pigment—not the same.) When red and blue light are mixed in the right proportions, we see magenta. Blue and green form cyan, and the mixture of red and green light produces yellow.

The **intensity** of electromagnetic radiation decreases as the inverse square of the distance from the source. Light also undergoes a **Doppler shift** similar to that for sound, i.e., a light source moving away from the observer appears to have a longer wavelength. Since red light is at the long wavelength end of the visible spectrum, an object moving away is said to be undergoing a **red shift.** A **blue shift**, then, would be a shift to the shorter wavelength end of the spectrum as an object moves closer.

Light has **momentum** (discussed further in Chapter 30), which is the ratio of its energy to the speed of light:

$$p = \frac{E}{c}$$

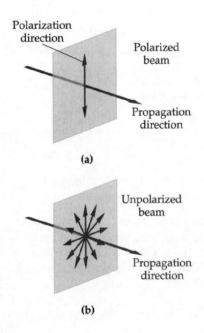

(a)

(b)

Polarization is a wave property of light that occurs when the electric field is restricted to one plane, as shown here. Polarizing film, for example, eliminates oscillations in all but one plane, cutting the light intensity in half. A polarizer only transmits light that has a component of the electric field aligned with the transmission axis of the polarizer. Two polarizers aligned perpendicular to each other would block light completely.

Reflection from some surfaces and scattering in the atmosphere are other methods by which light can be polarized.

Sample Questions

1. Ultraviolet light with a wavelength of 150 nm has what frequency?
    A. 2.0×10^{14} Hz
    B. 3.0×10^{14} Hz
    C. 1.0×10^{15} Hz
    D. 2.0×10^{15} Hz
    E. 3.0×10^{15} Hz

2. The distance to the Moon from Earth is about 4×10^8 meters. About how long would it take a laser light beam from Earth to travel to the Moon and back?
    A. 6 minutes
    B. 3 minutes
    C. 1 minute
    D. 30 seconds
    E. 3 seconds

3. Which of the following are properties of both electromagnetic waves and sound waves?
    I. They can be polarized.
    II. They transmit energy
    III. They can travel through a vacuum.
    A. **I** only
    B. **II** only
    C. **I** and **II** only
    D. **II** and **III** only
    E. **I, II,** and **III**

4. What is the wavelength and type of light emitted from the stimulated emission of a helium-neon gas mixture of frequency 4.75×10^{14} Hz?
    A. 630 nm, red
    B. 630 nm, green
    C. 500 nm, red
    D. 500 nm, green
    E. 500 nm, yellow

5. Which of the following ranks the electromagnetic radiations from lower frequency to higher frequency?
    A. red, infrared, radio
    B. blue, red, ultraviolet
    C. red, yellow, gamma
    D. blue, red, infrared
    E. radio, blue, infrared

SOLUTIONS TO SAMPLE QUESTIONS AND SAMPLE PROBLEMS

Multiple Choice Questions:

1. **D** $\quad f = \dfrac{c}{\lambda} = \dfrac{3 \times 10^8 \ m/s}{150 \times 10^{-9} \ m} = 2 \times 10^{15} \ Hz$

2. **E** The total distance to the Moon and back is 8×10^8 meters. At the speed of light, the time required is:

$$t = \frac{d}{v} = \frac{8 \times 10^8 \ m}{3 \times 10^8 \ m/s} = 2.7 \ seconds$$

3. **C** All waves transmit energy. Electromagnetic waves can be polarized, due to interactions of electric fields. Sound waves travel through matter and can neither be polarized nor travel through a vacuum.

4. **A** Laser light is produced in just such a way: "light amplification by the stimulated emission of radiation." The helium-neon laser's wavelength (which is red, incidentally), is:

$$\lambda = \frac{c}{f} = \frac{3 \times 10^8 \ m/s}{4.75 \times 10^{14} \ Hz} = about \ 0.6 \times 10^{-6} \ or \ 600 \times 10^{-9} \ m$$

This is a situation where a quick examination of the answer choices saves time in the calculation and allows an estimate to determine the answer. Once we see an answer in the 600-nm range, we recognize that as the long wavelength end of the visible range, or red.

5. **C** Yellow light is of higher frequency than red light, and gamma is the highest frequency on the scale.

▶ **Recommended for further practice (Walker, 3rd ed.):**
- Introduction in Section 25-1 on how EM waves are produced is optional.
- Spectra (in color) on page 846
- Chapter Summary on pages 860–862 (omit equations exception Section 25-3)
- Chapter Problems on pages 864–869: 1, 25, 29, 75

√ **Reminders:**
- Physicists use light as a general term referring to the entire range of the electromagnetic spectrum.
- Visible light is only a small portion of the electromagnetic spectrum, from about 400 nm (red) to 700 nm (violet).
- The speed of light, $c = 3 \times 10^8 \ m/s$, is a value you should remember.
- Wavelengths for light are commonly given in nanometers (nm), or 10^{-9} meter.

Chapter 26

Geometrical Optics

Equations

Speed of light in vacuum: $c = f\lambda$

Index of refraction: $n = \dfrac{c}{v}$

Snell's Law of refraction: $n_1 \sin\theta_1 = n_2 \sin\theta_2$

Critical angle: $\sin\theta_c = \dfrac{n_2}{n_1}$

Thin lens equation: $\dfrac{1}{f} = \dfrac{1}{s_i} + \dfrac{1}{s_o}$

Magnification: $M = \dfrac{h_i}{h_o} = -\dfrac{s_i}{s_o}$

Focal length and radius of curvature: $f = \dfrac{R}{2}$

Light travels at 3×10^8 m/s in a vacuum, but when it enters a medium, such as air, glass, or water, it slows down. The amount its speed is reduced is dependent on the **index of refraction** (n) of the material, which is the ratio of the speed of light in a vacuum to the speed in that material:

$$n = \frac{c}{v}$$

Since $c = f\lambda$, the speed alone cannot change. Frequency does not change—it defines the type of light—so when the speed is reduced, so is the wavelength.

When light strikes a surface, it may **reflect** or **refract** or both. The **Law of Reflection** says that when light reflects from a surface, the angle of incidence is equal to the angle of reflection, with both angles measured with the normal to the surface. To represent this, we draw a **ray diagram.**

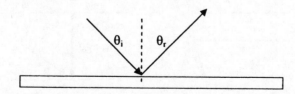

Ray diagrams are useful in analyzing light and optical systems. Here are some basic conventions used in making ray diagrams:

1. First, construct a **normal** line to the surface at the point the light makes contact.

2. Arrows are drawn to show the direction the wave front is traveling.
3. Measure all angles relative to the normal line—not to the surface.

A flat mirror, or **plane mirror**, reflects light from an object to create an image, according to the Law of Reflection. When light from the object strikes the mirror, it reflects back to the observer—but the light appears to have come from an object behind the mirror.

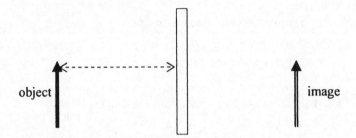

Some basic rules regarding reflection from a plane mirror:
1. The **image**, which is perceived by the observer, appears to be located at the same distance behind the mirror as the **object** is in front of the mirror.
2. The image is upright, or in the same orientation as the object, which means that it is **virtual.**
3. The image appears to be the same size as the object.

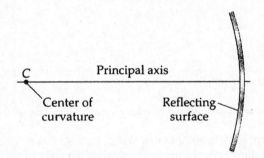

A **concave** mirror has the reflective side curved inward, so that light rays from a distance object are **converged**, or reflected to a single point, called the **focal point**. For a curved circular mirror, the **focal length** is one-half the **radius of curvature** of the mirror. For construction purposes, we will also use the **principal axis**, which is actually a radius line from the center of curvature to the center of the lens.

Now, set the focal point halfway between the center of curvature and the lens. Position the object on the principal axis. It helps to position the bottom of the object on the principal axis, because rays traveling along the principal axis will hit the center of the mirror—along the normal—and reflect straight back. So we know the bottom of the image will be somewhere along the principal axis. All we have to do now is locate the top of the image

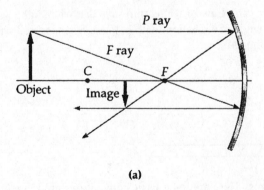

(a)

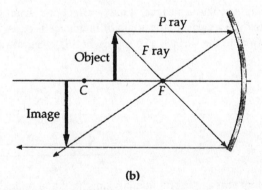

(b)

We will examine two cases for the concave mirror: (a) object located outside the radius of curvature, and (b) object located between the focal point and radius of curvature. As we'll see by following the rules below, a **real image** is produced in both cases, since the reflected rays intersect.

To draw the rays for the situation on the previous page, use the following simple steps (that will hold for many other cases—not just this one):

1. Draw the principal axis, from center of curvature to center of mirror (or lens).
2. Set the focal point.
3. Position the object on the principal axis. Since rays from a point on the axis will always reflect along the principal axis, the bottom of the object is already defined.
4. Draw a ray from the top of the object through the focal point to the mirror or lens. It will reflect or refract parallel to the principal axis.
5. Draw a ray from the top of the object, parallel to the principal axis. It will reflect (or refract) through the focal point.
6. These two rays should be enough to find the position of the object, but a third ray from the top of the object to the center of the mirror or lens will reflect forming equal angles with the principal axis. This third ray should meet the other two where the top of the object is located. If the rays meet, the image is a **real** image It could be projected on a screen, since light rays actually converge at that point.
7. At the point of intersection, draw the object from the principal axis.
8. If the rays do not converge, do what your eye and brain would do—extrapolate the rays to a virtual point and construct the **virtual** image. [It's recommended to draw these extrapolated rays with dashed lines, for clarity.] A virtual image cannot be projected on a screen.

The **mirror equation** can be used to calculate the position, orientation, and magnification of images, where f is the focal length, d_o or s_o is the distance of the object from the mirror, and d_i or s_i the distance of the image from the mirror

$$\frac{1}{f} = \frac{1}{s_i} + \frac{1}{s_o}$$

When using this formula with mirrors:

- The focal length is positive for concave mirrors (which converge light rays).
- The focal length is negative for convex mirrors (which do not converge light).
- A positive d_i means the image forms on the same side of the mirror as the object, so it is a real image.
- A negative d_i means a virtual image appears behind the mirror.
- Real images are inverted with respect to the object.
- Virtual images appear upright with respect to the object.
- The negative ratio of image distance to object distance, which is also the ratio of image height to object height, is the **magnification**: $M = \dfrac{h_i}{h_o} = -\dfrac{s_i}{s_o}$
- Negative magnification means the image is inverted and real.
- Positive magnification means the image is upright and virtual.

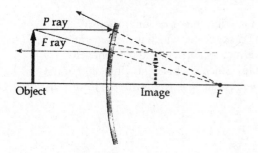

In this case, the reflected mirror surface is **convex**. Convex mirrors have a virtual focal point, since it is located behind the mirror—where light cannot actually travel. Two sets of rays are drawn here: (1) A ray parallel to the principal axis that reflects as if it came from the focal point. (2) A ray headed toward the focal point that reflects parallel to the principal axis. These reflected rays diverge, so we must construct the virtual image by extrapolating the rays backward, behind the mirror.

In summary, convex mirrors always form virtual images. Concave mirrors form virtual images when the object is inside the focal point and real images when the object is outside the focal point.

A mirror exhibits **specular reflection**, meaning the reflected rays are organized to form an image. Many objects are visible due to the light they reflect, but they do not form images. The reflected rays are sent off in varying angles, called **diffuse** reflection.

The **Law of Refraction**, or **Snell's Law**, says that the angles of incidence and refraction depend on the index of refraction:

$$n_1 \sin\theta_1 = n_2 \sin\theta_2$$

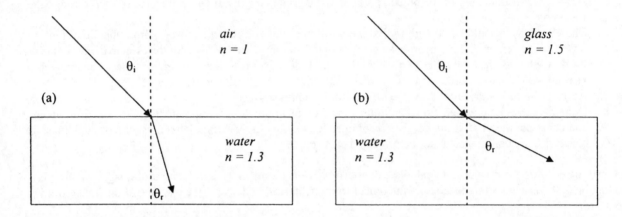

[Note: The index of refraction of air is 1.003. Considering significant figures, it's reasonable to use n = 1 for air.]

In diagram (a) above, the ray enters the glass at angle of incidence θ_1. Since the ray enters from air to glass (with a higher incidence of refraction), the angle of refraction is smaller, i.e., the ray refracts <u>toward the normal</u>. In diagram (b), the light is refracting from a medium with higher index of refraction to one with lower index of refraction, so the angle of refraction is larger than the angle of incidence, i.e, the ray refracts <u>away from the normal</u>. If the light enters at an angle of incidence along the normal, it will stay along the normal.

Upon refraction, light will change wavelength and speed—but <u>frequency does not change</u>. As mentioned previously, the index of refraction of the medium is an indication of the light speed in that material. Since frequency does not change, the wavelength must change in the same ratio:

$$n = \frac{c}{v} = \frac{\lambda_{vacuum}}{\lambda_{medium}}$$

The index of refraction is actually not a constant value for a particular material. It varies somewhat with the frequency of light—higher index for higher frequencies. This produces **dispersion,** which is the separation of white light into its component frequencies (or colors), since light will refract at a different angle for each frequency. A prism separates white light into colors, using this principle. Since the blue and violet end of the visible spectrum has highest frequency, these colors will refract at the largest angles. Red, with the lowest visible frequency, will refract least.

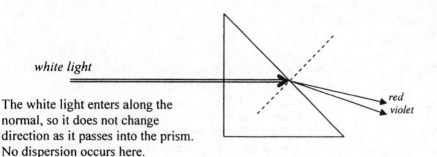

white light

The white light enters along the normal, so it does not change direction as it passes into the prism. No dispersion occurs here.

As the white light strikes this prism face at an angle to the normal, dispersion occurs. The violet end of the spectrum refracts at the largest angle, and red refracts least. The other colors appear in order in between.

[Note: Light entering an interface along a normal does not change frequency or direction, but it does change speed and wavelength.]

An interesting special case occurs when light enters a semicircular prism at the center of the flat side. Since any path the light ray takes through the prism is along a radius, as the ray emerges from the prism, it is along a normal on the curved side—and does not change direction.

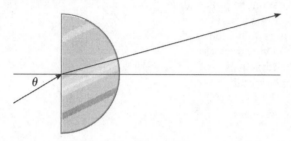

Another special case of refraction occurs when light goes from a medium of higher index of refraction (1) to a medium of lower index of refraction (2). When the light strikes the interface between the two media, both reflection and refraction occur. As the angle of incidence increases (diagram b), more of the light reflects and less refracts out of the medium. As the angle of incidence is increased, the angle of refraction (which is always larger than the angle of incidence) increases also. Then, at a special angle (diagram c), called the **critical angle**, the angle of refraction is 90°. At this angle, none of the light is refracted into the second medium. If the angle of incidence is increased further (diagram d), all of the light is reflected back into the first medium. This is **total internal reflection**, which only occurs inside a medium of higher index of refraction than the medium outside.

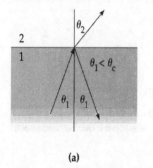 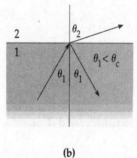 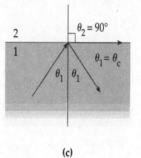 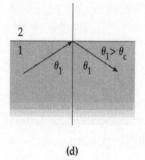

(a)   (b)   (c)   (d)

The critical angle can be determined from Snell's Law: $\qquad n_1 \sin\theta_1 = n_2 \sin\theta_2$
At the critical angle, $\theta_2 = 90°$, so: $\qquad\qquad\qquad \sin\theta_2 = 1.$

The formula for critical angle becomes: $\qquad\qquad\qquad \sin\theta_c = \dfrac{n_2}{n_1}$

The rules for mirrors can be applied, with a few modifications, to lenses.

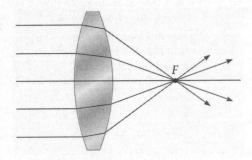

A **convex lens** is curved so that it is thicker in the middle than it is on the ends. This type of lens is also called a **converging lens**, since it is able to cause parallel light rays to intersect at a **focal point**. As with a mirror, this focal point is one-half the radius of curvature. The magnification of a convex lens is greater when the lens has a shorter focal length—or when the lens is thicker.

To locate an image, follow the same rules as outlined earlier for mirrors: (1) Draw the principal axes. (2) Set the focal points (including one on each side of the lens, since light may pass through either way. (3) Position the object on the principal axis. (4) Draw a ray (P ray) from the top of the object, parallel to the principal axis, to the lens and then through the focal point. (5) Draw a ray (M ray) straight through the middle of the lens. (6) Draw a ray (F ray) through the near focal point to the lens, then parallel to the principal axis as it emerges. (7) Locate and sketch the image.

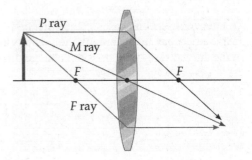

The diagrams below show that when the object is outside the focal point, a real image is formed (inverted, opposite side of lens). When the object is placed inside the focal point, the image formed is virtual (upright, same side of lens as object).

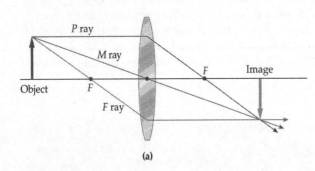

(a)

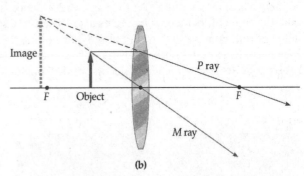

(b)

The **thin lens equation** can be used to calculate the position, orientation, and magnification of the image, where f is the focal length, d_o or s_o is the distance of the object from the mirror, and d_i or s_i the distance of the image from the mirror

$$\frac{1}{f} = \frac{1}{s_i} + \frac{1}{s_o}$$

It's no mistake that these variables and the equation look the same as the mirror equation. The only difference in applying the same rules is that light reflects from mirrors so real images form on the reflective side of mirrors—and light goes through lenses, so real images form on the opposite side of the lens from the object.

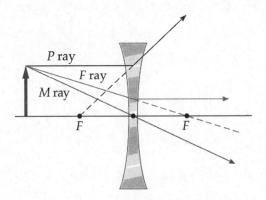

P ray

F ray

M ray

F   F

This **concave** or **diverging lens** does not converge light, so the focal points shown here are virtual. (When using the thin lens equation, the focal length has negative values.) The rays are constructed as follows: (1) Draw a ray parallel to the principal axis (P ray) , which will leave the lens as if it came from the near focal point. (2) Draw a ray toward the far focal point (F ray), which will exit the lens parallel to the principal axis. (3) Draw a ray (M ray) straight through the center of the lens. (4) Extrapolate the rays (which won't converge) to a virtual image on the same side of the lens as the object. <u>Diverging lenses do not form real images.</u>

Mirrors and lenses are often used in combination, particularly in optical instruments such as microscopes and telescopes—or the human eye in combination with a pair of glasses.

Sample Questions

1. An object is located at a distance of 2 cm from the front surface of a concave mirror with focal length 5 cm. Which of the following describes the image?
    - **I.**   real
    - **II.** upright
    - **III.** larger than the object
    - A. **I** only
    - B. **II** only
    - C. **I** and **II** only
    - D. **II** and **III** only
    - E. **I, II,** and **III**

2. When light passes from air into glass, which of the following combinations is true?

	frequency	wavelength	wave speed
A.	stays the same	stays the same	decreases
B.	stays the same	increases	increases
C.	stays the same	decreases	decreases
D.	decreases	decreases	stays the same
E.	increases	increases	stays the same

3. Light of frequency 1×10^{15} Hz has a wavelength of 200 nm in a certain medium. What is the index of refraction of that medium?
    - A. 1.0
    - B. 1.3
    - C. 1.5
    - D. 1.8
    - E. 2.0

4. A convex mirror produces an image that is 10 cm from the mirror of an object that is 20 cm from the mirror. What is the focal length of the mirror?
    A. 5 cm
    B. 10 cm
    C. 20 cm
    D. –5 cm
    E. –20 cm

5. Which angle is a critical angle in the diagram?

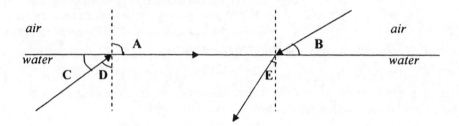

Sample Problems

1. Using the diagram below, find the angle of incidence. The index of refraction of the semicircular prism is 1.42. Assume it is surrounded by air.

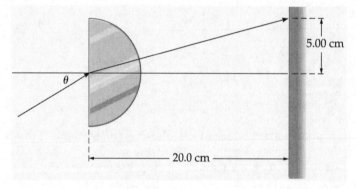

2. Construct the ray diagram for a diverging lens, with the object located between the focal point and the center of curvature. Describe the image.

3. If the index of refraction of water is 1.33, find the angle θ. Assume an index of refraction of 1.00 for the air above the oil and that the oil layer is of uniform thickness.

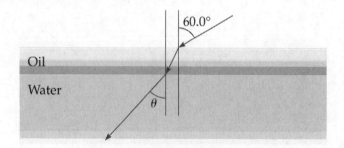

232

4. An object that is 4 cm tall is located 10 cm from a convex lens of radius of curvature 30 cm. Calculate—do not measure—the size, location, and orientation of the image.

SOLUTIONS TO SAMPLE QUESTIONS AND SAMPLE PROBLEMS

Multiple Choice Questions:

1. D Inside the focal point, the concave mirror is what we call a "magnifying mirror." The image is virtual, so it is upright. The image is also larger than the object.

2. C When light passes from air into a medium of higher index, such as glass, the frequency remains constant, but speed decreases in proportion to the index of refraction: $v = \dfrac{c}{n}$. If frequency is constant, wavelength has to decrease along with the speed: $v = f\lambda$

3. C First, calculate the wavelength of the light in a vacuum: $\lambda = \dfrac{c}{f} = \dfrac{3 \times 10^8 \ m/s}{1 \times 10^{15} \ Hz} = 3 \times 10^{-7} m$ or $300 \ nm$

The index of refraction, n, is the ratio of speed of light in a vacuum to speed in the medium, which is the same ration by which the wavelength is reduced in the medium:

$$n = \frac{c}{v} = \frac{\lambda_{vacuum}}{\lambda_{medium}} = \frac{300 \ nm}{200 \ nm} = 1.5$$

4. E A convex mirror forms only virtual images, since it cannot bring reflected rays to a focal point. Thus, the focal length is negative and only negative answers need be considered. Using the thin mirror formula, with the image distance negative, since the virtual image will appear behind the mirror:

$$\frac{1}{f} = \frac{1}{s_i} + \frac{1}{s_o}$$

$$\frac{1}{f} = \frac{1}{-10 \ cm} + \frac{1}{20 \ cm}$$

$$f = -20 \ cm$$

5. D Angle D is an angle of incidence that results in an angle of refraction equal to 90°, and therefore it is the critical angle. Critical angle is the angle of incidence when a ray travels from a medium of higher index of refraction to a medium of lower index of refraction (and the angle of refraction is 90°).

Free Response Problems:

1. First, find the refracted angle:
$$tan \ \theta_R = \frac{5cm}{20cm}$$
$$\theta = 14°$$

Apply Snell's Law:
$$n_1 \sin\theta_1 = n_2 \sin\theta_2$$
$$(1.00) \sin\theta = 1.42 \sin 14°$$
$$\theta = 20°$$

2.

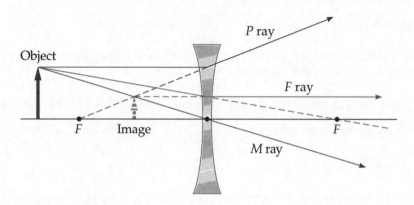

The image is **upright, virtual, and smaller** than the object.

3. At the first interface (air to oil), apply Snell's Law:

$$n_1 \sin\theta_1 = n_2 \sin\theta_2$$
$$(1.00)(\sin 60°) = n_{oil} \sin\theta_2$$

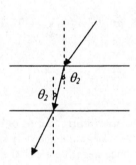

At the second interface (oil to water), apply Snell's Law again:

$$n_{oil} \sin\theta_2 = (1.33)\sin\theta$$

Compare the first and second equations:

$$(1.00)(\sin 60°) = (1.33)\sin\theta$$
$$\theta = 41°$$

4. The instructions to calculate—not measure—the final image are common on the AP* Exam. Use the thin lens equation, the magnification formula, and the proper sign conventions to determine the properties of the image. Remember that the focal length is half the radius of curvature, and a convex lens has a positive focal length.

$$\frac{1}{f} = \frac{1}{s_i} + \frac{1}{s_o}$$
$$\frac{1}{15\ cm} = \frac{1}{10\ cm} + \frac{1}{s_i}$$
$$s_i = -30\ cm$$

This negative value for the image distance indicates that the image is on the same side of the lens as the object—and thus it is **virtual**. The magnification is:

$$M = \frac{h_i}{h_o} = -\frac{s_i}{s_o}$$

$$M = \frac{h_i}{4\,cm} = -\frac{-30\,cm}{10\,cm}$$

We learn three things from this one calculation: (1) That the magnification is +3, meaning the image is 3 times the height of the object; (2) That the positive sign on the magnification indicates the image is **upright** with respect to the object; and (3) That the image is 3 times 4 cm, or **12 cm** tall.

▶ **Recommended for further practice (Walker, 3rd ed.):**
- Table 26-1 on page 880, image characteristics for mirrors
- Table 26-3 on page 893, image characteristics for lenses
- Rainbows, page 897
- Chapter Summary on pages 898–900
- Chapter Problems on page 902–908: 7, 13, 19, 23, 31, 37, 45, 47, 53, 57, 61, 67, 71, 101

√ **Reminders:**
- Real images are inverted, and virtual images are upright.
- Concave lenses and convex mirrors do not form real images.
- Real images can be formed when the object is placed outside the focal point of concave mirrors or convex lenses.
- Magnification is the positive ratio of image size to object size and the negative ratio of image distance to object distance. A negative magnification indicates the image is inverted with respect to the object.
- Focal length is ½ the radius of curvature.
- The index of refraction is the ratio of speed of light in vacuum to its speed in the material.
- Index of refraction varies for different colors of the spectrum.
- When light enters a medium from a vacuum, its speed and wavelength are reduced but frequency stays the same.

Chapter 27

Optical Instruments

Equations

Thin lens or mirror equation: $\dfrac{1}{f} = \dfrac{1}{d_o} + \dfrac{1}{d_i}$

Magnification: $M = \dfrac{h_i}{h_o} = \dfrac{-d_i}{d_o}$

Magnification of two optical elements: $M_T = M_1 M_2$

Knowledge of specific optical instruments, such telescopes, microscopes, and the human eye are not necessary for the AP* examination. However, this chapter includes discussion of combinations of lenses (or mirrors)—and these do show up occasionally. We will treat only the mathematics of combinations, but Walker's Chapter 27 contains interesting information on the function of the human eye. Further exploration of this topic after the AP* Exam is highly encouraged.

When two lenses or mirrors are placed in combination, the <u>image</u> from the first lens or mirror becomes the <u>object</u> for the second lens or mirror. For example, let's examine two lenses in combination, positioned 30 cm from each other. The first lens has a focal length of 10 cm, and the second lens has a focal length of 7 cm. The object is positioned 20 cm from the first lens.

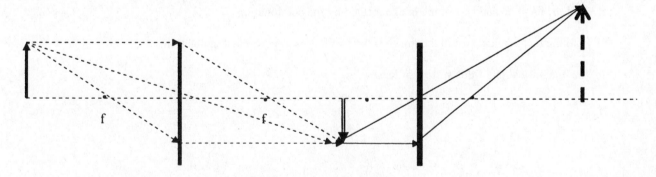

(1) Find the image for the first lens:

$$\frac{1}{f} = \frac{1}{d_o} + \frac{1}{d_i}$$

$$\frac{1}{10} = \frac{1}{20} + \frac{1}{d_i} \qquad\qquad d_i = 20\ cm$$

This creates a real image (inverted) that is 20 cm from the first lens and 10 cm from the second lens.

(2) Use the real image from the first lens as a real object for the second lens:

$$\frac{1}{f} = \frac{1}{d_o} + \frac{1}{d_i}$$

$$\frac{1}{7} = \frac{1}{10} + \frac{1}{d_i} \qquad\qquad d_i = 23\ cm$$

The final image is inverted from the object for that lens, so it is real and located 23 cm from the second lens, or 73 cm from the original object. The total magnification for a system of two lenses or mirrors is the product of their individual magnifications. The magnification for the first lens is $-d_i/d_o$ = -20/20 or -1. The magnification of the second lens is -23/10 or -2.3. The total magnification of the system is the product of the two magnifications:

$$M_T = M_1M_2 = (-1)(-2.3) = 2.3$$

The total magnification for this system is 2.3, meaning the final image is 2.3 times as large as the object and is (because it is positive) in the same orientation as the object.

It is important to note here that the answer will not necessarily be the same if the order of the lenses is reversed.

The refractive power of a lens, in diopters, is equal to the reciprocal of the focal length of the lens, in meters. A high refractive power, then, is a shorter focal length lens. (Although refractive power and diopters have not shown up on AP* Exams, in my experience, the concept of refractive power of a lens related to focal length could be very helpful in analyzing problems with lenses.)

Sample Problems

1. A 2 cm tall object is positioned 10 cm from a convex lens with focal length 5 cm. A concave lens with focal length –10 cm is located 20 cm from the convex lens.
   (a) Find the location and size of the image formed by the combination.

   (b) Find the location and size of the image if the two lenses are switched in position.

2. Find the magnification of this system of lenses.

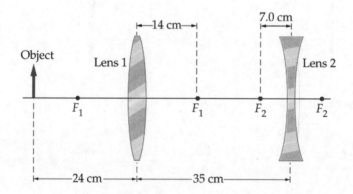

SOLUTIONS TO SAMPLE PROBLEMS

1. (a) Find the image formed by the first lens, using the thin lens equation:

$$\frac{1}{f} = \frac{1}{d_o} + \frac{1}{d_i}$$

$$\frac{1}{5} = \frac{1}{10} + \frac{11}{d_i}$$

$$d_i = 10 \ cm$$

This image is real (+ image distance), so it is inverted. The magnification is $-\dfrac{d_i}{d_o} = -\dfrac{10 \ cm}{10 \ cm} = -1$.

The image is the same size as the object, inverted, and located 10 cm from the second lens. Now, use this image as the object for the second lens.

$$\frac{1}{f} = \frac{1}{d_o} + \frac{1}{d_i}$$

$$\frac{1}{-10} = \frac{1}{10} + \frac{1}{d_i}$$

$$d_i = -5 \ cm$$

This image distance is negative, indicating that the image is on the same side of the lens as the object. Thus, it is located 5 cm toward the first lens, which is 15 cm from the first lens and 25 cm from the object. The

magnification for the second lens is $\dfrac{+5 \ cm}{10 \ cm}$, or $\frac{1}{2}$. It has the same orientation as the object used for this lens.

Since the object used for this lens was inverted, the final image is inverted with respect to the original object. The total magnification for the final image is the product of the two magnifications:

$$M_T = (-1)(\tfrac{1}{2}) = -\tfrac{1}{2} \ .$$

The image is **1 cm** tall.

(b) When the lenses are switched, we use the same steps but begin with the concave lens. First, find the image formed by the concave lens using the thin lens equation:

$$\frac{1}{f} = \frac{1}{d_o} + \frac{1}{d_i}$$

$$\frac{1}{-10} = \frac{1}{10} + \frac{1}{d_i}$$

$$d_i = -5 \ cm$$

This image distance is negative, indicating that the image is on the same side of the lens as the object. Thus, it is located 5 cm from the concave lens and 25 cm from the convex lens. The magnification for this lens is $+5cm/10cm$, or $\frac{1}{2}$, so it is half as large as the object and has the same orientation. Now use this image as the object for the convex lens.

$$\frac{1}{f} = \frac{1}{d_o} + \frac{1}{d_i}$$

$$\frac{1}{5} = \frac{1}{25} + \frac{1}{d_i}$$

$$d_i = 6.25 \ cm$$

This final image is located 6.25 cm on the far side of the second lens from the object, so it is a total of 36.25 cm from the original object. The magnification due to the second lens is $\dfrac{-6.25 \ cm}{25 \ cm} = -\frac{1}{4}$. The product of the two magnifications is: $M_T = (\frac{1}{2})(-\frac{1}{4}) = -\frac{1}{8}$. The final image is $\frac{1}{4}$ **cm tall** and is inverted with respect to the original object.

▶ **Recommended for further practice (Walker, 3rd ed.):**
- Section 27-2 on combinations of lenses
- Chapter Problems on page 932: 19, 21, 37, 43

√ **Reminder:**
- The total magnification of a lens system is the product of the magnifications of the individual lenses.

Chapter 28

Physical Optics: Interference and Diffraction

Wave fronts produced from the two edges of one opening or from two separate openings may interfere with each other, canceling where wave crests meet wave troughs, producing **destructive interference,** and reinforcing where waves meet in the same phase, producing **constructive interference**. This **superposition** of waves produces patterns, such as those shown below. When parallel wave fronts pass through two openings, they diffract at the openings and spread outward to interfere with each other. The change in direction, or **diffraction** of the waves as they pass through the small openings, produces a pattern of outgoing waves that interfere as shown below, with the arrows indicating the new directions for the wave fronts. Diffraction occurs for any type of wave passing through an opening that has a width in the same order of magnitude as the wavelength. Since the waves coming into the openings are one wave front, the waves are **in phase** with each other as they enter and exit the openings (i.e., at the same crest or trough position).

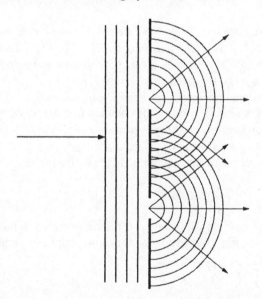

Interference patterns may be formed by any type of wave. Points of constructive interference are often called **antinodes,** such as points where water waves have high displacement, sound waves are loud, or light waves are bright. Points of complete destructive interference are called **nodes,** such as points where sounds are cancelled, water wave amplitude is low, and dark bands instead of light bands appear.

The double slit openings illustrated above and on the next page produce two sets of wave fronts that interfere with each other, producing a diffraction pattern on a screen. The light "fringes"—which may appear as light bands or bright spots—appear where the waves from each source meet in phase with each other. The dark fringes occur where the waves meet out of phase (or 180° out of phase) and destructively interfere. At the point labeled $m = 0$, called the **central maximum,** the waves from each opening have traveled the same distance, or the same **path length**. Since they were in the same phase when they left the openings—and have traveled the same distance—they are in phase at the central maximum, producing a **bright fringe**.

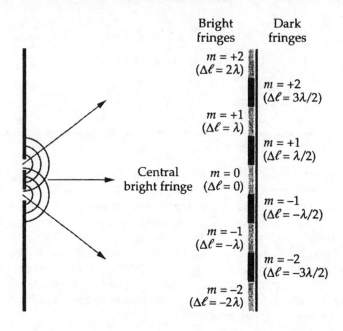

At $m = 1$ on either side of the bright fringe, the distance traveled by one wave is one entire wavelength greater than the distance traveled by the other wave, so the path length difference is λ. They are, then, in phase again and produce a bright fringe. At the other bright fringes, $m = 2$, $m = 3$, etc., the difference in path length for the waves meeting at that point are 2λ, 3λ, 4λ, respectively. At the "half-way" points—where the path length difference is $\frac{1}{2}\lambda$, $1\frac{1}{2}\lambda$, etc.—the waves are out of phase when they meet. At these points, the waves destructively interfere, canceling each other. We call these dark fringes or dark bands. The equation that describes this phenomenon, where m is the number of the fringe (whole numbers for bright fringes and multiples of $\frac{1}{2}$ for dark fringes), λ is the wavelength of the light, d is the distance between centers of adjacent openings, and θ is the angle between a line from the middle of the opening to the central maximum and a line to the fringe under consideration.

$$m\lambda = d \sin\theta$$

This equation will work for diffraction through a single slit (where d is the slit width), a double slit (where d is the distance between the centers), or a diffraction grating (where d is the separation between grating lines).

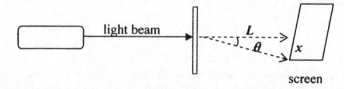

In the experimental arrangement above, x represents the distance from central maximum to the bright line selected ($m = 1,2,3$,etc.). L is the distance from the slit plate or grating to the screen, and θ is the angle between the light beam to central maximum and the beam to the bright line. To set up the equation:

$$tan \; \theta = \frac{x}{L}$$

$$\theta = tan^{-1} \; \frac{x}{L}$$

$$m\lambda = d \; sin[tan^{-1} \; \frac{x}{L}]$$

In most situations, this is what we will use. However, if the bright lines are very close together, meaning the angle is very small, we can assume: $sin \; \theta \approx \theta \approx tan \; \theta$

In this special situation, we can use the <u>small angle approximation</u>: $m\lambda = d \frac{x}{L}$ and $x_m \approx \frac{m\lambda L}{d}$

where x_m is the distance from central maximum to the "m^{th}" bright line on each side.

Thin film interference occurs when a thin film produces a variation of color reflections, depending upon the thickness of the film, such as the colors on soap bubbles or the colors seen on a thin layer of oil on water. This phenomenon occurs because the light reflected from the top layer of the film and the light reflected from the bottom layer of the film either constructively or destructively interfere with each other.

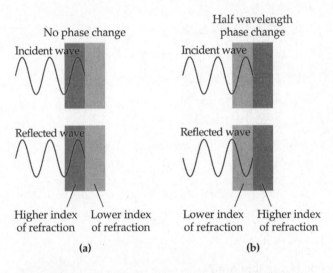

(a)   (b)

Before we examine the steps to the solution of such problems, we must mention that when light reflects from a surface, it may or may not undergo a **phase change**. When light reflects from an interface from higher index of refraction to lower index of refraction, it does not change phase. When light reflects from a surface from lower index of refraction to higher index, it changes phase by 180° (shifting the wave by ½)—putting it out of phase with the incoming wave. [See diagram (b).]

The thin film on the right has an index of refraction greater than 1 and is surrounded on both sides by air. (This could be a soap bubble.) The oncoming light partially reflects from the top surface as Ray 1, changing phase as it reflects, since it hits a boundary from lower to higher index. The oncoming light also partially refracts into the film, with no change in phase. <u>Refractions do not cause phase changes</u>. The light that refracts into the medium reflects from the lower surface of the film with no phase change (higher index to lower index). As that light beam, called Ray 2, refracts back into air, there is no phase change. Thus, Ray 1 and Ray 2 are <u>out of phase</u> with each other, since only Ray 1 has undergone a phase change.

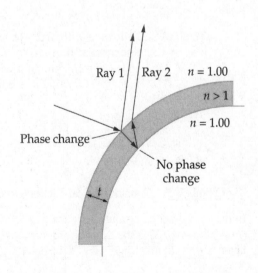

A color will not be seen in this situation <u>unless</u> the distance Ray 2 travels through the film ($2t$) is a multiple of ½ wavelength. This difference in path will also result in a change of phase for Ray 2, adding to the phase change due to reflection with an overall effect of the two rays being in phase with each other. Then we will see the color that has ½ wavelength equal to $2t$. <u>However, we must use the color's wavelength in the film, not in air:</u>

$$n = \frac{c}{v} = \frac{\lambda_{air}}{\lambda_{film}}$$

When thin films vary in thickness, different colors are visible in portions of the film of different thickness, with the color visible dependent on the film thickness and the index of refraction of the material under the film.

Sample Questions

1. Represented here are four sets of layers, with the index of refraction given for each layer. In which of the following cases would the light entering the boundary indicated change phase upon reflection?

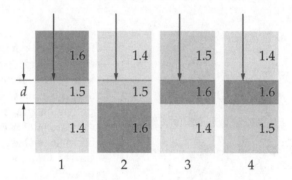

A. 1, 2, and 3 only
B. 1 and 3 only
C. 3 and 4 only
D. 1 and 2 only
E. 2, 3, and 4 only

2. Which of the following will affect the color reflection from a thin film?
    I.   thickness of film
    II.   index of refraction of medium above the film
    III. index of refraction of medium under the film
    A. I only
    B. II only
    C. II and III only
    D. I and II only
    E. I, II, and III

Questions 3-5. Consider the diffraction experiment setup below.

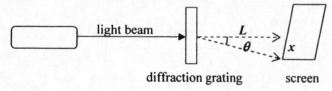

3. What will be the effect on the bright pattern on the screen if the light source is moved farther from the diffraction grating?
   A. Bright lines will be farther apart.
   B. Bright lines will be closer together.
   C. Bright lines will be less bright.
   D. The bright line pattern will begin to rotate.
   E. There will be no effect.

4. What will be the effect on the bright pattern on the screen if the screen is moved farther from the diffraction grating?
   A. Bright lines will be farther apart on the screen.
   B. Bright lines will be closer together on the screen.
   C. Bright lines will be brighter.
   D. The bright line pattern will begin to rotate.
   E. There will be no effect.

5. What will be the effect on the bright pattern on the screen if the light is replaced by a light of higher frequency?
   A. Bright lines will be farther apart on the screen.
   B. Bright lines will be closer together on the screen.
   C. Bright lines will be less bright.
   D. The bright line pattern will begin to rotate.
   E. There will be no effect.

Sample Problems

1. Determine the minimum thickness of plastic film ($n = 1.40$) that could be placed on a water surface ($n = 1.33$) to reflect green light of wavelength 500 nm.

2. A diffraction grating is placed 0.50 m from a screen. The diffraction grating is marked 750 lines/mm. Calculate the wavelength of the light that produces a second order maximum that is 0.60 m from the central maximum.

3. A single slit plate is set up so that it projects a set of bright and dark lines on a screen. The slit plate is 20 cm from the screen, and there appear to be 10 bright lines per centimeter width on the screen when light of wavelength 600 nm is used. What is the width of the slit?

SOLUTIONS TO SAMPLE QUESTIONS AND SAMPLE PROBLEMS

Multiple Choice Questions:

1. **E** In cases 2, 3, and 4, the light is entering from a material of lower index of refraction to higher index of refraction, where it will change phase.

2. **E** All three factors will affect the phases of the reflecting light beams, which will determine whether or not a certain color undergoes constructive interference. (Refer to the steps outlined in the Problem 1 solution.)

3. **C** Moving the light source farther away from the slit source will not affect the pattern on the screen, since the diffraction occurs at the slits. However, moving the light farther away will decrease the intensity of the light, making patterns less bright.

4. A Though the angles will not change, moving the slit source farther from the screen will project bright lines on the screen that are farther apart.

5. B A higher frequency light is of shorter wavelength. Decreasing wavelength on one side of the equation also decreases the angle on the other side of the equation, so the pattern moves closer together.

$$m\lambda = d\,sin\theta$$

Free Response Problems:

1.

Steps to solution of thin film problems:
1. Reflection at upper surface: Change in phase since the boundary is lower index to higher index.
2. Refraction into film: Never changes phase.
3. Reflection at lower surface: No change in phase here because it goes from higher index to lower index.
4. Refraction back into original medium: Never a phase change on refraction.
5. Compare the two reflected rays from upper and lower surfaces: In this case, they are out of phase—but we want them in the same phase.
6. Consider the effect of path length through film, $2t$: We need the second ray to switch phase to match the first ray, so the distance $2t$ must be $\frac{1}{2}\,\lambda$.

7. Calculate the wavelength in film: $n = \dfrac{\lambda_{air}}{\lambda_{film}}$

$$\lambda_{film} = \frac{500\ nm}{1.40} = 357\ nm$$

8. Determine film thickness: $2t = \frac{1}{2}\ (357\ nm)$
$$t = \textbf{89 nm}$$

2. First, determine the slit separation, d, from the value given:

$$750\ lines/mm \longrightarrow \frac{1\ mm}{750\ lines} = 0.0013\ mm/line = 1.3 \times 10^{-6}\ m/line$$

Then use the x and L values to determine the angle: $tan\ \theta = \dfrac{0.6\ m}{0.5\ m}$
$$\theta = 50°$$

Substitute known values and solve:
$$m\lambda = d\,sin\theta$$
$$(2)\lambda = (1.3 \times 10^{-6}\ m)(sin\ 50°)$$
$$\lambda = 5.0 \times 10^{-7}\ m = \textbf{500 nm}$$

3. First, since there are 10 bright lines per centimeter, the bright lines are 0.1 cm apart. Therefore, x is 0.001 m. Since the ratio of bright line spacing to the distance from slit to screen is so small, we can assume a very small angle. Therefore, use the small angle diffraction approximation, with the first order maximum:

$$x_m \approx \frac{m \lambda L}{d}$$

$$0.001 \ m = \frac{(1)(6 \times 10^{-7} \ m)(0.20 \ m)}{d}$$

$$d = 1.2 \times 10^{-4} \ m \text{ or } \textbf{0.12 mm}$$

▶ **Recommended for further practice (Walker, 3rd ed.):**
- Section 28-1 on superposition and interference for all types of waves
- Conceptual Checkpoint 28-3 on page 952, width of central bright fringe
- Section 28-5 on resolution and Rayleigh's Criterion (optional)
- Chapter Summary on pages 961–963
- Chapter Problems on pages 964–969: 3, 5, 7, 13, 17, 23, 25, 27, 39, 57, 65, 79

√ **Reminders:**
- Only use the small angle approximation for diffraction if the angle is quite small, i.e., values of x are a few millimeters and value of L is in meters.
- Don't forget, when calculating thin film thickness, to use the wavelength of the light in the film.
- When light refracts, it changes wavelength and speed, but it does not change frequency or phase.
- When light reflects, it changes phase only when it hits what might be called a "hard" boundary, i.e., lower index to higher index.

PART 5

MODERN PHYSICS

Chapter 29

Relativity

The topic of relativity was removed in recent years from the A.P. Syllabus. However, Walker's fascinating treatment of the topic in Chapter 29 would make challenging reading for the interested student.

Chapter 30

Quantum Physics

Equations

Energy of a photon: $E = hf$

Photoelectric effect: $K_{max} = hf - \phi$

Momentum of a photon: $p = \dfrac{E}{c} = \dfrac{hf}{c}$

de Broglie wavelength: $\lambda = \dfrac{h}{p}$

Mass-energy equivalence: $\Delta E = (\Delta m)c^2$

Though the derivation and treatment of the Bohr model of the atom has been removed from the AP* Syllabus, the student should have a general understanding of the energy levels of electrons. The concept of energy level "jumps" correlating to energy given up by an electron or absorbed by an electron is useful in calculating the corresponding frequency of photons absorbed or emitted. Problems given on the AP* Exam will provide a framework for the energy levels and ask students to determine possible corresponding wavelengths or frequencies of photons absorbed or emitted—or the converse.

$$0 \quad\rule{2cm}{1pt}\quad n = \infty$$

$(-13.6 \text{ eV})/9 \quad\rule{2cm}{0.4pt}\quad n = 3$ } Excited states

$(-13.6 \text{ eV})/4 \quad\rule{2cm}{0.4pt}\quad n = 2$

Energy emitted equal to hf

Absorption of energy equal to hf

$-13.6 \text{ eV} \quad\rule{2cm}{0.4pt}\quad n = 1$ Ground state

Max Planck's **quantum** hypothesis—a conclusion from observations of the radiation given off by blackbody objects—states that the radiation energy *(E)* given off is an integral multiple of constant *(h)* times the frequency *(f)*, where *h* is Planck's constant:

$$E = nhf$$

Albert Einstein took the idea of quantized light and proposed that light comes in bundles of energy called **photons**, with the energy of each photon proportional to its frequency:

$$E = hf$$

When making calculations using the above equation, use the Planck's constant value $h = 6.63 \times 10^{-34}$ $J \cdot s$ when the energy is in joules. When the energy is given in *electron volts,* use the Planck's constant value $h = 4.14 \times 10^{-15}$ $eV \cdot s$. [Remember that one electron-volt is the amount of energy required to move one electron through a potential difference of one volt.]

The **photoelectric effect** had been observed for years, but Einstein applied the photon theory to the photoelectric effect to study it extensively—for which he eventually received the Nobel Prize. The photoelectric effect is the absorption of light of certain frequencies by a metal, which then ejects electrons, producing an electric current. In the experimental setup below, photons of light shine onto a metal plate (E), which emits electrons. These electrons are attracted to a positively charged collector (C). This sets up a current in the circuit, which can be measured with the ammeter. The direction of electron flow in this circuit is the opposite of the current flow studied previously, which is from high potential to low potential.

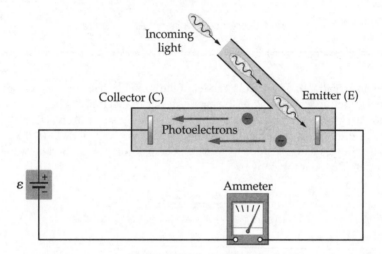

The energy of the incoming light depends on the frequency of the light, by $E = hf$. The minimum energy required for a certain metal to give off electrons is called the **work function, ϕ**. The frequency of the light that has this level of energy is called the **threshold frequency, f_o**. At light frequencies and energies below this minimum level, no electrons are given off by the metal—regardless of light intensity.

$$hf_o = \phi$$

If the light has frequency or energy above the minimum, the excess energy goes to providing the emitted electrons with kinetic energy, so the maximum kinetic energy of the emitted electrons is the difference between the energy provided by the light and the amount needed for the work function:

$$K_{max} = hf - \phi$$

Each metal has a unique threshold (cutoff) frequency and work function. The graph on the next page shows the different threshold frequencies for sodium and gold. As frequency increases, the emitted electrons gain kinetic energy. The slope of each line is Planck's constant.

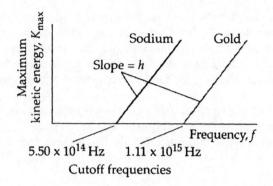

Slope = h

Sodium   Gold

Maximum kinetic energy, K_{max}

Frequency, f

5.50×10^{14} Hz 1.11×10^{15} Hz

Cutoff frequencies

Photons of light have energy and momentum but no mass. Thus, to determine the momentum of a photon, begin by considering the momentum of a particle with mass:

$$p = mv$$

For the mass of a photon, we substitute its energy equivalent, from $E = mc^2$: $m = \dfrac{E}{c^2}$

Then for velocity, we use the constant speed for all light in a vacuum, c:

$$p = mv = \frac{E}{c^2}\, c = \frac{E}{c}$$

Substituting from $c = f\lambda$ and $E = hf$, other forms for momentum of light can be derived:

$$p = \frac{E}{c} = \frac{hf}{f\lambda} = \frac{h}{\lambda}$$

The momentum of a photon, then, is proportional to its frequency and inversely proportional to its wavelength. Since photons have momentum, their momentum is conserved in collisions. The **Compton Effect** (proposed by Arthur Compton in 1923) uses this concept to explain the scattering that occurs when a photon collides with an electron at rest. As expected, the electron's increase in kinetic energy is matched by a decrease in kinetic energy of the photon. A decrease in kinetic energy of the photon would mean a decrease in frequency and an increase in its wavelength after the collision.

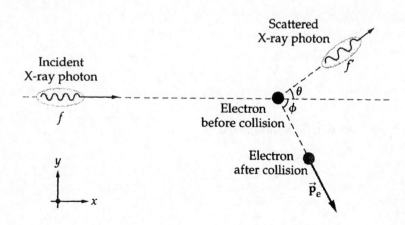

Incident X-ray photon

f

Scattered X-ray photon

f'

θ

Electron before collision

ϕ

Electron after collision

$\vec{P}_e$

y

x

In the previous example, the incident photon (X-ray in this case) has frequency f and energy hf. When it collides with the electron at rest, the momentum afterward has to be considered in separate x and y directions, since it is a vector. The x-component of the photon's final momentum plus the x-component of the electron's final momentum are equal to the photon's original momentum. Given information about the original and final frequencies or wavelengths, the scattering angles can be determined—or vice versa.

The photoelectric effect and the Compton effect exhibit the **wave-particle duality** of light—that light can behave both as a wave and as a particle. The **de Broglie Hypothesis** (also proposed in 1923) held that if light, which is a wave, can behave like a particle, then particles might behave like waves. The de Broglie wavelength, then, for any particle would be:

$$\lambda = \frac{h}{p}$$

Indeed, when high speed electrons are passed through double slits to a detection screen, light and dark bands are produced from the interference of the particles—in the same way that light and dark bands were produced earlier when we discussed diffraction of light. This phenomenon can be explained as diffraction of these particles as they pass through the openings, in the same way light is diffracted, exhibiting the wave properties of particles such as electrons.

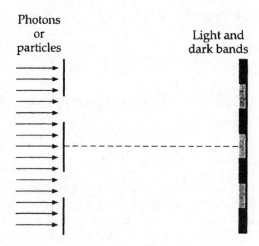

Sample Questions

1. What is the energy of a 200-nm photon?
    A. 10^2 J
    B. 10^{-2} J
    C. 10^{-10} J
    D. 10^{-18} J
    E. 10^{-32} J

2. Determine the momentum of the 200-nm photon.
    A. 3×10^2 N·s
    B. 3×10^{-10} N·s
    C. 3×10^{-15} N·s
    D. 3×10^{-20} N·s
    E. 3×10^{-27} N·s

3. A certain metal has a threshold frequency, or cutoff frequency, of 1.5×10^{15} Hz. What is the work function for this metal?
    A. 10^{-7} J
    B. 10^{-8} J
    C. 10^{-9} J
    D. 10^{-18} J
    E. 10^{-34} J

4. A photon of wavelength λ collides with an electron at rest. Which of the following is true about the collision?
          I. The photon wavelength after the collision is less than before.
         II. The photon kinetic energy after the collision is less than before.
        III. The photon frequency after the collision is less than before.
    A. I only
    B. II only
    C. III only
    D. I and II only
    E. II and III only

5. An electron makes an energy level transition from -13.6 eV to -3.4 eV. What is the energy of the photon absorbed for this transition?
    A. 3.4 eV
    B. 10.2 eV
    C. 13.6 eV
    D. 17.0 eV
    E. 20.2 eV

Sample Problems

1. A photon of wavelength 0.47 nm strikes an electron at rest. After the collision, the photon has a wavelength of 0.50 nm.

    (a) What is the frequency of the photon before the collision?

    (b) What is the frequency of the photon after the collision?

    (c) What is the speed of the electron after the collision?

2. The plot on the next page provides the results of a photoelectric experiment.

    (a) What is the threshold frequency for the metal used?

    (b) What is the work function for this metal?

    (c) Use data from this graph to determine a value for Planck's constant. (Show data used.)

    (d) How will this graph change if the intensity of light used in the experiment is increased?

    (e) How will this graph change if a different metal is used?

Kinetic Energy vs. Frequency

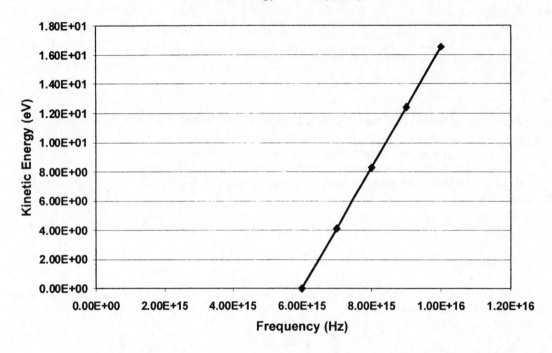

SOLUTIONS TO SAMPLE QUESTIONS AND SAMPLE PROBLEMS

Multiple Choice Questions:

1. D Energy of the photon is: $E = hf = \dfrac{hc}{\lambda}$

Selecting the right value of Planck's constant makes this one possible without a calculator. Since the answers are in Joules, choose the value: $hc = 1.99 \times 10^{-25} \ J \cdot m$. Round this value for a quick estimate:

$$E = \frac{2 \times 10^{-25} \ J \cdot m}{2 \times 10^{-7} \ m} = 10^{-18} \ J$$

2. E We can use the energy calculated previously (though AP* Exams don't usually require use of a previous answer on multiple choice).

$$p = \frac{E}{c} = \frac{1 \times 10^{-18} \ J}{3 \times 10^{8} \ m/s} = 0.33 \times 10^{-26} \ \text{or} \ 3 \times 10^{-27} \ N \cdot s$$

3. D The work function is the product of threshold frequency and Planck's constant:

$$\phi = hf_o = (6.63 \times 10^{-34} \ J \cdot s)(1.5 \times 10^{15} \ Hz) = 10 \times 10^{-19} \ \text{or} \ 10^{-18} \ J$$

4. E The photon will have less energy after the collision, as it has imparted some of its kinetic energy to the electron. If the photon has less energy, it has a lower frequency and longer wavelength.

5. B The energy absorbed is the change in energy: $\Delta E = E_f - E_o = -3.4 - (-13.6) = 10.2 \ eV$

Free Response Problems:

1. (a) The frequency of the photon before the collision is: $f = \dfrac{c}{\lambda} = \dfrac{3 \times 10^8 \, m/s}{4.7 \times 10^{-10} \, m} = 6.4 \times 10^{17} \, Hz$

(b) The frequency of the photon after the collision is: $f = \dfrac{c}{\lambda} = \dfrac{3 \times 10^8 \, m/s}{5 \times 10^{-10} \, m} = 6 \times 10^{17} \, Hz$

(c) The kinetic energy of the electron after the collision is equal to the loss in kinetic energy of the photon:

$$K_{electron} = K_{o(photon)} - K_{f(photon)}$$
$$\tfrac{1}{2} \, m_e v_e^2 = hf_o - hf_f$$
$$\tfrac{1}{2} \, (9.11 \times 10^{-31} \, kg) \, v_e^2 = (6.63 \times 10^{-34} \, J \cdot s)(6.4 - 6) \times 10^{17} \, J$$
$$v = 7.6 \times 10^6 \, m/s$$

2. (a) The threshold frequency is the lowest frequency at which electrons have kinetic energy, which is **6×10^{15} electron volts.**

(b) The work function is the product of threshold frequency and Planck's constant:

$$\phi = hf_o = (6.63 \times 10^{-34} \, J \cdot s)(6 \times 10^{15} \, Hz) = 4.0 \times 10^{-18} \, J$$
$$\text{or}$$
$$\phi = hf_o = (4.14 \times 10^{-15} \, eV \cdot s)(6 \times 10^{15} \, Hz) = \textbf{25 eV}$$

(c) Since $K = \phi - hf$ for a plot of K vs. f, the slope is Planck's constant, h. Use two values on the line to determine slope, e.g., $(6 \times 10^{15}, 0)$ and $(8 \times 10^{15}, 8.1)$.

$$slope = h = \dfrac{8.1 - 0}{8 \times 10^{15} - 6 \times 10^{15}} = \textbf{4.05} \times \textbf{10}^{-15} \, \textbf{eV} \cdot \textbf{s}$$

This compares quite favorably to the accepted value of 4.14×10^{-15} eV·s.

(d) Light intensity will not affect this graph. Increasing light intensity will increase the rate at which electrons are produced but not their individual energies.

(e) If a different metal is used, its threshold frequency will be different, so the graph will shift left or right but have the same slope (which is the constant h).

▶ **Recommended for further practice (Walker, 3rd ed.):**
- Emphasis on photoelectric effect on pages 1009–1013
- Emphasis on Compton effect on pages 1014–1016
- Wave-particle duality and de Broglie Hypothesis on page 1017–1021
- Chapter Summary on page 1026, Sections 1 through 5 only
- Chapter Problems on page 1030–1033: 15, 21, 25, 29, 33, 35, 41, 47, 51, 53, 57, 77

√ **Reminders:**
- Both energy and momentum are conserved during collisions of photons and electrons (Compton effect).
- The slope of *Kinetic Energy vs. Frequency* for a photoelectric effect experiment is Planck's constant.
- When making calculations with Planck's constant, select a value for the constant from the Fundamental Constants Sheet that makes the calculations most simple—and watch the units.

Chapter 31

Atomic Physics

Equations

Speed of light: $c = f\lambda$

Energy of a photon: $E = hf = pc = \dfrac{hc}{\lambda}$

[Note: The AP* Physics B Examination no longer includes the early models of atoms, including the Rutherford and Bohr models. However, the energy levels related to frequencies of photons absorbed or emitted are still included.]

The Bohr model of the atom, developed by Niels Bohr early in the twentieth century, described the motion of electrons in orbitals or energy levels around the nuclei of atoms. Although this model is not technically accurate, the model led the way for many developments in atomic theory during the rich historical era of "modern physics." Students in AP* Physics do not need to develop the model from basic principles of angular momentum and energy (as they have in years past), but they do need to have an understanding of the **quantum** principle, i.e., that electrons may make absorb or emit only specific amounts of energy in order to make the transitions among energy levels or even to escape and thus ionize the atom.

The diagram below represents the first four energy levels for electrons in a particular atom. Notice that the energies given for each energy level are negative, representing a potential energy "well," in which higher energy levels are less negative. Reaching a potential energy of zero would free the electron from that atom. Notice also that each subsequent level has an energy that varies with the square of the level, e.g., the $n = 2$ energy level has an energy that is one-fourth the ground state energy, and the $n = 3$ energy level has an energy that is one-ninth the ground state energy.

For an electron to move to a higher energy level, it must absorb exactly the amount of energy equivalent to the difference in energies between the two levels—otherwise no transition will take place. There are no allowed "jumps" intermediate to these levels. All possible energy transitions from lower energy to higher energy are shown with arrows on the diagram. Thus, the only energies that can be absorbed for the situation shown on the diagram below are found by taking $E_{final} - E_{original}$.

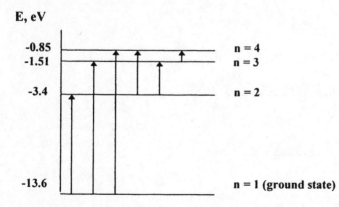

The possible energies for the transitions, in order from left to right, are:

(1) $E = -3.4 - (-13.6) = 10.2$ eV
(2) $E = -1.51 - (-13.6) = 12.09$ eV
(3) $E = -0.85 - (-13.6) = 12.75$ eV
(4) $E = -0.85 - (-3.4) = 2.55$ eV
(5) $E = -1.51 - (-3.4) = 1.89$ eV
(6) $E = -0.85 - (-1.51) = 0.66$ eV

Notice that all energy changes are positive, since in each case the electron must absorb energy to make the transition. The source of energy here is electromagnetic energy, or some form of light, with the quantity, or **quantum**, of energy equal to $E = hf$, where f is the frequency of light absorbed to make the transition and h is **Planck's constant**. For each of these transitions, there is a specific frequency or wavelength of light that will cause the transition. The frequency of light can easily be converted to a wavelength using the equation $c = f\lambda$. The same energy transitions are allowable for electrons to move from higher to lower energy levels, only by emitting comparable amount of energy—and thus emitting light of specific wavelengths and frequencies in the process. In each emission, the energy change has the same magnitude as the corresponding absorption but is negative, representing an emission of energy in the form of electromagnetic radiation.

Sample Questions

1. What wavelength of light would be emitted for an electron transition from n = 4 to n = 3, using the information in the chart on the previous page?
   A. 100 nm
   B. 200 nm
   C. 500 nm
   D. 1000 nm
   E. 2000 nm

2. Which transition comes closest to giving off visible light?
   A. n = 4 to n = 2
   B. n = 4 to n = 1
   C. n = 3 to n = 1
   D. n = 2 to n = 4
   E. n = 1 to n = 1

3. How much energy would it take to ionize a hydrogen atom with its electron in the ground state?
   A. 0.85 eV
   B. 1.51 eV
   C. 3.4 eV
   D. 13.6 eV
   E. 19.36 eV

SOLUTIONS TO SAMPLE QUESTIONS

Multiple Choice Questions:

1. **E** The energy change is 0.66 eV. Use the energy equation in the form:

$$E = \frac{hc}{\lambda} = \frac{1.24 \times 10^3 \, eV \cdot nm}{\lambda} = 0.66 \, eV$$

$$\lambda = 2000 \; nm$$

By using the equation in this form, the numbers are easy enough to manipulate without a calculator.

2. A First, let's check a broad range for visible light. We know visible light is from about 400 nm to 700 nm.
The energy equivalents would be: $E = \dfrac{hc}{\lambda} = \dfrac{1.24 \times 10^3 \; eV \cdot nm}{400 \; nm} = about \; 3 \; eV \; for \; the \; violet \; end \; of \; the \; spectrum$

$$E = \dfrac{hc}{\lambda} = \dfrac{1.24 \times 10^3 \; eV \cdot nm}{700 \; nm} = about \; 1.3 \; eV \; for \; the \; red \; end \; of \; the \; spectrum$$

The transitions that are closest are $n = 4$ to $n = 2$ and $n = 3$ to $n = 2$. The choice $n = 3$ to $n = 2$ is not given.
Choices B and C are too large, and choice D and E are energy absorptions, not emissions.

3.   D In the ground state, the electron would need to absorb a photon with exactly 13.6 eV of energy for the electron to gain the energy to leave the atom—and leave it ionized.

▶ **Recommended problems for further practice (Walker, 3rd ed.):**
- Hydrogen spectrum on page 1043–1045
- Chapter Summary on page 1064–1066, energy levels only from sections 2 and 3
- Chapter Problems on page 1067–1069: 17, 19, 57

√ **Reminders:**
- When using Planck's equation to convert energy to frequency or wavelength or vice versa, select the value from the Table of Information that makes the task easiest—a value for h or hc that will give the energy in joules or electron volts, as needed.
- When subtracting numerical values for energy levels to find transition values, always remember to keep the signs and use $\Delta E = E_{final} - E_{original}$.
- AP* students do not need to learn the names of energy transition series (Lyman, Balmer, etc.) or memorize numerical values—just be able to calculate values from given tables and/or recognize possible energy transitions.
- It's sometimes helpful to remember that the energy of each energy level (n) in an atom is equal to ground state energy divided by n^2. For example, the energy for energy level $n = 3$ is one-ninth of the ground state energy (negative, of course).

Chapter 32

Nuclear Physics and Nuclear Radiation

The fundamental particles that make up an atom are the **proton, neutron,** and **electron**. A proton, one of the basic constituents of an atomic nucleus, carries a fundamental charge of +1 and mass of +1, so we use the notation $_1^1 p$, where the subscript indicates the **charge** and the superscript indicates the **mass number** of the particle. The neutron, $_0^1 n$, is also normally found in the nucleus. **Electrons,** $_{-1}^0 e$, carry the fundamental charge of negative one, have no mass number, and exist in energy levels as they orbit the nucleus. An **alpha** particle is a helium nucleus, $_2^4 He$, meaning the particle consists of two protons and two neutrons, for a total mass of 4 a.m.u. A **beta** particle is a high-speed electron, $_{-1}^0 e$, with a negative one charge and no essential mass (about 1,830 electrons would have the mass of one proton). **Gamma rays** (γ) are a form of electromagnetic radiation—the most energetic, difficult to shield, and damaging of the basic nuclear particles and rays that we will discuss. A few others are worth mentioning—the neutrino, deuteron, and positron—as these come up occasionally on AP* tests. The **neutrino,** $_0^0 n$, has no charge and is essentially massless, though the determination of the mass of neutrinos is a major pursuit in physics research. The **positron,** $_1^0 p$, resembles a positive electron, and a **deuteron,** $_1^2 H$, is a hydrogen nucleus consisting of two protons—so the deuteron has twice the mass of a proton.

Mass and Charge of Particles in the Atom				
Particle	Mass (kg)	Mass (MeV/c^2)	Mass (u)	Charge (C)
Proton	1.672623×10^{-27}	938.28	1.007276	$+1.6022 \times 10^{-19}$
Neutron	1.674929×10^{-27}	939.57	1.008665	0
Electron	9.109390×10^{-31}	0.511	0.0005485799	-1.6022×10^{-19}

In nuclear equations, the charge and mass must be conserved, so in the simplest scenario, the sum of charges for reactants must equal the sum of charges in the products—and the same must be true for the mass numbers. In some reactions, however, the total mass of products is less than the total mass of reactants, indicating that some mass has been converted to energy, by Einstein's famous equation, $E = mc^2$. The "loss" in mass between reactants and products is often referred to as "mass defect." That mass goes into the equation for **m**, and **c** is the speed of light 3×10^8 **m/s.**

We can apply these concepts to further understanding of the proton-proton cycle for the fusion reactions on the sun. This is essentially a three-step cycle:

(1) Two protons (protium nuclei) combine to form one deuterium nucleus, a positron, and a neutrino:

$$_1^1 H + _1^1 H \rightarrow \ _1^2 H + _1^0 e + _0^0 \nu$$

In nuclear reactions, not only are linear momentum and mass-energy conserved, other properties are conserved, such as angular momentum, spin, charge, fermion number, charm, and strangeness. Conservation of all these properties ultimately defines exactly what particles are produced during the reaction. In the case above, one positron is produced in each of these combinations due to conservation of charge. Each proton on the left side of the equation has a positive charge, for a total of +2 prior to the fusion (i.e., add the lower numbers). The total mass number on the left side is 2 (add the upper numbers). On the right side, the newly formed deuterium has a charge of +1 and a mass number of 2. Production of the positron, then, balances the charge, bringing the total charge on the right side of the equation to +2. The reason the neutrino is also produced relies upon examination of conservation of all the other quantities mentioned above. For example, each proton consists of 2 "up"\" quarks and 1 "down" quark, while the deuterium is made up of a total of 3 "up" quarks and 3 "down" quarks. Though quarks don't seem to be conserved so far, the positron and neutrino properties allow "balance" or conservation of all other properties.

(2) In the second step of the cycle, a protium nucleus combines with a deuterium nucleus to form a helium-3 nucleus and energy in the form of gamma radiation. [Gamma results from a collision of a positron and an electron.]

$$ {}_1^1H + {}_1^2H \rightarrow {}_2^3He + \gamma $$

Notice here that the charge numbers on the bottom row balance, and the mass numbers on the top row ${}_1^1H$ balance. The gamma energy produced should be the equivalent of the exact mass deficit on the right side, using $E = mc^2$.

(3) In the third step of the cycle, two helium-3 nuclei combine to form one helium-4 nucleus and two protium nuclei.

$$ {}_2^3He + {}_2^3He \rightarrow {}_2^4He + {}_1^1H + {}_1^1H $$

Note the balance of both charge and mass number. This one reaction requires two of the first two reactions to provide the necessary two He-3 nuclei required to produce just one He-4. Thus, if we add up all three reactions, the net reaction looks like this:

$$ 4\ {}_1^1H \rightarrow {}_2^4He + 2{}_1^0e + \gamma + 2\nu $$

The charge, +4 on each side, balances; mass number also balances.

Sample Questions

1. What is species X in the following equation?

    $$ {}_{11}^{23}Na + X \rightarrow {}_{12}^{26}Mg + {}_1^1H $$

    A. alpha particle
    B. beta particle
    C. neutrino
    D. proton
    E. deuteron

2. Which of the following would be given off when one atom of tritium (${}_1^3H$) produces one atom of helium-3 (${}_2^3He$)?

    A. proton
    B. beta particle
    C. neutrino
    D. alpha particle
    E. positron

3. Which of the following nuclear reactions is not possible?

A. $_1^2H + _1^3H \rightarrow _2^4He + _0^1n$

B. $2\ _1^2H \rightarrow _2^4He$

C. $_1^2H + _1^3H \rightarrow _2^4He$

Sample Problems

1. In a nuclear reaction, the mass defect between reactants and products is determined to be 0.0026 kg. Find the energy given off, in: (a) joules and (b) electron volts.

2. Write the balanced nuclear equation for the capture of a proton by lithium-7 ($_3^7Li$) to produce beryllium-7 ($_4^7Be$) and a neutron.

3. On the sun, hydrogen fuses to helium, producing huge amounts of energy. When a kilogram of hydrogen fuses, the mass defect is about 0.0066 kg. How much energy (in joules) does this represent?

SOLUTIONS TO SAMPLE QUESTIONS AND SAMPLE PROBLEMS

Multiple Choice Questions:

1. **A** Adding the charges (subscripts) for reactants and products, we can see that X needs to have a charge of +2. Then, adding mass numbers for reactants and product (superscripts), we see that the species X needs a mass of 4 to balance both sides. The alpha particle, $_2^4He$, will balance the equation.

$$_{11}^{23}Na + _2^4He \rightarrow _{12}^{26}Mg + _1^1H$$

2. **B** To balance the equation $_1^3H \rightarrow _2^3He + X$, the charge has to be –1 to balance, and the mass needs to be zero. That would be an electron or beta particle, to create the following balanced nuclear equation:

$$_1^3H \rightarrow _2^3He + _{-1}^0e$$

3. **C** The charge numbers (subscripts) balance on both sides, but the mass numbers (superscripts) do not balance in this equation, so mass is not conserved as the equation is given.

Free Response Problems:

1. (a) Use the mass given to determine the amount of energy produced, using Einstein's equation:

$$E = mc^2 = (0.0026\ kg)(3 \times 10^8\ m/s)^2 = 2.3 \times 10^{14}\ J$$

(b) Convert kilograms to electron volts using the values given on the Table of Information:

$$1\ u = 1.66 \times 10^{-27}\ kg = 931\ MeV/c^2$$

$$m = (0.0026 \; kg)\left(\frac{931 \; MeV/c^2}{1.66 \times 10^{-27} \; kg}\right) = 1.46 \times 10^{27} \; MeV/c^2$$

Now use Einstein's equation again, paying careful attention to units from the previous answer:

$$E = mc^2 = (1.46 \times 10^{27} \; MeV/c^2)(c^2) = 1.46 \times 10^{27} \; MeV = \boldsymbol{1.46 \times 10^{33} \; eV}$$

[Alternate Solution: The student may also remember that 1 eV equals 1.6×10^{-19} J—the charge on one electron—and simply divide the answer to (a) by that number to obtain the answer to (b). You can also check your answer to (b) by multiplying it by 1.6×10^{-19} J/eV to see that you get the answer to part (a).]

2. Using what we know about a proton ($^1_1 p$) and a neutron ($^1_0 n$), write the complete equation:

$$^7_3 Li + ^1_1 p \rightarrow ^7_4 Be + ^1_0 n$$

Note that the charges (subscripts) and masses (superscripts) balance on both sides.

3. Use Einstein's equation:

$$E = mc^2 = (0.0066 \; kg)(3 \times 10^8 \; m/s)^2 = \boldsymbol{5.9 \times 10^{14} \; J}$$

▶ **Recommended problems for further practice (Walker, 3rd ed.):**
- Concepts only in Section 32-1
- Balancing nuclear equations in Section 32-3
- Concepts only in Sections 4, 5, and 6
- Chapter Problems on pages 1107–1109: 13, 15, 41, 43, 59

√ **Reminders:**
- When using $E = mc^2$ for mass-energy equivalence conversions, watch the units on mass, and use the Table of Information sheet for conversion values.
- The unit MeV/c^2 is commonly used by particle physicists as a unit for mass.
- Mass and energy—along with many other unique properties of matter—must be conserved in nuclear reactions.
- 1 eV = 1.6×10^{-19} J

SECTION III
THE LABORATORY

Each AP Examination contains at least one free response question that is designed to assess the student's ability to design laboratory experiments and/or critically analyze laboratory data. Though a set of particular physics experiments are not recommended in preparation for the exam, the best preparation for this assessment is extensive work in the physics laboratory. Students who have had that experience should be able to set up an experimental design for a given problem, regardless of familiarity or experience with that specific purpose or set of equipment. Students who have not had extensive laboratory experience should have an idea in advance of what is expected of good experimental design and develop a plan or approach to such problems. Even though you may have never performed such an experiment, there is no reason to leave this question blank! A wide variety of creative approaches may be entirely acceptable—and expected—on such questions. At the very least, give the question a try. Additionally, concept or "what would happen if" questions are often added at the end, and you may gain hints from these or have some idea how to answer them from your knowledge of physics concepts.

Often, the student is given a problem or purpose, then asked to select needed equipment, describe the experimental setup briefly, and discuss expected results. These descriptions need not be lengthy or extensive; as a matter of fact, information can often most quickly and succinctly be presented in itemized lists or tables—reducing time spent overall.

Here is a sample laboratory procedure outlining the key elements of experimental design. Commentary notes in italics provide general guidelines that are general to most situations.

Sample Laboratory Experiment

Determining the Index of Refraction for Lucite

Purpose: To determine the index of refraction for a solid rectangular piece of Lucite plastic.

Materials Needed: small laser, block of Lucite, protractor, paper
[Note: The student should list all necessary materials and avoid listing or checking extraneous materials.]

Background: [Here we want to provide information helpful to solution of the problem, discuss considerations that might reduce sources of error in the experiment, note safety considerations, and outline equations or mathematical derivations that would be pertinent.]

Index of refraction, n, is the ratio of speed of light in vacuum to speed of light in the medium. Since index of refraction varies with color, it would be better to use a small laser of one color or put a color filter on the light beam if a white light source is used. The accepted value from the *CRC Handbook* for Lucite is 1.42.

Equations: $n = c/v$
$n_1 \sin \theta_1 = n_2 \sin \theta_2$ *(Snell's Law)*

All angles should be measured from the normal to the surface, as shown on the next page.

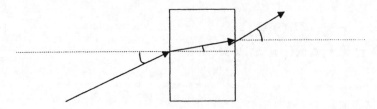

[Note: A labeled diagram is a concise way of clarifying and providing information.]

Since we will be reading and rounding measurements to no more than three significant digits, the index of refraction for air can reasonably be assumed to be 1.00. Angles can be estimated to the nearest ½ degree, so all readings will be recorded as 0 or 5 in the tenths place on the data table.

Procedure: [In a more formal report, this might take paragraph form. However, due to time constraints on an exam, it might be best to provide only key steps in bulleted form.]
1. Lay the Lucite piece on a large piece of paper.
2. Draw a normal, or perpendicular, line on the paper at the front surface of the plastic.
3. Shine the light beam onto the point of contact as shown on the diagram and trace the beam onto the paper.
   Also trace the exit beam and mark a normal line at that surface, as shown in the diagram.
4. Lift the Lucite piece and connect the line that would represent the beam's path through the Lucite.
5. Measure the incident angle to the normal and the refracted angle.
6. Repeat for several different incident angles and record all data in a table.

Data:
Table 1.

Angle of Incidence (degrees)	Angle of Refraction (degrees)
10.0	7.0
20.0	14.0
30.0	21.0
40.0	27.0
50.0	32.0
60.0	37.0
70.0	41.0
80.0	44.5

Chart 1.

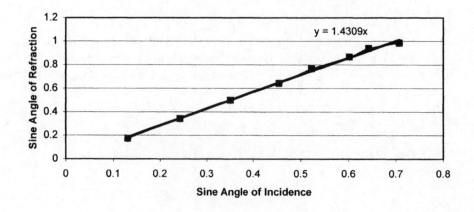

Sine Angle of Refraction vs Sine Angle of Incidence

$y = 1.4309x$

Analysis:

Since the graph is linear, the sine of angle of incidence is directly proportional to sine of angle of refraction. By Snell's Law, the slope of the line should be the index of refraction of the Lucite.

Calculation of slope: $n = \Delta y/\Delta x = (1-0.2)/(0.7-0.15) = 1.45$

Accepted value of index of refraction: 1.42

Calculation of percent error: $\% Error = (1.45-1.42)/1.45 = 0.02$ or 2%

The largest source of error in this experiment probably came in the measurement of angles using a protractor. The angle readings could only be estimated to the nearest half a degree. Additionally, since the lines were drawn by pencil on a light beam, the thickness of the pencil and the thickness of the light beam could cause variations up to half a degree just in drawing the lines.

SECTION IV
SAMPLE EXAMINATION IN THE AP* FORMAT

In this section, a full-length sample AP* Physics B Examination similar to the AP* format is provided.

The Table of Information provided here will be provided with both sections of the AP* Examination. Notice the fundamental constants are defined here, along with currently accepted values, units, and enough information to make some conversions. The symbols of common units of measure are defined, as are symbols and values for metric prefixes. Values of trigonometric functions are provided for common angles—particularly for the Multiple Choice section, where calculators may not be used.

The Equations for AP* Physics B are provided here and will only appear on the Free Response section of the AP* Exam. On the Equation Table, several explanations may be helpful:
1. Vector quantities (with some exceptions) are listed in bold type.
2. Subscripts indicate special cases, e.g., v_o means initial velocity.
3. The symbol Δ before a variable means "change in," e.g., $\Delta v = v_f - v_o$.
4. Equations are grouped by subject area.
5. Symbols used for the same quantity may vary, depending on context, e.g., r and d are both used for distance, depending on the equation. These are defined in the margin near the equations.
6. Conventions used in writing and scoring the exam are listed at the bottom (I through IV), e.g., "direction of conventional current flow is the direction of positive charge flow."

In the Multiple Choice section, seventy questions are to be answered in ninety minutes. To best simulate exam conditions, use only the Table of Information provided and do not use either the Equation Table sheet or a calculator. The answers to these questions, along with explanations, follow the full exam.

In the Free Response section, six questions are to be answered in ninety minutes. On this section, spend about fifteen minutes on each question. The Table of Information, sheet of equations, and a calculator should all be used while taking this section of the exam. Answers with full explanations follow the exam.

Instructions for sample scoring are on the last page of this section.

Acknowledgment: We are grateful to the College Board for allowing use of the AP* Table of Information and Physics B Equations for the sample examination.

CONSTANTS AND CONVERSION FACTORS		UNITS		PREFIXES		

CONSTANTS AND CONVERSION FACTORS

1 unified atomic mass unit,	$1\ u = 1.66 \times 10^{-27}$ kg
	$= 931$ MeV$/c^2$
Proton mass,	$m_p = 1.67 \times 10^{-27}$ kg
Neutron mass,	$m_n = 1.67 \times 10^{-27}$ kg
Electron mass,	$m_e = 9.11 \times 10^{-31}$ kg
Electron charge magnitude,	$e = 1.60 \times 10^{-19}$ C
Avogadro's number,	$N_0 = 6.02 \times 10^{23}$ mol^{-1}
Universal gas constant,	$R = 8.31$ J/(mol·K)
Boltzmann's constant,	$k_B = 1.38 \times 10^{-23}$ J/K
Speed of light,	$c = 3.00 \times 10^8$ m/s
Planck's constant,	$h = 6.63 \times 10^{-34}$ J·s
	$= 4.14 \times 10^{-15}$ eV·s
	$hc = 1.99 \times 10^{-25}$ J·m
	$= 1.24 \times 10^3$ eV·nm
Vacuum permittivity,	$\epsilon_0 = 8.85 \times 10^{-12}$ C^2/N·m^2
Coulomb's law constant,	$k = 1/4\pi\epsilon_0 = 9.0 \times 10^9$ N·m^2/C^2
Vacuum permeability,	$\mu_0 = 4\pi \times 10^{-7}$ (T·m)/A
Magnetic constant,	$k' = \mu_0/4\pi = 10^{-7}$ (T·m)/A
Universal gravitational constant,	$G = 6.67 \times 10^{-11}$ m^3/kg·s^2
Acceleration due to gravity at Earth's surface,	$g = 9.8$ m/s^2
1 atmosphere pressure,	$1\ atm = 1.0 \times 10^5$ N/m^2
	$= 1.0 \times 10^5$ Pa
1 electron volt,	$1\ eV = 1.60 \times 10^{-19}$ J

UNITS

Name	Symbol
meter	m
kilogram	kg
second	s
ampere	A
kelvin	K
mole	mol
hertz	Hz
newton	N
pascal	Pa
joule	J
watt	W
coulomb	C
volt	V
ohm	Ω
henry	H
farad	F
tesla	T
degree Celsius	°C
electron-volt	eV

PREFIXES

Factor	Prefix	Symbol
10^9	giga	G
10^6	mega	M
10^3	kilo	k
10^{-2}	centi	c
10^{-3}	milli	m
10^{-6}	micro	μ
10^{-9}	nano	n
10^{-12}	pico	p

VALUES OF TRIGONOMETRIC FUNCTIONS FOR COMMON ANGLES

θ	$\sin\theta$	$\cos\theta$	$\tan\theta$
0°	0	1	0
30°	1/2	$\sqrt{3}/2$	$\sqrt{3}/3$
37°	3/5	4/5	3/4
45°	$\sqrt{2}/2$	$\sqrt{2}/2$	1
53°	4/5	3/5	4/3
60°	$\sqrt{3}/2$	1/2	$\sqrt{3}$
90°	1	0	∞

The following conventions are used in this exam.

I. Unless otherwise stated, the frame of reference of any problem is assumed to be inertial.

II. The direction of any electric current is the direction of flow of positive charge (conventional current).

III. For any isolated electric charge, the electric potential is defined as zero at an infinite distance from the charge.

*IV. For mechanics and thermodynamics equations, W represents the work done on a system.

*Not on the Table of Information for Physics C, since Thermodynamics is not a Physics C topic.

ADVANCED PLACEMENT PHYSICS B EQUATIONS FOR 2006 and 2007

NEWTONIAN MECHANICS

$v = v_0 + at$

$x = x_0 + v_0 t + \frac{1}{2}at^2$

$v^2 = v_0{}^2 + 2a(x - x_0)$

$\sum \mathbf{F} = \mathbf{F}_{net} = m\mathbf{a}$

$F_{fric} \leq \mu N$

$a_c = \dfrac{v^2}{r}$

$\tau = rF \sin\theta$

$\mathbf{p} = m\mathbf{v}$

$\mathbf{J} = \mathbf{F}\Delta t = \Delta\mathbf{p}$

$K = \frac{1}{2}mv^2$

$\Delta U_g = mgh$

$W = F\Delta r \cos\theta$

$P_{avg} = \dfrac{W}{\Delta t}$

$P = Fv \cos\theta$

$\mathbf{F}_s = -k\mathbf{x}$

$U_s = \frac{1}{2}kx^2$

$T_s = 2\pi\sqrt{\dfrac{m}{k}}$

$T_p = 2\pi\sqrt{\dfrac{\ell}{g}}$

$T = \dfrac{1}{f}$

$F_G = -\dfrac{Gm_1 m_2}{r^2}$

$U_G = -\dfrac{Gm_1 m_2}{r}$

a =	acceleration
F =	force
f =	frequency
h =	height
J =	impulse
K =	kinetic energy
k =	spring constant
ℓ =	length
m =	mass
N =	normal force
P =	power
p =	momentum
r =	radius or distance
T =	period
t =	time
U =	potential energy
v =	velocity or speed
W =	work done on a system
x =	position
μ =	coefficient of friction
θ =	angle
τ =	torque

ELECTRICITY AND MAGNETISM

$F = \dfrac{1}{4\pi\epsilon_0}\dfrac{q_1 q_2}{r^2}$

$\mathbf{E} = \dfrac{\mathbf{F}}{q}$

$U_E = qV = \dfrac{1}{4\pi\epsilon_0}\dfrac{q_1 q_2}{r}$

$E_{avg} = -\dfrac{V}{d}$

$V = \dfrac{1}{4\pi\epsilon_0}\sum_i \dfrac{q_i}{r_i}$

$C = \dfrac{Q}{V}$

$C = \dfrac{\epsilon_0 A}{d}$

$U_c = \frac{1}{2}QV = \frac{1}{2}CV^2$

$I_{avg} = \dfrac{\Delta Q}{\Delta t}$

$R = \dfrac{\rho\ell}{A}$

$V = IR$

$P = IV$

$C_p = \sum_i C_i$

$\dfrac{1}{C_s} = \sum_i \dfrac{1}{C_i}$

$R_s = \sum_i R_i$

$\dfrac{1}{R_p} = \sum_i \dfrac{1}{R_i}$

$F_B = qvB \sin\theta$

$F_B = BI\ell \sin\theta$

$B = \dfrac{\mu_0}{2\pi}\dfrac{I}{r}$

$\phi_m = BA \cos\theta$

$\mathcal{E}_{avg} = -\dfrac{\Delta\phi_m}{\Delta t}$

$\mathcal{E} = B\ell v$

A =	area
B =	magnetic field
C =	capacitance
d =	distance
E =	electric field
$\mathcal{E}$ =	emf
F =	force
I =	current
ℓ =	length
P =	power
Q =	charge
q =	point charge
R =	resistance
r =	distance
t =	time
U =	potential (stored) energy
V =	electric potential or potential difference
v =	velocity or speed
ρ =	resistivity
θ =	angle
ϕ_m =	magnetic flux

FLUID MECHANICS AND THERMAL PHYSICS

$P = P_0 + \rho g h$

$F_{buoy} = \rho V g$

$A_1 v_1 = A_2 v_2$

$P + \rho g y + \frac{1}{2}\rho v^2 = \text{const.}$

$\Delta \ell = \alpha \ell_0 \Delta T$

$H = \dfrac{kA\,\Delta T}{L}$

$P = \dfrac{F}{A}$

$PV = nRT = Nk_B T$

$K_{avg} = \dfrac{3}{2}k_B T$

$v_{rms} = \sqrt{\dfrac{3RT}{M}} = \sqrt{\dfrac{3k_B T}{\mu}}$

$W = -P\Delta V$

$\Delta U = Q + W$

$e = \left| \dfrac{W}{Q_H} \right|$

$e_c = \dfrac{T_H - T_C}{T_H}$

A = area
e = efficiency
F = force
h = depth
H = rate of heat transfer
k = thermal conductivity
K_{avg} = average molecular kinetic energy
ℓ = length
L = thickness
M = molar mass
n = number of moles
N = number of molecules
P = pressure
Q = heat transferred to a system
T = temperature
U = internal energy
V = volume
v = velocity or speed
v_{rms} = root-mean-square velocity
W = work done on a system
y = height
α = coefficient of linear expansion
μ = mass of molecule
ρ = density

ATOMIC AND NUCLEAR PHYSICS

$E = hf = pc$

$K_{max} = hf - \phi$

$\lambda = \dfrac{h}{p}$

$\Delta E = (\Delta m)c^2$

E = energy
f = frequency
K = kinetic energy
m = mass
p = momentum
λ = wavelength
ϕ = work function

WAVES AND OPTICS

$v = f\lambda$

$n = \dfrac{c}{v}$

$n_1 \sin \theta_1 = n_2 \sin \theta_2$

$\sin \theta_c = \dfrac{n_2}{n_1}$

$\dfrac{1}{s_i} + \dfrac{1}{s_0} = \dfrac{1}{f}$

$M = \dfrac{h_i}{h_0} = -\dfrac{s_i}{s_0}$

$f = \dfrac{R}{2}$

$d \sin \theta = m\lambda$

$x_m \sim \dfrac{m\lambda L}{d}$

d = separation
f = frequency or focal length
h = height
L = distance
M = magnification
m = an integer
n = index of refraction
R = radius of curvature
s = distance
v = speed
x = position
λ = wavelength
θ = angle

GEOMETRY AND TRIGONOMETRY

Rectangle
$A = bh$

Triangle
$A = \dfrac{1}{2}bh$

Circle
$A = \pi r^2$
$C = 2\pi r$

Parallelepiped
$V = \ell w h$

Cylinder
$V = \pi r^2 \ell$
$S = 2\pi r \ell + 2\pi r^2$

Sphere
$V = \dfrac{4}{3}\pi r^3$
$S = 4\pi r^2$

Right Triangle
$a^2 + b^2 = c^2$
$\sin \theta = \dfrac{a}{c}$
$\cos \theta = \dfrac{b}{c}$
$\tan \theta = \dfrac{a}{b}$

A = area
C = circumference
V = volume
S = surface area
b = base
h = height
ℓ = length
w = width
r = radius

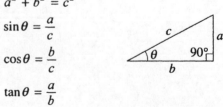

SAMPLE EXAM

MULTIPLE CHOICE
Time – 90 minutes
70 Multiple Choice Questions

Directions: Answers to these questions should be filled in on an answer sheet grid. No calculator or Formula Sheet is allowed, but you may refer to the Table of Information. It is recommended for you to use $g = 10$ m/s^2.

Questions 1-4.

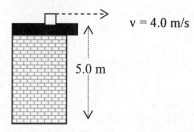

$v = 4.0$ m/s

5.0 m

A block is pushed horizontally off of a building at a speed of 4.0 m/s and hits the ground 5.0 meters below.

1. How long does it take the block to hit the ground once it leaves the building?
    A. 0.25 s
    B. 0.50 s
    C. 0 s
    D. 1.5 s
    E. 2.0 s

2. How far from the side of the building does the block land on the ground?
    A. 1.0 m
    B. 2.0 m
    C. 3.0 m
    D. 4.0 m
    E. 5.0 m

3. What is the closest approximation of the speed of the block when it hits the ground?
    A. 2.0 m/s
    B. 5.0 m/s
    C. 10. m/s
    D. 11. m/s
    E. 14. m/s

4. A second block falls from the building without any initial horizontal velocity. Select the correct combination of descriptions for each block's trip to the ground.

	Time for the Fall	Vertical Velocity Upon Impact	Horizontal Velocity Upon Impact
A.	same for both	same for both	same for both
B.	same for both	same for both	greater for first block
C.	greater for first block	same for both	greater for first block
D.	greater for second block	greater for second block	greater for second block
E.	greater for second block	greater for first block	same for both

5. A friction force of 50 N acts against a 10 kg object moving at 5 m/s. Over what distance will the friction force stop the object?
   A. 0.5 m
   B. 1.25 m
   C. 2.5 m
   D. 5 m
   E. 10 m

Questions 6-7. The system below consists of a mass M on the right and a mass m on the left connected by a light string pulled over a pulley with negligible mass and friction. When the system is released, M accelerates at a rate a downward and m accelerates upward.

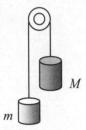

6. Determine the tension in the string as the objects accelerate.
   A. Mg
   B. mg
   C. $Mg + mg$
   D. $Mg - mg$
   E. $Mg - Ma$

7. If $M = 2m$, what is the acceleration, in terms of g?
   A. $\frac{1}{3}g$
   B. $\frac{1}{2}g$
   C. g
   D. $2g$
   E. $3g$

8. Which of the following is a correct free-body diagram for a box being pulled up a ramp by an attached string?

A. 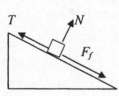 B. 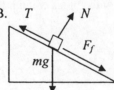 C.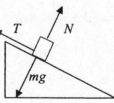

D. 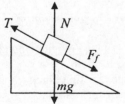 E.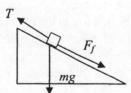

9. A baseball outfielder catches a 200 gram ball that is traveling at 20 m/s when it strikes the outfielder's glove. The ball is stopped in a distance of 10 cm. What is the average force applied to the ball?
    A. 200 N
    B. 400 N
    C. 2000 N
    D. –200 N
    E. –400 N

Questions 10-11. These questions refer to the two springs below, which have spring constants k_1 and $k_{2,}$, and x is the distance each one is stretched.

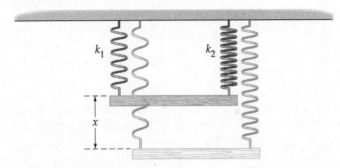

10. In the situation above, if spring 1 and spring 2 are both stretched a distance x, and $k_2 = 2k_1$, then the relationship between the potential energy stored in each spring is:
    A. $U_1 = \frac{1}{4} U_2$
    B. $U_1 = \frac{1}{2} U_2$
    C. $U_1 = \frac{1}{8} U_2$
    D. $U_1 = 2 U_2$
    E. $U_1 = 4 U_2$

11. The bar is removed and masses are added separately to each spring above, with m_2 on spring 2 equal to twice m_1, which is on spring 1. Then the masses are pulled down the same distance, released, and allowed to oscillate. If $k_2 = 2k_1$, compare the speeds of the masses as they pass through equilibrium.
    A. The speed of the mass on spring 1 is $\frac{1}{4}$ the speed of the mass on spring 2.
    B. The speed of the mass on spring 1 is ½ the speed of the mass on spring 2.
    C. The speed of the mass on spring 1 is equal to the speed of the mass on spring 2.
    D. The speed of the mass on spring 1 is twice the speed of the mass on spring 2.
    E. The speed of the mass on spring 1 is four times the speed of the mass on spring 2.

12. A box of mass m is pushed at constant velocity v with a force F across a horizontal surface. Which of the following is the formula for coefficient of kinetic friction?
    A. $\dfrac{mv}{F}$
    B. $\dfrac{mg}{F}$
    C. mgv
    D. $\dfrac{F}{mg}$
    E. $\dfrac{Fv}{mg}$

13. The uniform beam below has a mass of 5 kilograms and is 4 meters long. Two masses, each 10 kilograms, are positioned as shown, with one mass at the left and the other mass 3 meters from the left end. Approximately how far from the left end of the beam should a support be placed for the beam to remain in balance?

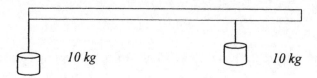

    A. 0.5 m
    B. 1.0 m
    C. 1.25 m
    D. 1.5 m
    E. 1.6 m

Questions 14-15. In a test of sheer willpower, an athlete attaches a 70-kg mass to a rope and runs the rope up over a nearly massless frictionless pulley. He then determines that it takes him 5 seconds to lift the mass to a height of 5 meters.

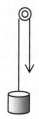

14. What is the average power generated by the athlete during each lift from the floor?
    A. 70 W
    B. 140 W
    C. 350 W
    D. 700 W
    E. 1750 W

15. What is the total work done by the athlete in lifting the mass and lowering it to the floor 20 times?
    A. 700 J
    B. 3,500 J
    C. 7,000 J
    D. 14,000 J
    E. zero

16. On a frictionless track, cart A of mass 1.0 kg moving to the right at 0.5 m/s collides elastically head-on with cart B of mass 1.0 kg moving to the left at 1.0 m/s. Which of the following is a possible result of the collision?
    A. The carts stick together and move together to the left at 0.25 m/s.
    B. The carts stick together and immediately stop.
    C. Cart A moves to the left at 0.5 m/s and cart B continues to move to the left, but at 0.25 m/s.
    D. Cart A moves to the left at 1.0 m/s and cart B moves to the right at 0.5 m/s.
    E. Cart A moves to the right at 0.25 m/s and cart B moves to the right at 0.5 m/s.

Questions 17-18. The graph below shows *Force vs. Time* for a 1.0 kg cart on a track striking a force sensor. The cart is initially moving at 2.0 m/s.

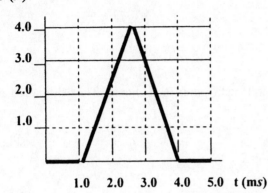

F (*N*)

17. What is the average magnitude of acceleration of the cart from 1.0 to 2.5 seconds?
    A. 0
    B. 2.0 m/s^2
    C. 3.0 m/s^2
    D. 3.5 m/s^2
    E. 4.0 m/s^2

18. What is the impulse on the cart from 1.0 to 4.0 seconds?
    A. 0
    B. 3 x 10^{-3} N·s
    C. 6 x 10^{-3} N·s
    D. –3 x 10^{-3} N·s
    E. –6 x 10^{-3} N·s

19. Each of the following diagrams represents a hollow tube. Rank the following from highest to lowest according to the frequency of the fundamental note that could be produced by a standing wave in each air column.

    I. open at both ends   **II.** open at both ends   **III.** closed at one end

    A. **I, II, III**
    B. **I, III, II**
    C. **II, III, I**
    D. **II, I, III**
    E. **III, I, II**

20. Which of the following is the equation for a wave of amplitude 0.25 m and frequency 40 Hz, if the position of the wave is 0 at time = 0 s?
  A. $x(t) = 0.25 \cos 80\pi t$
  B. $x(t) = 0.25 \sin 80\pi t$
  C. $x(t) = 40 \sin \pi t$
  D. $x(t) = 40 \cos \pi t$
  E. $x(t) = 0.25 \sin 40\pi t$

Questions 21-23.
A ball attached to the end of a string is swung in a vertical circle with radius **R**, as shown. The ball's speed at the top of the circle is *v*.

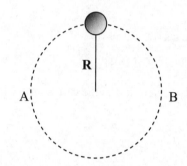

21. For the ball to move in a constant velocity around the circular path:
  A. The string tension must also be constant.
  B. The string tension must be greater when the ball is at the top of the circle.
  C. The string tension must the greater when the ball is at the bottom of the circle.
  D. Is impossible unless the radius is changed.
  E. Is impossible unless the ball's mass is changed.

22. If the ball is replaced by another ball with twice the mass, for the velocity at the top to remain equal to *v*:
  A. The tension must be equal to the square root of the previous tension.
  B. The tension must be equal to $\sqrt{2}$ times the previous tension.
  C. The tension must stay the same as before.
  D. The tension must double.
  E. The tension must be tripled.

23. When the string is taut and is in a position parallel to the floor (point A or point B), the centripetal force is provided by:
  A. string tension + weight of ball
  B. string tension – weight of ball
  C. string tension and gravitation
  D. weight of ball – string tension
  E. string tension only

24.

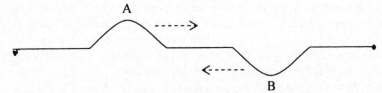

Point A and point B of two wave pulses are 4.0 meters apart at t = 0 s, and the crests are each 3.0 m from the ends of a 10 meter long string that is tied in position at both ends. Each wave is moving with velocity 2.0 m/s in the direction indicated on the diagram above. Which of the following diagrams below best represents the pulses on the string after 4.0 s?

A.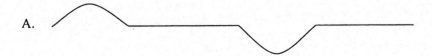

B.

C.

D.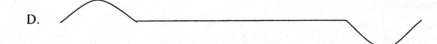

E.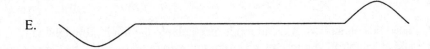

25. A large open tank with diameter 10 meters is filled with water to a depth of 20 meters. Which is the best estimate of the total fluid pressure at the bottom of the tank?
   A. 100 kPa
   B. 200 kPa
   C. 300 kPa
   D. 400 kPa
   E. 500 kPa

26. The Continuity Equation, $A_1v_1 = A_2v_2$, describes the rate of flow of an incompressible fluid as cross-sectional area of the flow changes. This equation is based upon the idea that:
   A. Fluid pressure must be equal at all points of flow.
   B. The rate of mass flow must be maintained.
   C. The density of the fluid must change in proportion to the rate of flow.
   D. Velocity will change in direction proportion to the cross-section of the pipe in which the fluid flows.
   E. An object immersed in the flowing fluid will maintain a constant rate of flow.

27. A ball is floating on the surface, with one-third of the ball below water level. The ball is pushed under water. Which of the following statements applies to the situation when the ball is completely submerged?
   A. The buoyant force on the ball remains the same because the ball's actual mass is the same.
   B. Once the ball is completely submerged, the buoyant force on it will increase as it is pushed deeper.
   C. The water pressure on the ball is the same at every point on the ball's surface.
   D. The buoyant force on the ball is three times as much as when it was floating.
   E. The buoyant force on the ball is one-third as much as when it it was floating.

28. A can of carbonated soda is shaken and then the tab top lid opened to allow the soda to spray into the air. If the soda initially sprays to a height of 50 cm, what was the soda pressure in the can when it was first opened? (Assume the soda to be mostly water.)
   A. 1 kPa
   B. 5 kPa
   C. 10 kPa
   D. 50 kPa
   E. 500 kPa

29. Doubling the absolute temperature of a an ideal gas will have what effect on the average translational kinetic energy of its molecules?
   A. ¼
   B. ½
   C. remain unchanged
   D. double
   E. quadruple

30. Doubling the absolute temperature of a system of ideal gas will have what effect on the pressure of an ideal gas, assuming volume remains constant?
   A. ¼
   B. ½
   C. remain unchanged
   D. double
   E. quadruple

31. A liquid is enclosed and insulated in a container. A metal rod is inserted into the liquid, through the container wall, to heat the liquid at a controlled rate. Which of the following will produce the highest rate of conduction of heat through the rod into the liquid?
   A. Replace the metal rod with a glass rod.
   B. Replace the existing rod with a longer rod of smaller diameter.
   C. Adjust the temperature outside the container so it is closer to the temperature of the liquid.
   D. Replace the existing rod with a longer rod of larger diameter.
   E. Replace the existing rod with a shorter rod of larger diameter.

32. The total energy of a system, or the sum of all the forms of energy possessed by the atoms or molecules of a system is called:
   A. heat
   B. radiant energy
   C. internal energy
   D. translational kinetic energy
   E. blackbody radiation

Questions 33-34. The following pressure-volume diagram shows three stages of a thermodynamic cycle A-B-C for an ideal gas.

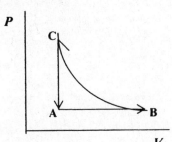

33. Which step(s) could be isothermal?
   A. only AB
   B. only BC
   C. only CA
   D. AB and BC
   E. BC and CA

34. In which step is no work done?
   A. only AB
   B. only BC
   C. only CA
   D. AB and BC
   E. AB and CA

Questions 35-36. Initially, metal sphere X is charged to a potential of 10,000 volts, with a total charge on its surface of +Q. Metal spheres Y and Z are initially uncharged. Spheres Y and Z are the same size as sphere X. All three spheres are held by insulated stands.

sphere X   sphere Y   sphere Z

35. Sphere X is connected by a conducting wire to sphere Y. The wire is then removed and used to connect sphere Y to sphere Z. After the wire is again removed, what is the potential on sphere Z?
   A. 10,000 V
   B. 5,000 V
   C. 2,500 V
   D. 1250 V
   E. 0

36. What is the charge on sphere Z after the procedure described in problem 35?
   A. +Q
   B. + ½ Q
   C. + ¼ Q
   D. + ⅓ Q
   E. –Q

37. Four equal positive charges of 1 μC are held on the corners of a square that is 2 meters on a side. What is the magnitude of the electric field at the center of the square?

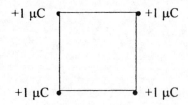

+1 μC   +1 μC

+1 μC   +1 μC

    A. 0
    B. 4×10^{-6} N/C
    C. 4.5×10^{3} N/C
    D. 9×10^{3} N/C
    E. 1.8×10^{4} N/C

38. Two helium nuclei, each with a charge of +2e, are located 1 nm apart. What happens to the force between them if the nuclei are moved twice as far apart, to 2 nm?
    A. It drops to zero.
    B. It is one-fourth as great.
    C. It is one-half as great.
    D. It is twice as great.
    E. It is four times as great.

39. Consider a resistor of length l and cross-sectional diameter d. Which of the following will produce the largest resistance?
    A. Make a new resistor of length $2l$ and diameter $2d$.
    B. Connect two of the original resistors in series.
    C. Connect three of the original resistors in series.
    D. Connect two of the original resistors in parallel.
    E. Connect three of the original resistors in parallel.

40. A capacitor with capacitance C is connected in series with a resistor R and voltage supply V. Which of the following will produce the largest charge on the capacitor?

	Capacitance	Resistance	Voltage
A.	C	R	V
B.	C	$4R$	V
C.	$2C$	$2R$	$2V$
D.	C	$4R$	$2V$
E.	$2C$	$4R$	V

41. A 500 μF capacitor is charged to 10 V, storing 5×10^{-3} C of charge in the capacitor. A second 500 μF capacitor is connected in parallel with the first, and the capacitors charged in the same manner as before. What is the resulting charge on each capacitor?
    A. 250 μC
    B. 500 μC
    C. 1000 μC
    D. 2500 μC
    E. 5000 μC

Questions 42-44. In the circuit below, each of the bulbs has a resistance of 400 ohms, and $\varepsilon = 10$ volts. Assume negligible resistance in the switch and connecting wires.

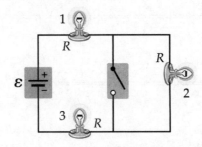

42. The equivalent resistance (or load) in the circuit with the switch open is:
    A. 0.008 Ω
    B. 133 Ω
    C. 400 Ω
    D. 800 Ω
    E. 1200 Ω

43. The equivalent resistance (or load) in the circuit with the switch closed is:
    A. 0.005 Ω
    B. 200 Ω
    C. 400 Ω
    D. 800 Ω
    E. 1200 Ω

44. The comparative brightness of the bulbs with the switch closed:
    A. 1 = 2 = 3
    B. 1 > 2 > 3
    C. 1 < 2 < 3
    D. 1 > 3 and 2 = 0
    E. 1 = 3 and 2 = 0

45. A circuit is set up with a power supply, an uncharged capacitor, and a resistor. Which of the following is the best sketch of the current flow through the resistor from the time the connections are first made until the capacitor is charged?

A.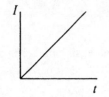

B.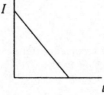

C.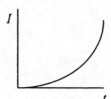

D.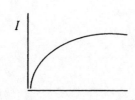

E.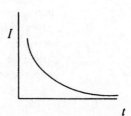

Questions 46-48. Two wires carry currents in opposite directions, as shown below. The wires are separated by a distance of 0.02 meter, and points P and Q are located 0.01 meter above and below the bottom wire.

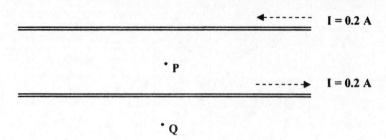

46. What is the magnetic field strength at point P, due to the top wire?

    A. $\dfrac{\mu_0}{20\pi}$

    B. $\dfrac{10\mu_o}{\pi}$

    C. $\dfrac{\mu_0}{10\pi}$

    D. $\dfrac{\mu_o \pi}{10}$

    E. $\dfrac{0.2\mu_0}{\pi}$

47. What is the direction of the magnetic field at point P, due to both wires?
    A. out of the page, perpendicular to the plane of the page
    B. into the page, perpendicular to the plane of the page
    C. none, the fields cancel
    D. to the right, parallel to the wires
    E. to the left, parallel to the wires

48. Compare the magnetic field strength at point Q to the magnetic field strength at point P.
    A. $B_P = B_Q$
    B. $B_P = \frac{1}{2} B_Q$
    C. $B_P = \frac{1}{4} B_Q$
    D. $B_P = \frac{1}{9} B_Q$
    E. $B_P = 3 B_Q$

49. A string fixed at both ends is set into oscillation by a constant frequency generator. Increasing the tension on the string as it oscillates will have what set of effects?

	Wavelength	Wave pulse velocity
A.	increases	increases
B.	increases	stays the same
C.	stays the same	increases
D.	decreases	decreases
E.	decreases	stays the same

50. A wire carrying a current directed upward on the page extends through a magnetic field, as shown below. What is the direction of the magnetic force on the section of wire in the field?

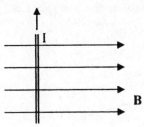

    A. to the right, in the plane of the page
    B. to the left, in the plane of the page
    C. toward the top of the page, in the plane of the page
    D. into the page, perpendicular to the plane of the page
    E. out of the page, perpendicular to the plane of the page

51.

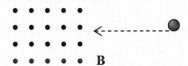

A negatively charged particle moving from the right enters a uniform magnetic field directed out of the page, as shown. So that the particle is not deflected from its path as it moves through the magnetic field:
    I. Make sure the particle's speed is very large.
    II. Add an electric field in the same region that points up on the page.
    III. Add an electric field in the same region that points down on the page.

    A. **I** only
    B. **I** and **II** only
    C. **I** and **III** only
    D. **II** only
    E. **III** only

52. An observer hears the sound from a source that is emitting a sound of constant frequency. In which case will the observer hear the highest frequency sound?
    A. The observer is moving at 10 m/s toward a stationary source.
    B. The observer is moving at 10 m/s away from a stationary source.
    C. The source is moving at 10 m/s toward a stationary observer.
    D. The source and observer are each moving at 10 m/s away from each other.
    E. The source and observer are each moving at 10 m/s toward each other.

A large copper hoop with a radius of 1 meter is located near the Earth's surface in a region where the Earth's magnetic field dips to the right at a 60° angle. Assume the magnetic field strength is about 10^{-4} T in this region.

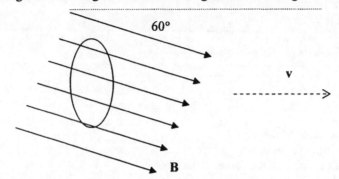

53. The hoop is open to the right, with the plane of the hoop perpendicular to the ground. It is held in that position as it is moved to the right at 2 m/s. Estimate the magnetic flux through the hoop.
   A. 0
   B. $0.5\pi \times 10^{-4}$ Wb
   C. $\pi \times 10^{-4}$ Wb
   D. $2\pi \times 10^{-3}$ Wb
   E. $3\pi \times 10^{-3}$ Wb

54. The hoop is again open to the right, with the plane of the hoop perpendicular to the ground. It is held in that position as it is moved to the right at 2 m/s. Estimate the EMF induced in the hoop.
   A. 0
   B. 1×10^{-4} V
   C. 3×10^{-4} V
   D. 5×10^{-3} V
   E. 9×10^{-3} V

55. Which action with the hoop will induce the largest current in the hoop while it is in this field?
   A. moving the vertical hoop to the right at constant velocity
   B. rotating the vertical hoop around a horizontal axis that is perpendicular to the plane of the hoop
   C. rotating the vertical hoop around a horizontal axis across the hoop, in the plane of the hoop
   D. dropping the hoop in such a way that it falls straight to the ground without rotating
   E. holding the hoop stationary in the position described above

56, Which of the following is not electromagnetic?
   A. microwave
   B. infrared waves
   C. visible light
   D. sound waves
   E. X-rays

57. A beam of light is incident along the normal from air into glass. Which of the following will change as the light moves from air to glass?

    I. frequency of the light
    II. speed of the light
    III. wavelength of the light

    A. I only
    B. I and II only
    C. II and III only
    D. I, II, and III
    E. II only

58. In a darkened room, a beam of white light shines through a magenta filter onto a reflective red surface and then into a camera. What color will be developed in the camera film?
    A. red
    B. blue
    C. magenta
    D. white
    E. no color

59. Total internal reflection can only occur if:
    A. The light wavelengths are within the visible range.
    B. The incident beam is in a medium of higher index of refraction.
    C. The incident beam is along the normal to the interface between two media.
    D. The angle of refraction is less than the angle of incidence.
    E. The angle of incidence is less than the critical angle.

60. In which of the following cases can a real image be formed?

    I. Convex lens, object outside focal length
    II. Concave lens, object inside focal length
    III. Concave mirror, object outside focal length

    A. I only
    B. III only
    C. I and III only
    D. II and III only
    E. I, II, and III

61. A beam of light is directed from air into a glass prism. Which of the following diagrams best illustrates the path of the beam through the glass and back into the air?

A. 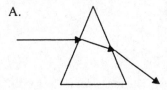   B. 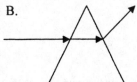   C.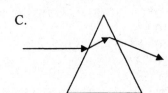

D.    E.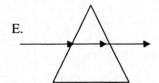

62. This experiment projects a red laser light beam of wavelength λ through a diffraction grating labeled 750 lines/mm onto a screen that is positioned a distance l from the diffraction grating. The diffraction grating has a distance d between adjacent lines. The distance between the central maximum and first order bright line is x.

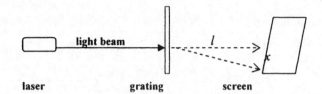

    In order for the bright lines produced on the screen to appear closer together, what change could be made in the above experiment?
    A. Replace the red laser with a green laser.
    B. Move the laser farther from the diffraction grating.
    C. Move the diffraction grating farther from the screen.
    D. Replace the diffraction grating with one that is labeled 800 lines/mm.
    E. Rotate the diffraction grating by a small angle within the same plane.

63. Which of the following could produce the largest real image of an object?
    A. convex mirror, $f = -5$ cm, with object 3 cm from center of mirror
    B. concave lens, $f = -5$ cm, with object 3 cm from center of lens
    C. convex lens, $f = 5$ cm, with object 3 cm from center of lens
    D. convex lens, $f = 10$ cm, with object 12 cm from center of lens
    E. concave mirror, $f = 15$ cm, with object 10 cm from center of lens

64. A thin film of oil on water causes us to see a green reflection of light. Which of the following must be true?
    I.   The light source must be only green light
    II. The oil must be of lower index of refraction than the water.
    III. Other colors present in the incident beam underwent destructive interference.
    A. I only
    B. II only
    C. III only
    D. I and II only
    E. II and III only

65. What is an appropriate estimate of the energy in photons of wavelength 600 nm?
    A. 3×10^{18} J
    B. 3×10^{8} J
    C. 3×10^{-6} J
    D. 3×10^{-9} J
    E. 3×10^{-19} J

66. In a nuclear reaction, the products have less total mass than the reactants. The mass defect is 3×10^{-6} kg. Determine the corresponding amount of energy this mass defect represents.
    A. 3×10^{-6} J
    B. 9×10^{-12} J
    C. 9×10^{2} J
    D. 2.7×10^{11} J
    E. 2.7×10^{12} J

The diagram represents the electron energies for the first four energy states of an atom, with energies given in electron volts.

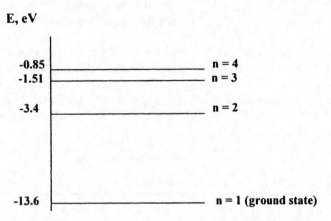

67. Which of the following energy emissions is not possible for this set of energy states?
    A. −12.75 eV
    B. −12.09 eV
    C. −13.6 eV
    D. −10.2 eV
    E. −1.89 eV

68. Which of the following electron energy transitions would produce a photon of highest frequency?
    A. n = 4 to n = 3
    B. n = 4 to n = 2
    C. n = 4 to n = 1
    D. n = 1 to n = 3
    E. n = 1 to n = 2

69. How much energy must be given to an electron in the ground state for it to ionize the atom?
    A. 0.85 eV
    B. 1.51 eV
    C. 3.4 eV
    D. 13.6 eV
    E. 19.36 eV

70. A photon of wavelength λ collides with a stationary electron, causing the photon to be deflected at an angle θ and an increase in the photon's wavelength. This is a description of:
    A. Photoelectric Effect
    B. Compton Effect
    C. Zeeman Effect
    D. X-ray diffraction
    E. Relativity

END OF PART I

Free Response
Time – 90 minutes
6 Free Response Questions

Directions: Answer all questions, showing your work in the space provided after each question. A calculator is allowed, and you may refer to the Formula Sheet and to the Table of Information while working these problems.

1. (15 points) The graph below describes the motion of an object of mass 2 kg as it moves across a level tabletop and subsequently falls to the floor below. The object hits the floor after 1.2 s and stops instantly.

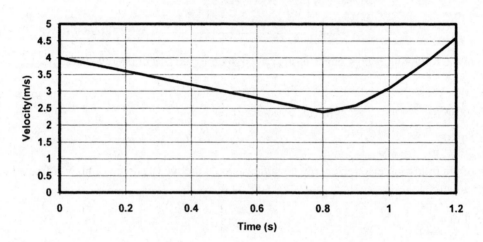

(a) At what time on the graph does the object leave the table? Justify your answer.

(b) What is the object's acceleration while it is moving across the table?

(c) How far across the table has the object moved after 0.5 s?

(d) Assuming no other horizontal forces other than friction acting on the object while it is on the table, calculate a value for the coefficient of friction.

(e) How high is the table top from the floor?

2. (15 points)

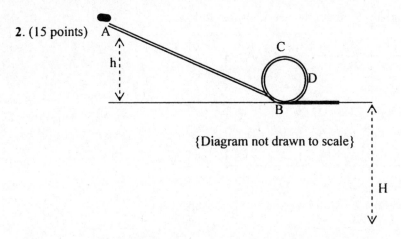

{Diagram not drawn to scale}

A small car of mass m is released at height h on a steel track. The car rolls down the track and through a loop of radius R. At the end of the track, the car rolls off the track, which is positioned a height H above the floor. Neglect friction and the small amount of rotational motion of the wheels of the car. Solve in terms of h, m, R, H, and g.

(a) Find the velocity of the car at point B (bottom of the loop).

(b) Find the velocity of the car at point C (top of the loop).

(c) Determine the height h at point A such that the car just barely makes contact with the loop at point C as it goes through the loop.

(d) When the car is moving at minimum speed, what provides the centripetal force on the car:
   (i) at point B?

   (ii) at point C?

   (iii) at point D (side of loop)?

(e) Determine the distance from the end of the track that the car will land on the floor.

3. (15 points) Use the following circuit diagram to answer the questions that follow.

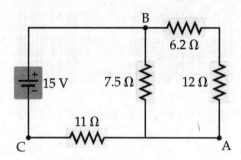

(a) Calculate the equivalent resistance of the 7.5-Ω, 6.2-Ω, and 12-Ω resistors.

(b) What is the current through the 11-Ω resistor?

(c) Determine the potential difference between points A and B.

(d) Determine the power output by the 15 V battery.

(e) If the 6.2-Ω resistor is removed from the circuit above, would the current through the 12-Ω resistor increase or decrease? Justify your answer.

4. (15 points) A right triangular glass prism is used to demonstrate dispersion of white light into a rainbow of colors. Initially, a narrow beam of white light is shone perpendicular to one face, as shown below.

(a) Draw the path of the light in the prism and as it comes out of the prism and hits the screen at right. Show any color separation by labeling the red end of the spectrum as a ray with **R** on it, and label the violet end of the spectrum as a ray with **V** on it.

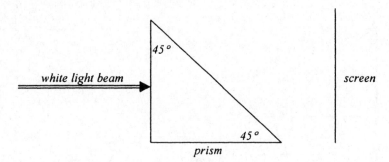

(b) If the index of refraction for red light of frequency 3.2 x 10^{14} Hz is 1.52 in the glass prism, calculate:

(i) the speed of this red light inside the prism

(ii) the frequency of this red light inside the prism

Now the light source is kept stationary and the prism is turned so that the light is directed onto the center of the widest face, as shown below.

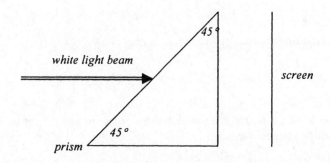

(c) Again, draw the path of the light in the prism and as it comes out of the prism and hits the screen at right. Show any color separation by labeling the red end of the spectrum as a ray with **R** on it, and label the violet end of the spectrum as a ray with **V** on it.

(d) How will the pattern of the colors on the screen appear different in this situation, compared to the pattern produced in part (a)?

(e) If the entire setup as shown directly above is submerged in water, with index of refraction 1.33, how will the color pattern on the screen be different, compared to part (c)?

5. (15 points) A thermodynamic process takes place in three stages, as diagrammed below. In stage I, one mole of an ideal gas is allowed to expand at constant pressure to a volume of 0.5 m³. In stage II, 5000 joules of heat are removed from the gas. In stage III, the gas is cooled at constant volume to a pressure of 1.0 x 10⁵ Pa.

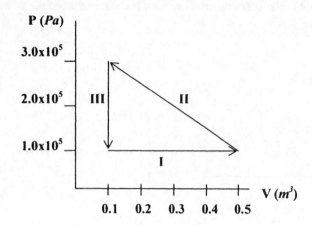

(a) Calculate the work done in stage I, and indicate whether the work is done by the gas or on the gas.

(b) What is the temperature of the gas at the beginning and end of the 3-stage process?

(c) Determine the change in internal energy during Stage II.

(d) Does the gas undergo a temperature increase or a temperature decrease during Stage I?
Justify your answer.

(e) For the entire cycle, determine:

(i) work done, and indicate whether the work is done by the gas or on the gas

(ii) heat exchange, and indicate whether there is a net heat loss or net heat gain

6. (15 points)

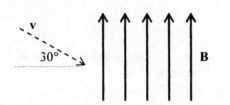

+y *(toward top of page)*

+x *(to the right)*

+z *(out of the page)*

A proton with velocity $v = 3 \times 10^6$ m/s moves at an angle as shown into a uniform magnetic field of strength $B = 4 \times 10^{-4}$ T in the +y direction. Use the scheme shown above to indicate directions on your answers.

(a) Determine the magnitude and direction of the magnetic force on the proton as it first enters the field.

(b) Calculate the orbital radius of the proton in the field.

(c) Describe the subsequent path of the proton as it travels through the field.

(d) Describe the motion of the proton as it leaves the magnetic field, assuming no fringe effects.

Now an electric field **E** is added to the same region, along with the magnetic field.

(e) What are the strength and direction of the electric field needed so the proton travels through both fields without being deflected?

END OF EXAMINATION

MULTIPLE CHOICE ANSWERS AND EXPLANATIONS

[Note: 10 m/s^2 is used for g.]

1. **C** Since the object has only horizontal velocity when it leaves the table, the initial vertical velocity is zero. The time it takes the object to drop vertically depends only on the height of the table:

$$s_y = v_{oy}t + \tfrac{1}{2} gt^2$$
$$5.0 \ m = 0 + \tfrac{1}{2} (10 \ m/s^2)t^2$$
$$t = \sqrt{\frac{(2)(5)}{10}} = 1 \ s$$

2. **D** The horizontal displacement from the edge of the table, or range, depends on the horizontal velocity and time the object is in the air. We assume no acceleration in the horizontal direction, if air friction is minimal:

$$s_x = v_{ox} t + \tfrac{1}{2} at^2$$
$$s_x = (4.0 \ m/s)(1.0 \ s) + 0 = 4.0 \ m$$

3. **D** The question asks for speed when the object hits the ground, which will be the vector resultant of both the vertical and horizontal speeds. The horizontal speed is assumed constant at v_x = 4.0 m/s, so first find the vertical speed when the object hits the ground, then use the Pythagorean Theorem to find the resultant of the vertical and horizontal components:

$$v_y = v_o + at$$
$$v_y = 0 + (10 \ m/s^2)(1.0 \ s) = 10 \ m/s$$
$$v = \sqrt{4^2 + 10^2} = \sqrt{116}$$

Since we have no calculator to obtain an exact answer, we choose an answer somewhat greater than 10.

Alternate Solution: The total energy of the object as it leave the top of the building (K + U) should be the same as the total energy just before it hits the ground (all kinetic):

$$K_{top} + U_{top} = K_{bottom}$$
$$\tfrac{1}{2} mv_0^2 + mgh = \tfrac{1}{2} mv^2$$
$$\tfrac{1}{2} (4.0 \ m/s)^2 + (10 \ m/s^2)(5.0 \ m) = \tfrac{1}{2} v^2$$
$$v^2 = 116 \ (same \ as \ above)$$

4. **B** Both blocks make the same vertical trip to the ground, so the time of fall and final vertical velocity is the same for both. Obviously, the first block has a horizontal velocity upon impact and the second block has none.

5. **C** The work done by the friction force in stopping the object is equal to the loss in kinetic energy (both are negative):

$$W = F_f d = \tfrac{1}{2} mv^2$$
$$(50 \ N)d = \tfrac{1}{2} (10 \ kg)(5 \ m/s)^2$$
$$d = 2.5 \ m$$

Alternate Solution: Use Newton's Second Law to determine the acceleration of the object:

$$\Sigma F = ma$$
$$-50 \ N = (10 \ kg)(a)$$
$$a = -5 \ m/s^2$$

Then use a kinematic equation to determine the distance:

$$v_f^2 = v_o^2 + 2as$$
$$0 = (5\ m/s)^2 + 2\ (-5\ m/s^2)(s)$$
$$s = 2.5\ m$$

6. **E** Write Newton's Second Law for the mass M, with downward direction positive:

$$\Sigma F = ma$$
$$Mg - T = Ma$$
$$T = Mg - Ma$$

7. **A** Write Newton's Second Law for the entire system, with direction of motion positive:

$$\Sigma F = ma$$
$$Mg - mg = (M + m)a$$
$$2mg - mg = 3ma$$
$$a = \frac{mg}{3m} = \frac{g}{3}$$

8. **B** This diagram correctly shows the normal force (N) perpendicular to the surface, the tension force (T) pulling the object up the ramp, the friction force (F_f) opposing the direction of motion, and the gravitational force (mg) down, or toward the center of Earth.

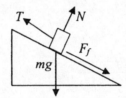

9. **E** First, calculate the acceleration of the ball:

$$v_f^2 = v_o^2 + 2as$$
$$0 = (20\ m/s)^2 + 2a(0.10\ m)$$
$$a = -2000\ m/s^2$$

Then use Newton's Second Law to determine the force:

$$\Sigma F = ma = (0.2\ kg)(-2000\ m/s^2) = -400\ N$$

Alternate Solution: Set the work required to stop the ball equal to the ball's loss in kinetic energy.

$$\tfrac{1}{2}\ mv^2 = F_{ave}d$$
$$\tfrac{1}{2}\ (0.2\ kg)(20\ m/s)^2 = F(0.10\ m)$$
$$F = 400\ N$$

Since the force opposes the motion of the ball and the ball initially has a positive velocity, the force must be negative, or $-400\ N$.

10. **B** The potential energy of a spring is $\tfrac{1}{2} kx^2$. If the second spring has twice the k value, then $U_1 = \tfrac{1}{2} U_2$.

11. **C** The kinetic energy at equilibrium is equal to the potential energy of each spring at the point it is released:

$$\tfrac{1}{2}\, mv^2 = \tfrac{1}{2}\, kx^2$$

$$v = x\sqrt{\frac{k}{m}}$$

If the second spring has twice the k value and also twice the mass, then the two velocities are the same.

12. **D** The object is moving at constant velocity, so the net force horizontally is zero, and the friction force equals the force F. On a level surface, the normal force equals the weight of the object, mg.

$$F_f = \mu N$$

$$\mu = \frac{F_f}{N} = \frac{F}{mg}$$

13. **E** In the diagram below, the weight of the stick has been added at the middle of the stick (2.0 meter point), and x is labeled as the unknown distance from the left end to the pivot. To balance, the net torque on the stick must be zero:

$$\tau_{clockwise} = \tau_{counterclockwise}$$

$$(5\ kg)(10\ m/s^2)(2\ m - x) + (10\ kg)(10\ m/s^2)(3\ m - x) = (10\ kg)(10\ m/s^2)(x)$$

$$10 - 5x + 30 - 10x = 10x$$

$$40 = 25x$$

$$x = 1.6\ m$$

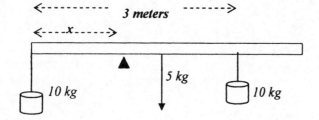

Alternate Solution:
(1) The pivot is supporting 25 kg, so the force upward of the pivot is $(25\ kg)(10\ m/s^2)$, or 250 N.
(2) Calculate the torques about the left end of the stick.

$$\tau_{clockwise} = \tau_{counterclockwise}$$

$$(5\ kg)(10\ m/s^2)(2\ m) + (10\ kg)(10\ m/s^2)(3\ m) = (250\ N)(x)$$

$$x = \frac{400\ N \cdot m}{250\ N} = 1.6\ m$$

14. **D** Power is work divided by time, which is equal to change in potential energy divided by time:

$$P = \frac{W}{t} = \frac{mgh}{t} = \frac{(70\ kg)(10\ m/s^2)(5\ m)}{5\ s} = 700\ W$$

15. **E** The work done by the athlete on each lift is the increase in potential energy of the object lift, which is positive. However, as the object is lowered, the potential energy decreases to zero, so an equal magnitude of negative work is done on the object in lowering it back to the floor. After twenty repetitions, the net work is zero. In other words, the object ends up back on the floor with no potential energy, so no net work is done on the object.

16. **D** This question is easy if you remember that in a head-on elastic collision between two equal masses, the objects exchange velocities. If necessary, a quick examination of the two equations that are applicable here— conservation of momentum and conservation of kinetic energy—shows that 0.5 m/s and 1.0 m/s are the answers. Since the objects can't pass each other on the track, they have to exchange velocities. For the sake of practice, the equations are given below :

$$p_o = p_f$$
$$(1\ kg)(0.5\ m/s) + (1\ kg)(-1.0\ m/s) = (1\ kg)v_a + (1\ kg)v_b$$
$$-0.5 = v_a + v_b$$

$$K_o = K_f$$
$$\tfrac{1}{2}\ (1\ kg)(0.5\ m/s)^2 + \tfrac{1}{2}\ (1\ kg)(-1.0\ m/s)^2 = \tfrac{1}{2}\ (1\ kg)v_a^2 + \tfrac{1}{2}\ (1\ kg)v_b^2$$
$$1.25 = v_a^2 + v_b^2$$

17. **B** Between $t = 1.0$ and 2.5 seconds, the force increases from 0 to 4 newtons. The average force during this interval is 2 N. Use Newton's Second Law to determine average acceleration:

$$\Sigma F = ma$$
$$a = \frac{F}{m} = \frac{2\ N}{1\ kg} = 2\ m/s^2$$

18. **E** Impulse, J, is change in momentum. From Newton's Second Law:

$$\Sigma F = \frac{\Delta p}{\Delta t}$$

Thus, the impulse is equal to $F\Delta t$, which is the area under the graph line in this case.

$$J = F\Delta t = \tfrac{1}{2}\ Bh = \tfrac{1}{2}\ (3\ ms)(4\ N) = 6\ N\text{-}ms\ or\ 6\ x\ 10^{-3}\ N\text{-}s$$

We are asked for the impulse <u>on</u> the cart, so we choose the negative answer.

19. **A** The fundamental wavelength produced by the closed tube is four times its length, while the wavelength produced by each open tube is twice its length. Tube III has the longest wavelength and lowest frequency, assuming the velocities to be the same in each tube, by $v = f\lambda$. Tube I has the shortest wavelength and highest frequency.

20. **B** The form for the wave equation is $x(t) = A\ sin2\pi ft$ or $x(t) = A\ cos2\pi ft$, depending upon the position of the oscillator at $t = 0$. The sine form fits the situation $x = 0$ m when $t = 0$ s, so we eliminate choices A and D. By substituting 40 Hz for f and 0.25 m for the amplitude, A, we get the answer.

21. **C** At the top of the circle, the centripetal force $\frac{mv^2}{R}$ is provided by both the weight of the ball and the tension in the string. At the bottom of the circle, the centripetal force is equal to $T\text{-}mg$, so the tension has to be greater. Thus, to maintain constant speed, the tension must vary—greatest at the bottom and least at the top.

22. **D** Centripetal force is $\frac{mv^2}{R}$, which equals $mg + T$. $T = \frac{mv^2}{R} - mg$, so doubling the mass also doubles the value of T.

23. **E** Centripetal force is provided by the net force toward the center of the circle. When the ball is in a horizontal position, the only force that is centripetal is the string tension.

24. **D** Each wave travels a distance of 8 meters during the 4 seconds ($d = vt$), and each wave also inverts, or changes phase, when it reaches the end of the string. Since each wave is 7 meters from the end of the string toward which it is initially heading, it inverts at the end and returns 1 meter. Thus, the crest of each wave is one meter from the end of the string and in an inverted position.

25. **C** It's a good "rule of thumb" to remember that each 10-meter depth of fresh water exerts about 1 atmosphere of pressure:

$$P = \rho g h = (1000 \ kg/m^3)(10 \ m/s^2)(10 \ m) = 1 \times 10^5 \ Pa, \ [where \ 1 \ atm = 1.01 \times 10^5 \ Pa]$$

The total fluid pressure will be the water pressure plus atmospheric pressure. At a depth of 20 meters in water, we estimate two atmospheres of water pressure then add 1 atmosphere for air pressure above it, for a total of 3 atmospheres or 3.03×10^5 Pa—about 300 kPa.

26. **B** The continuity equation for fluids is $\rho_1 A_1 v_1 = \rho_1 A_1 v_1$, showing that the rate of mass flow (kg/s) remains constant. If the fluid is incompressible, the density stays constant and cancels, leaving: $A_1 v_1 = A_1 v_1$. This equation describes: "the change in velocity is inversely proportional to cross-sectional area of flow."

27. **D** When the ball floats, it submerges in the water only far enough to displace its own weight, which is equal to the buoyant force. The buoyant force is equal to the weight of displaced water. Pushing the ball under water causes it to displace three times as much water, thus making the buoyant force on it three times as great.

28. **B** The soda will spray to a height so the pressure, $\rho g h$, is equal to the pressure inside the can. This is a modification of Bernoulli's Principle:

$$P = \rho g h = (1000 \ kg/m^3)(10 \ m/s^2)(0.5 \ m) = 5000 \ Pa$$

29. **D** The equation for average translational kinetic energy of an ideal gas is $K = \frac{3}{2} kT$. If the absolute temperature is doubled, the kinetic energy will be doubled.

30. **D** The ideal gas equation is $PV = nRT$. Since number of moles of gas (n), the ideal gas constant (R), and volume (V) all remain constant, doubling the temperature would also double the gas pressure.

31. **E** The rate of heat conduction through a material is given by the formula $\dfrac{kA\Delta T}{d}$, where k is the conductivity of the material transferring the heat from one chamber to another, A is the cross-sectional area of the conductor, ΔT is the difference in temperature (temperature gradient) between the two chambers, and d is the distance through which the heat is conducted. In this case, we don't want glass (a poor conductor with low k value), and we want a large temperature difference between the liquid inside and the air outside the container. A rod of larger cross-sectional area and small diameter will produce the highest rate of heat flow.

32. **C** The statement is the definition of internal energy.

33. **B** Since $PV = nRT$, isothermal would imply that the products of all pairs of P and V values would be constant. Mathematically, that will produce a hyperbolic curve. The curve for step BC could represent such a set of values.

34. **C** Work done <u>by</u> the gas is $-P\Delta V$. For the process CA, ΔV is zero, so no work is done.

35. **C** In the first connection, spheres X and Y share the electrons, leaving Q/2 on each sphere. Each sphere will then also have a equal potentials that are proportional to the charges, so X and Y now have potentials of 5,000 V each. When Y is connected to Z, the charge is again shared, leaving Q/4 on each sphere and 2,500 V on each.

36. **C** (See explanation for #35.) Note: After both steps of charge transfer, the total charge on all three spheres is Q, so total charge is conserved.

37. **A** Electric field is radially outward in all directions from each positive charge. At the center of the square, the fields produced by charges on opposite corners are equal in magnitude but opposite in direction, therefore canceling each other and making the net electric field at the center equal to zero.

38. **B** The Coulomb force $F = \dfrac{kq_1q_2}{r^2}$ is an inverse square law, such that doubling r reduces the value of F to one-fourth its previous value.

39. **C** Resistance can be calculated with the formula $\dfrac{\rho\, l}{A}$. Connecting three in series produces three times the resistance of one resistor. Substituting the other changes for l and A does not produce that great an increase. It should be noted that connecting resistors in parallel serves to decrease equivalent resistance each time another resistor is added.

40. **C** Since $Q = CV$, the largest charge is obtained with the largest product of capacitance and voltage. Increasing the resistance only increases the charging time for the capacitor.

41. **E** Two capacitors in parallel add to produce an equivalent capacitance $2C$. Since $Q = CV$, doubling the value of C also doubles Q, with an equal amount of charge distributed to each capacitor. Thus, each capacitor still holds a charge of Q.

42. **E** With the switch open, there are three 400-ohm resistors in series. The equivalent resistance is the sum of the three, or 1200 ohms.

43. **D** With the switch closed, resistor 2 is effectively "shorted out;" i.e., the current goes through the switch path instead of through resistor 2. The equivalent resistance is the sum of resistors 1 and 3, or 800 ohms.

44. **E** With the switch closed, no current goes through bulb 2, so it has no brightness. Bulbs 1 and 3 have the same resistance and the same current, so they are the same brightness.

45. **E** The current through the resistor decreases exponentially as the capacitor voltage increases, reducing the voltage across the resistor. In other words, the total voltage change throughout the circuit has to remain constant (Kirchoff's Loop Rule), so an increase in capacitor voltage means a decrease in resistor voltage.

46. **B** A current-carrying wire has a magnetic field encircling it that has a magnitude:

$$B = \frac{\mu_o I}{2\pi r} = \frac{\mu_o(0.2\ A)}{2\pi(0.01\,m)} = \frac{10\mu_o}{\pi}$$

47. **A** Using the right-hand rule, with the thumb in the direction of current flow in the top wire and curled fingers representing the direction of magnetic field lines, the field due to the top wire is out of the page at point P. Repeat for the bottom wire. The field at P due to the bottom is out of the page. Since both fields point in the same direction, the total field will be out of the page at point P.

48. **E** Using the right-hand rule again, we see that the fields due to the two wires add at point P (i.e., same direction) and subtract at Q, so it is logical to choose $B_P > B_Q$, without needing a calculation. (Also, the field at Q due to the top wire is less thatn the other field, because the distance is larger.)

49. **A** Increasing the tension in the oscillating string will results in an increase in velocity of the pulse along the string: $v = \sqrt{\dfrac{T}{\mu}}$, where T is the tension in the string and μ is the linear density of the string.

From the equation $v = f\lambda$, an increase in velocity at constant frequency results in an increase in wavelength.

50. **D** Use the right hand rule, with index finger in direction of current or charge flow, extended fingers in direction of field lines, and thumb extended in direction of force. $F = I\,l \times B$

51. **E** The magnetic force on a particle is: $F = qv \times B$. The particle will have a force on it, regardless of its speed, so **I** is not an answer. By the right hand rule, the magnetic force on a positively charged particle is upward on the page. The force on this negatively charged particle is down on the page. Adding an electric force upward on the page could produce a zero net force. For a negatively charged particle, the force is in the opposite direction of the field ($F = qE$), so the electric field needs to be downward on the page.

52. **E** When the observer and source move toward each other, wave crests from the source reach the observer more frequently, resulting in a perceived higher frequency—the Doppler Effect. The effect will occur when either moves toward the other, but both moving toward each other results in the highest relative velocity between them and the greatest frequency shift.

53. **B** Magnetic flux depends on the area of the hoop and the strength of field lines directed through the open hoop:

$$\Phi = B \cdot A$$

In this situation, $B \cos 60°$ describes the magnetic field line components that are directed through the plane of the hoop, and $A = \pi r^2$, so : $\Phi = (10^{-4}\ T \cos 60°)(\pi)(1m)^2 = $ about ½ $\pi \times 10^{-4}\ Wb$

54. **A** Induced emf is the rate of change in flux. As the hoop is moved to the right, the flux through the hoop remains the same, so no emf is induced.

55. **C** Assuming a uniform magnetic field, moving the hoop straight to the right or holding it stationary in the field will have the same result—no change in flux and no subsequent induced emf. Dropping the hoop (as long as it does not rotate as it drops) keeps the hoop in a steady orientation in the field, thus no change in flux and no induced emf. Rotating the hoop around an axis through its center, perpendicular to the plane of the hoop, does not change the flux through the hoop; thus there is no induced emf. However, rotating the hoop about an axis that runs across the plane of the hoop, through the center, will alternately reduce and increase the number of lines of magnetic flux through the hoop. In this manner, the change will result in an induced emf.

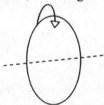

56. **D** Sound is a longitudinal wave that requires a medium for transmission. All the others are electromagnetic.

57. **C** As the light travels from air into glass, it decreases its speed by the equation $n = \frac{c}{v}$, where n is the index of refraction of the glass and v is the speed of the light in glass. Then, using the equation $v = f\lambda$, the wavelength also decreases. The frequency does not change.

58. **A** As white light, which is a mixture of all colors, is directed onto the magenta filter, only red and blue light will pass through, since magenta is a mixture of red and blue light. The red surface appears red because it absorbs all colors except red. The blue light is absorbed by the surface and the red light reflects onto the camera film.

59. **B** Total internal reflection occurs as light exits a medium of higher index into a medium of lower index of refraction, such that the refracted angle is at least 90°.

60. **C** If an object is located outside of the focal point of a convex lens or concave mirror, a real image can be formed. Concave lenses only form virtual images (as do convex mirrors).

61. **A** First, add a normal line at each point where the light beam crosses an interface. At the first interface, from air into glass, the light bends toward the normal (lower index of refraction to higher index of refraction). At the second interface, from glass back into air, the light bends away from the normal (higher index of refraction to lower index of refraction).

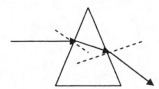

62. **A** By the equation $m\lambda = d\sin\theta$, using a green laser of shorter wavelength would decrease θ, moving lines together. Moving the grating farther from the screen increases l, but θ doesn't change, so x has to increase. Moving the laser back has no effect, since the diffraction occurs only when the light passes through the diffraction grating. A grating with 800 lines per mm means a smaller distance between lines and smaller d and thus a larger θ, moving lines apart.

63. **D** Convex mirrors and concave lenses cause light to diverge, so no real images form. Convex lenses and concave mirrors are able to form real images as long as the object is placed outside the focal point.

64. **C** The incident light can be a mixture of colors but must contain green frequencies. Other colors will undergo destructive interference, dependent upon index of refraction of the oil and the thickness of the oil film.

65. **E** The key here is to select the value for Planck's constant from the information sheet that is easiest to use. Since we want to find energy in joules, select the value for the constant that has wavelength units (meters) and energy units found in the answers (joules):

$$E = hf = \frac{hc}{\lambda} = \frac{2 \times 10^{-25} J \cdot m}{6 \times 10^{-7} m} = 0.33 \times 10^{-18} J = \text{approx. } 3 \times 10^{-19} J$$

Notice that we chose a value for hc, after substituting from the equation $c = f\lambda$. We also converted 600 nm to 6×10^{-7} meters. These are common substitutions of which you should be aware.

66. **D** The "missing" mass has been converted to energy. Find the energy equivalent of the mass:

$$E = mc^2 = (3 \times 10^{-6} kg)(3 \times 10^8 m/s)^2 = 27 \times 10^{10} \text{ or } 2.7 \times 10^{11} J$$

67. **C** Each emission is found by using $\Delta E = E_f - E_o$. So the possible emissions will be for electron "jumps" downward on the chart, where the energy is lower, e.g., $(-13.6 \text{ eV}) - (-3.4 \text{ eV})$ produces an emission of -10.2 eV (answer D). Answer B coincides with a jump from $n = 3$ to $n = 1$. Answer A is the value for $n = 4$ to $n = 1$, and answer E is the jump from $n = 3$ to $n = 2$. Answer C is not possible, as -13.6 eV is the ground level—there is no lower level—and there is not other combination that produces that energy difference. This answer should be initially obvious.

68. **C** Only electron transitions from higher to lower energy levels would result in emissions of photons, so you can immediately eliminate answer choices D and E. By the equation $E = hf$, higher frequency photons would be produced by higher energy transitions, i.e., a greater difference in energy levels.

69. **D** Since the ground state electron is in a potential energy "well" of -13.6 eV, adding that amount of energy would be the exact amount necessary for an electron in that energy state to escape and ionize the atom.

70. **B** The problem is a description of the Compton Effect.

FREE RESPONSE SOLUTIONS AND SCORING RUBRIC

1. [15 points]

[2 points] The object leaves the table top at **0.8 second**, because the velocity begins to increase as the object is no longer affected by friction with the table and now falls under the influence of gravity.

[3 points] The acceleration is constant during the first 0.8 second, since the plot is linear. The acceleration is the slope for that interval. Using the data points (0, 4) and (0.5, 3):

$$acceleration = slope = \frac{3\ m/s - 4\ m/s}{0.5\ s - 0} = -2\ m/s^2$$

[3 points] Using the equation $s = v_o t + \frac{1}{2} at^2$,

$$s = (4\ m/s)(0.5\ s) + \frac{1}{2}(-2\ m/s^2)(0.5\ s)^2 = 1.75\ or\ \textbf{1.8 m}$$

With the values given, one or two digits on the answer would be appropriate.

Alternate Solution: Determine the displacement by finding the area under the graph for the first 0.5 seconds. This space between the graph line and the x-axis is a trapezoid:

$$s = area = \frac{1}{2}(B+b)h = \frac{1}{2}(4\ m/s + 3\ m/s)(0.5\ s) = 1.75\ or\ \textbf{1.8 m}$$

[4 points] Since the table top is horizontal, the normal force is equal to the weight of the object, so we use Newton's Second Law for each direction:

$$\Sigma F_y = 0 \qquad\qquad \Sigma F_x = ma_x$$
$$N - mg = 0 \qquad\qquad F_f = ma_x$$
$$N = mg = (2\ kg)(9.8\ m/s^2) = 19.6\ N. \qquad F_f = (2\ kg)(-2\ m/s^2) = -4\ N.$$
(The negative meaning it opposes the motion.)

Now, use the formula $F_f = \mu N$:

$$\mu = \frac{4\ N}{19.6\ N} = \textbf{0.20}$$

[3 points] Based upon the answer to part (a), the object is falling for the last 0.4 second of its motion. Using the formula for the vertical motion only:

$$s = v_{0y}t + \frac{1}{2}gt^2$$
$$s = (0)(0.4\ s) + \frac{1}{2}(9.8\ m/s^2)(0.4\ s)^2 = \textbf{0.78 m}$$

Note: In this case, g was chosen as positive, i.e., the downward direction was positive. The displacement, then, was positive since it was in the downward direction.

---

2. [15 points]

(a) [3 points] Using conservation of energy, the potential energy at A should equal the kinetic energy at B:

$$mgh_A = \frac{1}{2}mv^2_B \qquad \text{(Cancel the mass and substitute given variables.)}$$
$$gh = \frac{1}{2}v_B^2$$

$$v_B = \sqrt{2gh}$$

(b) [3 points] Using conservation of energy, the potential energy at A should equal the sum of potential and kinetic energies at C:

$$mgh_A = mgh_C + \tfrac{1}{2}\, mv_C^2 \quad \text{(Cancel the mass and substitute given variables.)}$$
$$gh = g(2R) + \tfrac{1}{2}\, v^2 \quad \text{(Height at C is twice the radius, so } h_c = 2R.\text{)}$$
$$v_c = \sqrt{2gh - 4gR}$$

(c) [3 points] For the car to barely make contact, the speed is a minimum so that only the car's weight provides the centripetal force:

$$F_c = mg$$
$$\frac{mv^2}{R} = mg \quad \text{(Cancel mass.)}$$
$$v = \sqrt{gR}$$

Using what we have already derived in part (b):

$$\sqrt{2gh - 4gR} = \sqrt{gR}$$
$$2gh - 4gR = gR$$
$$2gh = 5gR$$
$$h = \frac{5}{2}R \text{ or } 2.5\,R$$

(d) [1 point each]
    (i) At B, the net centripetal force is provided by normal force from the track minus the car's weight.
    (ii) At C, when the car is moving at minimum speed, only the car's weight provides centripetal force.
    (iii) At point D, only the normal force from the track provides the centripetal force. (The weight of the car does not contribute to the centripetal force, since it acts perpendicular to the direction of centripetal force.)

(e) [3 points] Use the value for velocity derived for point B as the horizontal velocity when the car leaves the track and remember that there is no acceleration in the horizontal direction and no initial velocity in the vertical at the instant the car leaves the track:

$$s_y = v_{oy}t + \tfrac{1}{2}\, gt^2 \qquad\qquad\qquad s_x = v_{ox}\, t$$
$$H = (0)t + \tfrac{1}{2}\, gt^2$$
$$t = \sqrt{2gH} \quad\longrightarrow\quad s_x = \sqrt{2gh}\,\sqrt{2gH} = 2g\sqrt{hH}$$

3. [15 points]

(a) [3 points] First, add the 6.2-Ω and 12-Ω resistors that are in series to get the equivalent resistance in that branch. Then we can treat that resistance as a parallel resistance to the 11-Ω resistor to find the equivalent of all three. We can use the parallel resistor equation, but it is easier in this case to use the "product over sum" rule, which applies when there are just two resistors in parallel:

$$R_{eq} = \frac{product}{sum} = \frac{(18.2\ \Omega)(7.5\ \Omega)}{18.2\ \Omega + 7.5\ \Omega} = 5.3\Omega$$

(b) [3 points] Find the total resistance on the circuit by adding the 11-Ω resistor, which is in series: $R_T = 16.3\ \Omega$
Then use Ohm's Law to find the current flowing from the battery, which will all flow through the 11-Ω resistor:

$$I = \frac{V}{R} = \frac{15V}{16.3\ \Omega} = \boldsymbol{0.92\ A}.$$

(c) [3 points] Find the voltage across the 11-Ω resistor, using Ohm's Law: $V = IR = (0.92\ A)(11\ \Omega) = 10.1\ V$
There needs to be a 15 volt drop around the circuit branch, so subtract this voltage from 15 V to find the voltage
drop or potential difference between A and B: $V_{AB} = 15\ V - 10.1\ V = \boldsymbol{4.9\ V}$

(d) [3 points] $P = VI = (15\ V)(0.92\ A) = \boldsymbol{13.8\ W}$ [or 14 W to two significant figures]

(e) [3 points] Removing the resistor reduces the equivalent parallel resistance to $R_{eq} = \dfrac{(7.5)(12)}{7.5 + 12} = 4.6\ \Omega$

The new total resistance is 15.6 Ω. We can already see that this reduction in resistance will result in an increase
in circuit current. More of that current will now go through the 12 ohm resistor, since there is now less resistance
in that parallel branch. Thus, the 12 ohm resistor receives **more** current.

---

4. [15 points]

(a) [4 points]

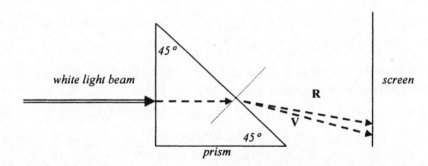

Since the incident beam strikes along the normal, it does not change direction in the prism. Going from higher
index of refraction (prism) to lower index (air), the light will take a direction away from the normal, with the light
of higher frequency (violet) refracting more than the red light.

(b) (i) [2 points} The index of refraction is defined as the ratio of speed in a vacuum to speed in the medium.
(Note: We're assuming an index of refraction in air of 1.00.)

$$v = \frac{c}{n} = \frac{3 \times 10^8\ m/s}{1.52} = \boldsymbol{1.97 \times 10^8\ m/s}$$

(ii) [1 point] The frequency does not change, so $f = \boldsymbol{3.2 \times 10^{14}\ Hz}$

(c) [4 points]

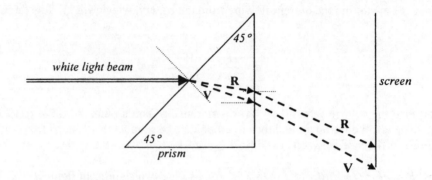

Each color will bend toward the normal when moving into the prism and then bend away from the normal when moving from glass back into air. The normal line should be drawn in to clarify the answer.

(d) [2 points] This process further separates the colors, so they will be farther apart and lower on the screen.

(e) [2 points] The light will still bend toward the normal going into the prism, but not as much, since the difference between the indices of refraction is less. Then, upon exiting the prism, they will again bend away from the normal, but not as much. Thus, the colors will be closer to each other and higher on the screen.

---

5. [15 points]

(a) [3 points] Work done: $W = P\Delta V = (1.0 \times 10^5 \, Pa)(0.4 \, m^3) = 40,000 \, J$. Since the gas expands, the work is done by the gas. (Note: 1 Pa = 1 N/m^2, so 1 Pa·m^3 = 1 N·m = 1 J)

(b) [3 points] The temperature at the beginning and at the end of the process is the same, since the gas returns to the same conditions of pressure and volume. Use the ideal gas law:

$$PV = nRT$$
$$T = \frac{PV}{nR} = \frac{(1.0 \times 10^5 \, Pa)(0.1 \, m^3)}{(1 \, mole)(8.31 \, J/mol \cdot K)} = 1200 \, K$$

Watch units as you work this one out, and use the universal gas constant given on the Table of Information sheet.

(c) [3 points] Use the First Law of Thermodynamics, $\Delta U = Q + W$, where ΔU is change in internal, Q is heat (5000 joules removed, according to the problem), and W is work (with positive work done on the gas). The work for Stage II is the area under that line, which is a rectangle (equal in size to the answer to part (a)) plus a triangle.

$$W = area = 40,000 \, J + \tfrac{1}{2} \, (0.4 \, m^3)(2.0 \times 10^5 \, Pa) = 80,000 \, J$$

This work is positive, since it is done on the gas, causing reduction in volume. The value of Q is negative, since the problem says it was removed from the gas. Now, substitute and solve:

$$\Delta U = Q + W = -5000 \, J + 80,000 \, J = 75,000 \, J$$

(d) [2 points] Pressure, number of moles, and the gas constant remain unchanged for Stage I. When we apply the ideal gas equation, $PV = nRT$, we can see that the volume increase that occurs in State I must also result in a **temperature increase** in the gas.

(e) (i) [2 points] Net work done for the cycle is the area inside the closed figure. That area was calculated above:

$$W = area\ inside = \frac{1}{2}\ (0.4\ m^3)(2.0\ x\ 10^5\ Pa) = \textbf{40,000\ J}$$

There is more compression of the gas than expansion of the gas during the cycle, so the net work is **on** the gas.

(ii) [2 points] For the cycle, the temperature change is zero, so there is no change in internal energy. Thus:

$$Q = -W = \textbf{--40,000\ J}$$

This heat is **given off** by the gas, since Q is negative.

---

6. [15 points]

(a) [3 points] We'll use the right-hand rule to determine the force, but only the component of velocity that is perpendicular to the magnetic field will produce a force on the proton. That component is $v\ cos\ 30°$. (The $v\ sin\ 30°$ component is antiparallel to the field and will produce no force.) The magnitude of the force is then:

$$F = q(v\ cos\ 30°)\ B = (1.6\ x\ 10^{-19}\ C)(3\ x\ 10^6\ m/s)(cos\ 30°)(4\ x\ 10^{-4}\ T) = \textbf{1.7\ x\ 10^{-16}\ N}$$

Using the right-hand rule with the velocity component perpendicular to the field:
 1. Index finger points to the right on the page (**v**).
 2. Other fingers point toward top of the page (**xB**).
 3. Thumb points **outward from page** (**F**).

(b) [4 points] The proton will move in a circle due to the magnetic force, with centripetal force provided by the magnetic force:

$$qvB = \frac{mv^2}{r}$$

$$r = \frac{mv}{qB} = \frac{(1.67x10^{-27}\ kg)(3x10^6\ m/s)}{(1.6x10^{-19}\ C)(4x10^{-4}\ T)}(cos\ 30°) = \textbf{68\ m}$$

The values for mass of the proton and fundamental charge, q, are obtained from the Table of Information sheet.

(c) [2 points] The component of velocity perpendicular to the magnetic field causes the proton to move in a circle, and the velocity component parallel to the field will cause the proton to continue its motion downward on the page. Thus, the composite motion is **helical, downward on the page**. (Note: The question asks for the path only, so it is not necessary to discuss speeds.)

(d) [3 points] As the proton leaves the field, it will leave **at constant velocity on a straight line path tangent to its velocity** at the moment it exits the field. Its velocity will be **v**, since there has been no force in the direction of velocity to accelerate the proton. (Note: Since this question asks for a description of motion, it is implied that a discussion of speed and acceleration as well as path are necessary.)

(e) [3 points] To counterbalance the magnetic force outward from the page (+z *direction)*, the electric field needs to exert a force on the proton that is equal in magnitude to the electric force (1.7×10^{-16} N) and into the page (in the −z direction). For a positive charge, the electric force is the same direction as the electric field, so the electric field is **into the page** or in the **-z direction**. The electric field strength must be:

$$|F_E| = |F_B|$$
$$qE = qv_\perp B$$
$$E = v \cos 30°B = (3 \times 10^6 \text{ m/s})(\cos 30°)(4 \times 10^{-4} \text{ T})$$
$$E = 1.0 \times 10^3 \text{ N/C}$$

SCORING YOUR SAMPLE EXAM

If you have taken the sample exam according to the directions on each section and have used the time limits suggested for each section, you can use the following formulas to gain an estimate of your performance on an AP* Physics B Examination.

1. Use the answer key for the Multiple Choice section to score your answers on that section.
2. Count the number of questions answered correctly, then subtract $\frac{1}{4}$ times the number answered incorrectly. from that total. (Questions left blank do not count in the calculation.)
3. After the subtraction, multiply that number by 1.286 to determine your **Multiple Choice Score.**
4. Use the rubric provided to assign scores to your work on each question of the Free Response section.
5. Add the scores for the six questions to obtain your **Free Response Score.**
6. Add the scores for the two sections to find a test total.

Multiple Choice Section Scoring: (90 points)	
Number of question answered correctly	(a)
Number of questions answered incorrectly*	(b)
Subtotal	(c)
Subtotal X 1.286	(d)
Free Response Section Scoring: (90 points)	
Use recommended points from answer key to obtain a total point value for all six questions	(e)
Exam Total: Add (d) to (e) **(180 points)**	

*Questions left blank do not count in this total.

Compare your exam total to the scale below to get an idea of your equivalent AP* score.

124 - 180	5	A
95 - 123	4	B
59 - 94	3	C

This scale is a composite of published AP* scales for several different tests over several different years, so it should only be used as an approximation of your predicted performance on the AP* Exam. The more important part of the exercise here is to examine your performance on various types of questions and use the answers as tools to avoid making similar mistakes again. The exam has been purposely designed with a variety of question styles to illustrate the wide variety of techniques one might use to determine answers without the aid of a calculator.

Note to Students: On the actual AP* Physics B Exam, the total percentages of topics on both the Multiple Choice and Free Response sections will be aligned with the topic percentages shown in the topic outline in Section I. For example, kinematics should represent 7% of the entire exam. Thus, if there is a kinematics question on the Free Response section, that already represents 8% of the exam, so the Multiple Choice section would be adjusted lower on kinematics. On this sample exam, however, it was thought to be a better practice exam if the Multiple Choice section was designed to fully represent the topic percentages. That section of the practice exam alone gives you a good overview of topic coverage.

Note to Teachers: When you examine the Free Response Examination for a given year, be aware that even though that portion of the exam may not seem to follow the topic percentages, the Multiple Choice section that you were not able to examine was adjusted to proportionally represent topic percentages.